Concern for Geography

WILLIAM GEORGE VICTOR BALCHIN
Professor of Geography, University College of Swansea. 1954–1978

Concern for Geography

A Selection
of the Work of
Professor W. G. V. Balchin
M.A. (Cantab), Ph.D. (London)
F.R.G.S., F.R.Met.S.

Published by his colleagues on the occasion of his retirement, after twenty-four years, from the Foundation Chair of Geography at University College of Swansea, University of Wales

This is Volume

No......10.

of a Limited Edition of

Five Hundred Copies

Published by the Department of Geography, University College of Swansea, 1981.
The contents of this volume were selected, edited and compiled by members of
Professor W. G. V. Balchin's Department.

The compilers wish to acknowledge and to express their appreciation for the
cooperation extended by Publishers, Professional Societies, Organisations, Col-
laborators and Authors in producing material, offering advice and permitting
reprint.

Copies of this volume may be obtained from the Head of the Department of
Geography, University College of Swansea, Swansea, West Glamorgan, SA2 8PP,
U.K.

Printed in England by Henry Ling Limited at the Dorset Press, Dorchester
ISBN No. 0 9507384 0 9

Contents

Foreword

This Foreword is written on the day when Professor W. G. V. Balchin becomes an Emeritus Professor of the University of Wales and hands over the responsibility of the Headship of the Department of Geography in the University College of Swansea to his successor, Professor R. H. Greenwood, after twenty-four years of loyal and devoted service in that office. It is an appropriate moment to look back over that period which has been successful for the Department and the College and, for Professor Balchin himself, I believe, a very happy and satisfying time. This volume is a way of paying lasting tribute to his achievement as a geographer and as the first Head of the Swansea Department and to his contribution to the life of the College as a whole. Not only has he served as Professor of Geography and a member of Senate for nearly a quarter of a century, but he was also Dean of the Faculty of Science from 1959 to 1961 and Vice-Principal of the College from 1964 to 1966. Moreover, in recent years he did something that no other member of the College has done when he resumed the additional and heavy responsibilities of a Vice-Principal for a further three sessions following on the tragic death of Professor Charles Gittins in 1970.

Geography in Swansea – as Professor Balchin's own chapter in this volume makes clear – first developed, as it did in several other universities, within the Department of Geology. Geology in Swansea has always enjoyed a very high reputation associated as it is with names such as Sir Franklin Sibly (the first Principal of the College), Sir Arthur Trueman (who became Chairman of the University Grants Committee), T. Neville George (a Fellow of the Royal Society who recently retired from the Chair of Geology in the University of Glasgow) and Frank Rhodes (who was installed as President of Cornell University a few months ago). Geography was first formally taught in the Department of Geology from 1931, first by D. Trevor Williams and later, after the Second World War, by B. H. Farmer (now Reader in Geography in the University of Cambridge and Director of the South Asian Studies Centre and a Fellow of St. John's College) and Miss Pegi John (now the wife of Mr. D. W. Hopkins, Dean of the Faculty of Applied Science and Senior Lecturer in the Department of Metallurgy and Materials Technology in Swansea). Mr. John Oliver (now Professor of Geography in the James Cook University of North Queensland in Australia) and Miss Gillian Groom were then appointed and were responsible for the first Honours courses in Geography and the planning of a separate Department of Geography. In 1954 they were joined by Dr. Balchin, at that time Lecturer in Geography at King's College, London, following his appointment as the first holder of the newly-established Chair of Geography. Within two years the geographers moved into new premises in the Natural Sciences Building, and the Swansea Department was for several years a show-piece as an example of a purpose-built department for geographers from other British universities and elsewhere. In the years since then it has grown steadily in size, strength and quality under Professor Balchin's guidance. Today, with more than 600 students and a teaching staff of twenty-four, it ranks not only as the largest single academic department in the University College of Swansea but also as one of the major departments of geography in Britain.

The Department of Geography in Swansea, about which Professor Balchin has written in this volume, is more than anything else his memorial in the College. We shall always remember him with gratitude and admiration for what he has built up from small beginnings over the years. But there are other sides, too, to Professor Balchin, W.G.V.B., William, Victor, Bill, Billy B. – the name used depends on the standing of the speaker and on the circumstances, but all of them are indicative of affection and respect for the person concerned. This volume of a selection of his papers reveals both the range of his interests and the diversity of his contribution to his subject. There is geomorphology (his first love and the theme of his Ph.D. thesis and much of his earlier published work); microclimatology (a war-time interest); water resources and natural hazards (problems and challenges that have engaged his attention in more recent years); and graphicacy (an aspect of geography that has been his particular concern and reflects his life-long involvement in cartographic matters). The papers also remind us of his special knowledge of certain areas – notably Cornwall and, of course, South Wales and particularly the Swansea area. *Swansea and its Region,* published in 1971 under his editorship, is among the most comprehensive and successful of the important series of handbooks prepared for the annual meetings of the British Association for the Advancement of Science. Another paper reminds us of the interest that he showed – more than any other geographer – in the criteria involved in the siting of the new universities of the early 'sixties. He has always been a shrewd observer of the academic scene, especially where geography and geographers are concerned, and still possesses a remarkable knowledge of his professional colleagues in Britain and overseas.

Nationally Professor Balchin has contributed a great deal to both geography and cartography. It is not easy to do justice to his achievements in a single paragraph. He has worked particularly for the Geographical Association on whose Council he has served since 1949 and of which he was a Trustee from 1955 to 1976 and President in 1971. I believe that he has not missed one of the Association's Annual Conferences since the end of the Second World War. He has also attended nearly every annual meeting of the British Association for the Advancement of Science during that period and, in the year following the Swansea meeting, in which he had been so closely involved, was President of Section E (Geography). His contribution to the work of the Royal Geographical Society has included membership of its Council at several periods and of its various committees including the Education Committee, of which he is at present the Chairman. Over the years he has attended many of the congresses of the International Geographical Union and the associated cartographic conferences. I recall that at one of these – the Washington, D.C., Congress of 1952 – Bill and his friend and colleague, Norman Pye, arrived direct from a two-man expedition to the Arizona Desert. The latest, the Moscow Congress of 1976, was his first visit to the U.S.S.R., though it would be an overstatement to say that he particularly enjoyed that occasion. By contrast he had a very successful and happy visit to Australia in 1976 when he attended a conference on natural hazards in Canberra and then saw a number of Australian universities where he made contact with many geographers and others with Swansea associations.

As professional colleagues Bill and I have known each other for more than thirty years. During the last four of these I have been a close colleague of his in Swansea as Principal of the College which has in it what has been widely, and rightly, known up till now as Professor Balchin's Department. There is no doubt that it is one of the most distinguished and productive, and certainly the most highly and efficiently organized, of all Departments of Geography in Britain. In commending this volume to a wider audience and in joining in the tribute of his departmental colleagues to Bill Balchin as a man and as a geographer, I take this opportunity of thanking him for all that he has done both for Geography and for the University College of Swansea. We wish him and his wife Lily (who has been a wonderful support for him, always in the background and ever ready to play her part) every happiness in their new home in Mrs. Balchin's native county of Yorkshire.

Robert W. Steel
Principal, University College of Swansea

1 August 1978

Professor Balchin – An Appreciation

R. H. GREENWOOD

This volume has been compiled to celebrate two closely related events – the retirement of Professor Balchin after twenty-four years of distinguished service as Foundation Professor of Geography at the University College of Swansea and the Silver Jubilee of the Department which is very much Professor Balchin's creation. An editorial committee has made a selection of publications which they regard as a representative sample of his written contributions to many aspects of geography and which characterise the evolution of a successful and innovating academic's professional interests over a period of forty-one years. They have seen value in including several articles which are less readily accessible now than when they appeared in print to complement papers from professional journals with a wider circulation and they wish to acknowledge with appreciation the sanction of the original publishers for their reproduction. The inclusion also of records of the Department's staff and graduates is a pleasant tribute to the past and present colleagues of Professor Balchin and the large numbers of graduates who have benefited by his guidance.

Bearing in mind the dual purpose of this volume, it is very much a corporate production and it is a pleasure to express my deep appreciation to those who have contributed to its compilation – in particular to Professor Steel for writing the Foreword which summarises Professor Balchin's notable contribution to the life of the University College of Swansea, to my colleagues on the editorial committee – Jack Davies, Guy Lewis, Colin Rouse and Clive Tomlinson – who have not only helped to select the papers but provided generously of their time and advice in many aspects of production, publicity and finance – and not least to Bill Balchin, not merely for being an honoured subject of a Festschrift but for writing a departmental history especially for it and for scouring his records to produce a comprehensive bibliography. I am equally appreciative of the professional skills of the printers and of their patience and tolerance of the foibles and distractions of the academic 'publishers'. There is more than meets the eye in the technology of producing a book of this kind and the skilful blending of differing styles and formats to make a visually acceptable whole and their painstaking attention to detail have played an important role in ensuring that the technical quality of the book is commensurate with its academic content.

Born at Aldershot on the 20th June 1916, William Balchin's taste for geography matured in the context of science studies at the Farnborough Grammar School from which in 1934 he won a State Scholarship which enabled him to read for the Geographical Tripos at St. Catharine's College, Cambridge – then as now a centre of excellence for aspiring geographers. Under the influence of Frank Debenham, Alfred Steers and Vaughan Lewis it is hardly surprising that his special interests focused in the realm of geomorphology and two years as a graduate supervisor at Cambridge gave him opportunities to sample field research in denudation chronology, coastal morphology and Arctic landforms. The West Spitsbergen paper is representative of his early work published between 1937 and 1941.

With the outbreak of war Mr. Balchin moved to the Hydrographic Department of the Admiralty to join an augmented team which was assembled to compile maps and charts for service requirements. This took him to Bath where with characteristic perspicacity he immediately bought a house and, thus established, he married Lily Kettlewood, the sister of one of his closest undergraduate friends. Their son and first daughter were both born during their time at Bath, Joan's birth coming perilously close to the infamous 'Baedecker' raids when Bathonians spent their nights in Anderson shelters or in the basement beneath the stoutest table they could muster. The Balchin home was damaged during these raids but the family was happily unscathed.

Wartime permitted scant opportunities for spare time research but, maybe stimulated by the dreadful winter of 1939–40 and modestly financed by a Leverhulme Research Fellowship, William Balchin collaborated with his Admiralty colleague Norman Pye in the establishment of a series of meteorological stations at which local variations in climate could be measured. The two papers recording the findings of this work generated renewed interest in local climates as well as some controversy about the relevance of the term micro-climatology to this kind of research.

At the end of the war Mr. Balchin was appointed Lecturer in Geography at King's College, London where, under the expert direction of the legendary figure of S. W. Wooldridge, he was able to pursue in depth his major interest in erosion surfaces. His work on Exmoor earned him a Ph.D. and, extending this work to Cornwall, he published several papers on West Country landscapes and a book on Cornwall, both of which are represented in this volume. His bibliography reveals a continuing interest also in climatology and cartography during his nine years at London and the beginning of a lifelong involvement with the Geographical Association for which he was the Honorary Annual Conference Organizer, 1950–54. In 1952, he attended his first I.G.U. Congress at Washington, presenting a paper on the evidence for Late Tertiary eustatic changes in western Europe, and he proceeded thence to explore – again in collaboration with Norman Pye – some of the features of the arid morphology of Arizona which is the subject of their 1954 paper.

In 1954 came Dr. Balchin's appointment to the first Chair of Geography at the University College of Swansea at the comparatively early age of 38. This provided abundant scope for the deployment of his undoubted flair for organisation and administration. As Robert Steel has explained in his Foreword, geography had been taught in Swansea since 1931 and the small geography section of the Department of Geology and Geography had become very active in the early post-war years with the appointment of three very able young geographers – Benny Farmer, John Oliver and Gillian Groom – who, housed modestly in the old buildings at the rear of the Abbey and teaching a growing intake of undergraduates, gave much of their time and thought to planning new courses to lead to an honours degree, to acquiring a range of basic equipment and an enlarged map collection and to designing new accommodation commensurate with their ambitions for an expanding and well found department.

Dr. Balchin's appointment as Foundation Professor of a newly autonomous department, therefore, gave him every opportunity for innovation. His first priority was the consolidation of teaching and research in the physical aspects of geography, where the main strength of staff expertise was concentrated, with considerable support on the cartographic side, and great benefits derived from the attractive field environment of the Swansea region for studies in Pleistocene and coastal geomorphology, climatology and hydrology. The move into the new Centre Block of the Natural Sciences Building in 1957, which bore the unmistakable stamp of Professor Balchin's meticulous attention to detail and his ambitions for the Department's growth, provided optimum opportunities for close working relationships with the Departments of Geology, Botany

5

and Zoology and this was further strengthened to the mutual advantage of the four Departments when wings were added to the Natural Sciences Building in 1960. The design and equipment of the new building attracted considerable interest nationally as Geography Departments elsewhere were also involved in building and expansion programmes and the paper that Professor Balchin wrote for the 1963 I.B.G. Conference which was held at Swansea has proved to have been of more than historical interest.

The continuous growth and diversification of the Department extended through to the early 1970s, making Swansea one of the largest Geography Departments in the country measured in terms of both staff and student numbers which have stabilised in the vicinity of 28 academic and 11 technical and secretarial staff and 600 students and this story is told by Professor Balchin in his chapter on departmental history. The Principal of the College supplements this in his Foreword by referring to the escalation of Balchin's College obligations in the 1960s which began with his election as Dean of Science and reached a peak during his two terms of office as Vice-Principal, both offices carrying a multiplicity of committee involvements. Reminiscing about this period, Bill Balchin has been heard to reflect wryly that he spearheaded the College's administrative diversification which was necessitated by the academic expansion in the post-Robbins era. After his term as Dean, the Faculty divided itself into two and it was not long before each Dean had the help of a Sub-Dean, and after his term as a lone Vice-Principal it became expedient to share the expanding administrative burden among three Vice-Principals!

Despite these commitments, Professor Balchin found time for active participation in the work of many national bodies – the Councils of the Geographical Association and the Royal Geographical Society, the British National Committee for Geography, the British National Cartography Committee, the Nature Conservancy, the Second Land Utilisation Survey and Section E of the British Association for the Advancement of Science. The federal structure of the University of Wales also opened avenues for the deployment of his organisational skills – among them his appointment as a member of the Court of Governors of the National Museum of Wales and of the Council of St. David's University College, Lampeter.

Such involvements not unnaturally diverted his research interests toward certain aspects of national planning, two in particular holding his attention in the late 1950s and early 1960s. In the first place, he considered that new technology in industry and agriculture and the escalating demands of electricity generation and consumer affluence were likely to create demands for water at a faster rate than the current supply plans allowed and that investigations should be undertaken to review the most efficient means of transferring more of the potential water surplus from highland Britain to the more highly urbanised lowlands. In the second place, he was deeply interested in the optimum location of new universities which were to be required in the post-Robbins expansion era. Noting that the historical sequence Oxbridge, London, Civic, Redbrick could best be complemented by 'County Town' sites with as even a geographical distribution as the demand patterns warranted, he promoted a plan for the establishment of further new universities which coincided remarkably closely with the distribution which subsequently came about. These two interests are represented by three papers in this volume, and a glance at the bibliography reveals that both themes were extended by a study of water policy in the United States (1967) and Canadian university expansion (1966) in consequence of study tours of North America.

The American visits also served to diversify Professor Balchin's research interests by alerting him to the anomaly that even arid areas can periodically suffer devastating floods. A visit to Puerto Rico provided him with evidence of destructive tropical cyclones. He returned to 'temperate' Britain to find floods following wet spells at times

6

of abnormal tidal surges. These complementary experiences provided the incentive for the study of man-made disasters which was the subject of his 1972 Presidential Address to Section E of the British Association and provided the opportunity to make his first visit to Australia in 1977 to participate in an international conference on the subject of Natural Hazards.

Meanwhile, the selection of Swansea as the venue for the British Association meeting in 1971 required the publication of the customary Scientific Survey. Professor Balchin was its editor and the introductory chapter which he wrote is included in this volume. His Department prepared most of the maps and diagrams for the book and very effective use was made of an earlier survey of the then derelict industrial area of the Lower Swansea Valley which was based on specially flown photographic air cover.

By 1971, the quantitative revolution in geography had reached its climax and although the Swansea department took this disturbing innovation in its stride and its members had become conditioned to concertina computer tabulations Professor Balchin consistently adhered to the philosophy that 'geography is about maps' and that statistical analysis should complement rather than displace cartographic representation in the training of undergraduates. His 1972 Presidential Address to the Geographical Association was the first of a series of papers – some translated into several languages – with 'graphicacy' in the title. The most widely read of these appeared in *The Times* in April 1977 under the heading 'Replacing the Three R's with the Four Aces' in which he promoted graphicacy as the fourth essential component of basic educational techniques to complement literacy, numeracy and articulacy. The fuller exposition of this argument which appeared in the *American Cartographer* in 1976 has been selected for this volume, this neatly closing the circle of geographical interests and representing a no less fundamental appraisal of the value of cartography than was implicit in the production of wartime charts discussed in the B.B.C. interview with Freddie Grisewood in 1942. Practical endorsement of the departmental commitment to cartography followed when, in 1978, a new degree in Topographic Science became available.

Reviewing the full range of Professor Balchin's published work and the context in which the significant contributions were conceived, one can readily appreciate the logical progression of his interests from early research into the intricacies of physical processes to the appraisal of national policies for the optimum utilisation of resources. Indeed, an intrinsic characteristic of his work is the blending of academic insight and thoroughness with the perception of practical applications and resourcefulness in problem solving. It is these qualities, coupled with his aptitude for identifying problems before they become acute and for formulating policies that outflank them before a critical situation develops, that brought Professor Balchin success as a Departmental Head and University Administrator. As was written of him on an earlier occasion, he has been 'dedicated to improving the system but has done so in ways that avoid time-wasting upheaval because he explored the full implication of changes before they were implemented and always worked on the principle that administrative machinery should serve and not distract a university's goal of academic achievement'.

In the Balchin vocabulary, however, 'administrative machinery' embraced not only the paraphernalia of development strategy, policy making and committee work but the maintenance of harmonious working relations within his Department. Willing to give independence to his colleagues in the organisation and presentation of courses and in the development of their research, he curbed periodic excesses of enthusiasm by such mild but disarming approaches as 'where would you put it?' (when asked for a particularly expensive piece of equipment) and 'how could you possibly examine it?' (when pressure was exerted for radical changes of syllabus). Beneath his quiet

7

personality and unobtrusive perceptiveness there was a strong confidence in his capacity to direct the growth of his Department and the welfare of his colleagues in the most efficient and productive fashion and these qualities commanded their loyalty, liking and respect.

Three annual social occasions that obviously gave him particular pleasure were the beginning of session party at which newcomers were formally welcomed in the College Senior Common Room and the notable events of the previous session were reviewed after sweet sherry, ham sandwiches and pastries had been dispensed; the end of session party which was usually held in the Balchins' spacious home – and garden, weather permitting – with Bill himself presiding over the bar in the conservatory to ensure that justice was done to all his guests and that just one bottle of sauternes remained unopened at the close of the party; and the formal dinner to honour the External Examiner which served both to maintain the more gracious traditions of community life and to fortify his colleagues for a four hour meeting to review the final fruits of each year's examining marathon. By comparison, the Christmas celebrations were less ambitious, as was perhaps fitting for the solemnity of the occasion and also having regard to the fact that the menu was traditionally subsidised by the annual surplus of the Departmental Tea Club and the generosity of the ladies of the Department. Suitably spaced at significant stages of the academic year, these functions contributed much to the departmental *esprit de corps*.

In more ways than one, Professor Balchin's retirement marked the end of an era, for it coincided with the onset of austerity in university finance, the need to consolidate rather than to diversify and to maximise the utility of existing resources. But the anticipated rigours of the 1980s will be less harsh and adaptations to new constraints will be less severe because of the sound and broadly based foundations and the wisely deployed resources that were so carefully and persistently established. It is perhaps symbolic that the anglepoise lamp on the professorial desk has been extinguished and the sweet sherry has disappeared from the professorial cupboard, but a more austere future should present no intractable problems to the Department.

Professor Balchin's erstwhile Swansea colleagues have enjoyed compiling the material for this commemorative volume; they hope that it will bring the pleasures of reminiscence and an awareness of a real sense of achievement to its recipient and that it will be valued by those who have been associated with the Swansea Department of Geography and by the larger fraternity of geographers who have enjoyed association with Bill Balchin. They extend their continued good wishes to Bill and Lily in their new home at Ilkley for a long, happy and satisfying retirement.

Geography in the University College of Swansea 1920–1978

by W. G. V. BALCHIN

Despite efforts by the citizens of Swansea in the eighteen-eighties and at the turn of the century it was not until 1920 that a University College at Swansea emerged. An important landmark was the appointment of the Royal Commission under the chairmanship of Viscount Haldane during the First World War 'to enquire into the organisation and work of the University of Wales and its three constituent Colleges and into the relations of those Colleges and other institutions in Wales providing education of a post-secondary nature'. The Royal Commission, although faced with a heavy agenda, nevertheless devoted much time and energy to a searching examination of the claims put forward by the citizens of Swansea for the establishment of a University College. The outcome was a recommendation in 1918 that a further University College be established in Swansea but with the proviso that humane as well as technical and scientific studies should be provided.

The gift of Singleton Abbey and a surrounding area of 19 acres of parkland, plus an additional area of 15 acres for playing fields, together with a sum of £60,000, all from the Corporation of Swansea, launched the new College in 1920 under the Principalship of Sir Franklin Sibly – a distinguished geologist from Newcastle. Needless to say, Geology was among the first seven science departments of 1920, to be followed by five Arts departments in 1921.

At this time Geography itself was a newly emergent university subject and chairs in the subject were confined to London, Liverpool and Aberystwyth. It may come as a surprise to many therefore to learn that Geography was studied and taught in Swansea right from the beginning of the College in 1920. This took the form of a special course of lectures and practical work for Geography teachers which was given at the new College on Saturday mornings during the first two terms by Dr. A. E. Trueman, who had been appointed Head of the Department of Geology, and Mr. S. W. Rider of Gowerton Grammar School. This course proved very popular and 78 students drawn from all the towns in the region participated. This number was almost as great as the total number of full time students registered by the newly emergent College. The course arose as a result of the growing interest in Geography at the school level and the need for qualifications by interested teachers. A Certificate of Proficiency was awarded to those teachers who successfully completed the course.

The Saturday morning course was continued into subsequent years by Dr. Trueman and Mr. Rider but the numbers gradually declined as the local teachers acquired the necessary qualifications. It was then decided to cater for intending teachers of Geography by instituting in the session commencing October 1927 a Certificate Course in Geography which was taken in conjunction with the Final or Honours Courses in Geology, supported by a course in Surveying in the Department of Engineering. No less than eleven students opted for this combination in October 1927. Out of the course there emerged in 1929 the classic book on the Physical and Economic Geography of South Wales by A. E. Trueman and S. W. Rider.

The popularity of the Certificate course in Geography contributed in no small measure to the upgrading of Geology into a Professorial Department – Dr. A. E. Trueman becoming Professor at the beginning of the session commencing October 1930. In the session 1930–31 the University approved the institution of courses in Geography up to the standard of the Final degree and Mr. D. Trevor Williams M.A. was appointed as a Lecturer in Geography as from October 1931 within a newly constituted Department of Geology and Geography under Professor A. E. Trueman. Mr. Williams was a graduate of Aberystwyth and was a Reader in Geography at the University College of Exeter at the time of his appointment. Subsidiary classes in Geography were started in October 1931 and Final courses in October 1932.

Professor A. E. Trueman resigned from his Swansea chair in 1933 on his appointment to Bristol University and was replaced by Professor T. Neville-George, then only 29 years in age, but fortunately also considerably interested in matters geographical as a result of his research work in geomorphology. The twin development of Geology and Geography pioneered by Professor Trueman was carried forwards by Professor Neville-George and it is significant that during the nineteen-thirties there were at times more Final Geography students in the Department than Final Geology students. It was during this period that the combined Department expanded into the first floor area of Singleton Abbey where laboratories were created to meet the growing needs of Geology and Geography.

The pressure of work falling upon Mr. Williams as the sole teacher for the Subsidiary and Finals courses in Geography was of course considerable and in October 1934 Mr. M. L. T. Sinclair B.Sc. was appointed as a Temporary Assistant Lecturer for one year to help Mr. Williams. Assistance was also forthcoming from the geology section for the work in physical geography. Despite the difficulties Mr. Williams maintained a steady output of research work in the fields of historical and economic geography.

This pattern of work and activity continued up to the outbreak of the Second World War in 1939 and although Honours degrees in Geography were still unobtainable at Swansea the Department began to attract research students in Geography. The first of these, Mr. E. J. Howell was awarded an M.Sc. in 1938, and subsequently a Ph.D., shortly before becoming Head of the Department of Geography in Gordon Memorial College, Khartoum – so initiating an interesting link which has continued to the present day.

Although the campus of the University College of Swansea became a hive of activity during the Second World War it was mainly related to evacuated Government departments: formal teaching in the College declined dramatically. In the Department of Geology and Geography further complications arose as a result of the involvement of both Professor Neville-George and Mr. D. T. Williams in the newly constituted Ministry of Town and Country Planning. Eventually Mr. Williams resigned from his College post in order to become a full time member of the Ministry of Town and Country Planning and in October 1945 Miss Pegi Bowen John took over the Geography responsibilities as a Temporary Assistant Lecturer until the appointment of Mr. B. H. Farmer M.A. as a Lecturer in Geography. Miss John (better known to many in Swansea as Mrs. Pegi Hopkins of Glanmôr Girls and Bishop Gore Schools) then reverted to the post of Departmental Demonstrator.

The combined Department also lost Professor Neville-George to Glasgow in 1946 and the new Head was Professor Duncan Leitch. Numbers in the College began to rise rapidly with the return of ex-service students and by 1947–48 the combined department had 235 registered students and the problem of accommodation was acute.

A further change in the arrangements for Geography was about to take place as Mr. Farmer returned to St. John's College, Cambridge, as a Fellow and Miss John resigned

University College of Swansea Campus, circa 1958, with the first of the new buildings, Natural Sciences, in the foreground. Geography occupies the nearest quarter of this building in this view.

following her marriage. Two new appointments were made as from October 1948, Mr. John Oliver of University College, Dundee, became Lecturer in Geography and Miss Gillian E. Groom, from the University of Birmingham, Assistant Lecturer in Geography. The Geography section of the combined department then consisted of a small room (now a store room) and a lecture room in the south-west corner of the inner courtyard of Singleton Abbey. The staff room had to accommodate all the maps, survey equipment, lecturers' desks and files needed by Geography. Technical assistance was provided by the legendary technician in Geology, Mr. Trevor Marchant, notable at this time as the only member of the Department who possessed a car!

Significant changes were, however, about to take place. The pressure of numbers forced an improvement in accommodation and in 1952 Geography moved into the house in the cobbled courtyard released by the retirement of the Registrar, Mr. Drew. Separate rooms became available for the members of staff whilst two small lecture rooms, a small map library, laboratory and dark room were created. Pressure was also mounting for the provision of Honours courses in Geography and the development of a separate department. Professor Duncan Leitch in Geology, Professor David Quinn in History and Professor Benjamin Farrington in Classics were all strong supporters on Senate of this proposal.

The *sine qua non* of university expansion is however land for building and Swansea's second great chance came in 1950 when, in part due to the negotiating skill of Principal J. S. Fulton (later Lord Fulton), the Corporation gave to the College a further twenty-six acres of Singleton Park alongside the land of its earlier gifts. This enabled an imaginative development plan for a college of 2,000 students to be drawn up. This plan envisaged the elimination of all the inter-war temporary buildings and their replacement by a central College House backed by Halls of Residence and surrounded by four major buildings housing Pure Sciences, Natural Sciences, Applied Sciences and Arts.

In the early 1950s, the academic section of the College under the greatest pressure and with the worst accommodation was the Natural Science group. The decision was therefore made to construct the Natural Sciences Building first and expand the two Departments of Biology and Geology, with Geography, into four separate Departments of Botany, Zoology, Geology and Geography. A million pound project was submitted to the University Grants Committee and sympathetically received (Sir Arthur Trueman was then Chairman!) but the resources available meant that the building would have to be constructed in two phases.

Concurrently, efforts were being made to extend the Geography courses to include Honours: the Senate and Council eventually approved this step in the session 1952–53. Honours courses were instituted as from October 1953 and additional assistance became available with the appointment of Mr. F. V. Emery from Oxford as an Assistant Lecturer. The University was next approached so that a Chair of Geography and separate Department of Geography could be instituted. Dr. W. G. V. Balchin, then a Lecturer at King's College, London, was appointed to the foundation Chair as from the 1st August 1954.

In the same year work had also started on the centre block of the Natural Sciences Building and for the next two years the staff of the new Geography Department, along with their colleagues in Geology, Botany and Zoology, were fully extended with the preparation of detailed drawings for the layout and equipment of the new building. The centre block, costing over half a million pounds, was opened in time for the October 1956 session. The acquisition of the new accommodation now permitted a policy of planned expansion to take place in which accommodation, equipment, staff and then students followed in that order. It was during this period that Mr. John Oliver became a Senior Lecturer, and Dr. Maling, Dr. Cousens, Mr. Manners (subsequently a Reader at

University College, London) and Miss Glenys Thomas (subsequently Mrs. Glenys Bridges) joined the staff: Mr. Emery returned to Oxford to a Fellowship.

The new state of equilibrium in the expanded Department of Geography was, however, shortlived. The mounting national pressure for university places led not only to the foundation of several new universities in the early nineteen-sixties but also to the continued expansion of the established universities. Additional finance provided by the Government enabled work to start in 1959 on the erection of the wings of the Natural Sciences Building. The staff of the Department were then engaged in another planning exercise, providing the architects with detailed drawings of all the fittings and equipment needed in the wing. The completion of the building in October 1960 resulted in an 'H' shaped building covering over 100,000 square feet of floor space at a cost of £800,000. At the time it was one of the largest university buildings underwritten by the U.G.C.

The building was of considerable interest to geographers since Swansea now possessed one of the first Departments of Geography to be planned on the drawing board. The accommodation available included a lecture laboratory for each of the three undergraduate years, a general lecture theatre seating 120 and a smaller theatre seating 60, staff rooms, research rooms, a departmental office, a drawing office, a set of photographic rooms, store rooms, a large map library and rolled map store. Special laboratories were also included for advanced undergraduate and postgraduate research work in geomorphology, hydrology, pedology, cartography and photogrammetry. Facilities for meteorology included a work room and an observation enclosure whilst a garage was also provided for a Land-Rover and Minibus. A large library serving all four departments was also part of the building.

Interesting features of the equipment in the Department included power-operated blackout curtains in the lecture-laboratories and extensive use of cork panelled walls for display purposes. Most of the staff and research rooms had special fitted service benches including hot and cold water points, gas and electrical points, a telephone point, a tracing frame and drawer and cupboard facilities. The map library was planned initially to absorb 50,000 maps with future storage facilities for another 50,000 maps (it currently houses 80,000) and the library very rapidly became the largest collection of maps in South Wales. The physical laboratory was equipped with full gas, electrical and water services together with vacuum and compressed air, and the initial apparatus included an earth sculpture tank, stream flume and wave trough. The pedological unit was equipped with standard apparatus for soil and pollen analysis and had rooms for micro-pedology, soil crushing and soil chemistry together with a constant temperature balance room. A set of four photographic rooms housed a large horizontal camera and copying units as well as the standard photographic equipment. Photogrammetric apparatus included a Santoni Stereocartograph III, a Zeiss Stereotope, Bausch and Lomb Multiplex equipment, a Watts Radial Line Plotter and Zeiss Slotted Template equipment. Class sets of meteorological apparatus, survey equipment and binocular stereoscopes with parallax bars were also provided.

It is little wonder that, with this wealth of accommodation and equipment and the investment of over a quarter of a million pounds in the subject, the Department of Geography at Swansea soon became a focus of attention as a whole succession of new departments of Geography began to emerge both at home and overseas in the expanding university situation of the nineteen-sixties. The annual departmental reports record many of the requests for assistance which were received during the next few years and by 1967 over fifty universities and institutions from all over the world had sought building, development and equipment information and advice from the Department. Professor Balchin undertook a tour of emergent university departments of

After twenty years of new building, University College of Swansea Campus, circa 1978. Geography occupies parts of the two nearest buildings in this view.

14

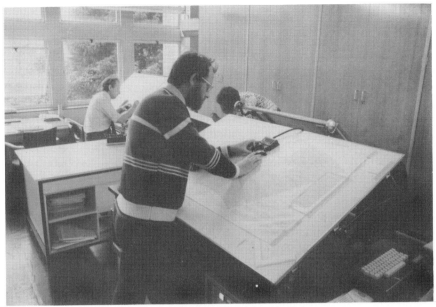

above: Staff in the Cartographic Unit.

below: A corner of the Map Library.

Geography in Eastern Canada in 1965 and provided a great deal of necessary data; assistance was also provided to a large number of United Kingdom institutions whilst later in the sixties the planning and equipping of the Department of Geography at St. David's University College, Lampeter, was wholly undertaken at Swansea prior to the appointment of any geography staff at Lampeter.

The addition of the wing in 1960 enabled a new and third phase of expansion to begin. The first year intake of Arts and Science students in Geography was doubled from 60 to 120 with a consequential doubling of honours and general classes in the ensuing second and third years. During this phase Mr. H. R. J. Davies, Dr. Graham Humphrys, Dr. E. M. Bridges, Mr. H. J. R. Henderson and Mr. C. Tomlinson joined the permanent staff. The link with Khartoum which had commenced with Dr. Howell's wartime appointment at the Gordon Memorial College (later to become the University College of Khartoum) was maintained by the appointment of Mr. H. R. J. Davies who had served for five years in Khartoum, and it was further strengthened when Mr. John Oliver was seconded to Khartoum for two years from October 1961 as Professor and Head of Department. During this phase of expanding student numbers the Department also experimented with the appointment of Tutors to assist in laboratory, tutorial and field work.

While the new building provided a wealth of library, lecturing and laboratory facilities, care was taken not to lose sight of the fact that Swansea is situated in the midst of a natural field laboratory. The Gower Peninsula illustrates a wide range of normal and coastal processes of erosion and accretion, while the immediate hinterland demonstrates normal and glaciological morphology. South Wales as a whole also exhibits a wide variety of economic and historical landscape changes. Thus, for both undergraduate teaching as well as the encouragement of research, the Department is enviable in having so close at hand such a great variety of terrain. Finally the availability of transport enabled a balance to be achieved at all levels between field-work, library work and laboratory work.

It was during the phase between the opening of the centre block of the Natural Sciences Building and the construction of the wings that Professor Balchin initiated some interesting research in the Department on university location in Great Britain. Information and memoranda were supplied, on request, to a number of authorities including the Association of University Teachers, and to promotion committees in Norwich, Coventry, Gloucester, Hereford and the Isle of Thanet. Professor Balchin broadcast on this topic on 21st November 1958 and was also invited by the Mayor and City Council of Hereford to address a public meeting in Hereford on 19th March 1959. During the summer vacation of 1959 the Department was asked to submit a memorandum on this topic to the newly constituted U.G.C. Committee on New University Institutions. Further information was also supplied to the promotion committees at York, Norwich and Gloucester.

Approval for new universities at Norwich and York was announced in April 1960 and at Canterbury, Colchester and Coventry in May 1961, whilst Lancaster followed shortly afterwards. Along with Sussex which had gained approval in 1958 this group of seven new universities formed the spearhead of the great expansion of the sixties. There is clear evidence that the analytical work undertaken in Swansea played a significant part in the selection of the seven from a large number of proposals. These universities were the last to be established in Britain along traditional historical and geographical lines.

The construction of the wings of the Natural Sciences Building was paralleled by the building of College House and the first two Halls of Residence on the campus. The completion of all these buildings by 1961 enabled the College to offer unique facilities

16

left:
E.D.M. and Theodolites for Field Surveying.

below:
Mapping from Aerial Photography with the Stereosimplex IIc Plotter.

for conferences and the early sixties are well remembered in Geography for the succession of local and national conferences and exhibitions organised by the Department. In the Lent term of 1962 a conference on 'North America' was organised in conjunction with the local branch of the Geographical Association and this was followed in the Easter vacation by a conference on 'Geography in the Secondary School' organised in conjunction with the Department of Education. During the summer vacation a further Ministry of Education conference on 'Geography' was held.

In the Christmas vacation of 1962–63 the Institute of British Geographers held one of its more memorable annual conferences. Despite the heavy snowfalls, over 250 geographers attended although all the field excursions had to be cancelled. In the Easter vacation of 1963, Swansea was selected as the venue for the Geographical Association's national Spring Conference and over 300 teachers were in attendance.

Five major conferences in two years meant a heavy load of additional work and responsibility for all the members of the academic, secretarial and technical staff of the Geography Department. In addition to the administrative and organisational details which these meetings entailed, members of the department contributed over 30 lectures, conducted over 40 excursions, mounted a great variety of exhibitions and also produced a play for the entertainment of the Geographical Association's Spring Conference. There is little doubt that these activities did a great deal to place Swansea firmly on the 'geographical' map of Britain.

In October 1960, a large Map Exhibition was organised jointly with the Ordnance Survey as part of the Swansea Festival. This attracted over 3,000 visitors including over 1,000 senior pupils from forty colleges and schools throughout South Wales. In the Lent term of 1961 an exhibition of maps and photographs covering recent developments in China was mounted. During the Summer term of 1961 a further exhibition was mounted in connection with the work of the Second Land Utilisation Survey of Britain. This was followed in the Michaelmas term of 1961 by an exhibition dealing with the work of the Schools Service Division of the Museum of Wales. Exhibitions organised in connection with the five conferences mentioned above were also made available to students in the Department.

Members of staff also found themselves with a further major commitment during the long vacation of 1964 as most were involved in the various symposia, excursions and field meetings organised for the 20th Congress of the International Geographical Union which was opened by Her Majesty the Queen in London in July 1964. A number of field excursions also visited, or were based upon, Swansea, before and after the main meetings of the Congress.

Two further major national conferences followed in the long vacation of 1965 when the British Cartographic Society and the British Soil Society both met in Swansea with the Department of Geography acting as host.

During this period the Department also became heavily involved in the Lower Swansea Valley Project, contributing a considerable amount of expertise in the fields of survey, cartography, land-use, climatology, hydrology, pedology and social geography. The investigation culminated in the publication of the Report in May 1967.

The continued growth in both staff and student numbers during the early nineteen-sixties led to approval for a second chair within the Department and this was advertised during the session 1965–66. Few were surprised when Mr. John Oliver, with his experience of the Khartoum Department, and with his prolonged period of service in the Swansea Department, was elected to this chair from October 1966.

By this time a fourth phase of expansion was in progress, partly as a result of the Robbins report of 1963, and partly because of the institution within the College of a new Faculty of Economic and Social Studies and the introduction of American Studies, in all of which Geography was asked to participate. Unlike the earlier phases of expansion, however, when accommodation came first to be followed by equipment, staff and then students, after 1964 the students arrived first, and were followed by staff, equipment and finally additional accommodation. The Natural Sciences Building could not contain this further expansion and after three uncomfortable years in which staff and students were scattered over the campus, the first of the Annexes was acquired and converted to the use of Geography.

Annex A was an old Arts Building of the nineteen-twenties which became available when Mathematics was rehoused during the session 1966–67. Professor Oliver then took charge of this Annex with its office, eight members of staff, two technicians, research rooms and a lecture-laboratory. In size the addition approached that of the centre block of the Natural Sciences Building. During this fourth phase of expansion Dr. D. T. Herbert, Dr. W. K. D. Davies (subsequently Professor at Calgary University), Dr. D. M. Harding (subsequently at the University College of North Wales), Dr. J. A. Edwards and Mr. G. B. Lewis joined the staff while the number of tutorships was increased to six.

Student numbers continued to grow in the late sixties and further changes occurred around 1970 when a second Annex was acquired. This was the Cedar Hut north of the Arts Hall which previously had housed the Department of German. This was taken over for further staff rooms and research rooms for Geography. At this time Professor John Oliver took up the offer of the Foundation Chair of Geography in the new James Cook University at Townsville, Queensland, Australia and almost paradoxically was replaced by Professor R. H. Greenwood who had been Head of the Department of Geography at the University of Queensland, Brisbane, Australia. Professor Greenwood's appointment reflected the need to meet the growing responsibilities of the Department in the field of Human Geography. By this time a pattern of two chairs, one physical, one human, had developed in most university departments of geography in the United Kingdom.

During the early seventies and after the acquisition of Annex B, further staff additions included Dr. W. C. Rouse, Dr. L. Symons, Dr. A. H. Perry, Dr. C. J. Thomas and Mr. T. Fearnside. The department also decided to experiment with a graduate administrative assistant's post to counter the growing amount of paper work involved in running the department. This post was filled in the first instance by Miss E. J. Rees and subsequently Miss S. E. Ashton. This was another pioneer experiment by the Swansea Geography Department and, like the graduate map librarians and graduate cartographers, has not only proved successful but has been copied by other university departments of geography.

Despite the extensive facilities of the Natural Sciences Building, Geography by this time was now scattered in four different places on the campus. A somewhat similar fate had befallen the other natural science subjects of Botany, Zoology and Geology (which had acquired Oceanography in addition) and accommodation problems were acute. College numbers were by now well past the 3,000 mark and the original Natural Sciences Building had been designed for a College of 1,800–2,000.

A considerable effort was hence made in the early seventies to find a solution to this acute accommodation problem. Various imaginative schemes were prepared and submitted to the U.G.C. but Treasury constraints on new science buildings in the country eliminated the sensible solutions and in the end the U.G.C. was only able to provide sufficient capital to replace the four old huts dating from the 1920s which, after fifty years, were at the end of their useful life. Construction of the 'extension' to the Natural Sciences Building began in 1973 and was completed in time for occupation in October 1975. N.S.B. West and N.S.B. East, linked by a covered bridge at first floor

Table 1
The growth in the number of students registered for Geography courses in the University College of Swansea 1931–1979

1931–32	28	1955–56	118
1932–33	50	1956–57	138
1933–34	61	1957–58	134
1934–35	54	1958–59	138
1935–36	50	1959–60	133
1936–37	47	1960–61	131
1937–38	31	1961–62	172
1938–39	33	1962–63	210
1939–40		1963–64	260
1940–41		1964–65	300
1941–42		1965–66	350
1942–43		1966–67	392
1943–44	17	1967–68	442
1944–45	14	1968–69	463
1945–46	25	1969–70	488
1946–47	46	1970–71	513
1947–48	74	1971–72	516
1948–49	81	1972–73	578
1949–50	69	1973–74	585
1950–51	68	1974–75	565
1951–52	76	1975–76	529
1952–53	64	1976–77	579
1953–54	72	1977–78	603
1954–55	89	1978–79	651

level, bring together the greater part of the Department once more, but 'outliers' still exist and the lack of accommodation inhibited any further dramatic developments in the mid seventies.

During the early seventies the Department was much involved in preparatory work for the visit of the British Association for the Advancement of Science to Swansea in September 1971. The compilation of the *Scientific Survey of Swansea and its Region* under the editorship of Professor Balchin involved all the service staff and most of the academic staff over a two year period. The Department also acted as host for Section E of the Association during the meeting and contributed extensively to the excursion programme. At this time also the Department undertook the preparation of an *Atlas for Community Development in Africa* for UNESCO together with an *Amenity Study on the Towy-Brianne Water Supply Scheme* for the West Glamorgan Water Board.

The theme of growth and expansion which had dominated the first twenty years of life in the independent Department of Geography was slowed but not halted in the mid-seventies. Along with the rest of the country the College and hence the Department faced acute financial problems which inhibited current activities as well as development. Problems arose with equipment, staff and accommodation most of which were related to insufficient funding of the Department in relationship to the student burden the Department was carrying. Some members of staff began to show signs of the increased pressures and regretfully Miss Gillian E. Groom had to seek an early retirement in 1976 owing to ill health. At the time of writing this account Miss Groom still holds the record for the longest service in Swansea in Geography, having been a member of College for 28 years.

above: The North Laboratory.

below: The Departmental Lecture Theatre.

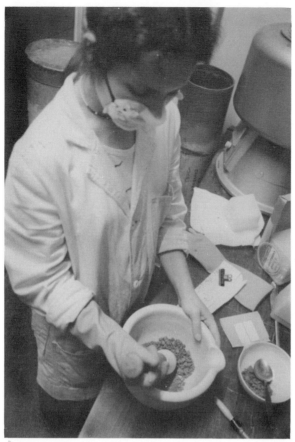

left:
Pedology Laboratory Work.

below:
Part of the Physical Geography
Laboratory.

22

During the mid-seventies, changes to the permanent academic staff were largely related to replacements, Mr. R. P. D. Walsh replaced Dr. D. M. Harding and Mr. M. Fielding replaced Miss G. E. Groom. Probably one of the main reasons for the success of the Department of Geography at Swansea during its first twenty-five years has been the relative stability of the permanent academic staff. Only six members of staff have resigned or retired during this period – Mr. F. V. Emery (to an Oxford Fellowship), Mr. G. Manners (to a Readership at University College, London), Professor J. Oliver (to the Foundation Chair at Townsville, Queensland, Australia), Dr. W. K. D. Davies (to a Professorship at Calgary University), Dr. D. M. Harding (to a Lectureship at University College of North Wales) and Miss G. E. Groom (retired owing to ill health). There has, however, been a continual input of young members of staff as a result of the success of the tutorship scheme. The complement of tutors rose to six by the mid-sixties and has been maintained at this number for well over a decade. The tutorship has always been regarded as a first step towards a career in higher education and appointments have always been highly selective. Well over 30 tutors have now been trained at Swansea and apart from one appointment in the Civil Service all have gone on to posts in universities, colleges of education or polytechnics.

One consistent aspect of Departmental life throughout the first twenty-five years has been the pioneer work undertaken in field studies and field work. That field work would figure largely in the degree structure at Swansea was a *sine qua non* in view of the location of the Department in the midst of a varied field laboratory with such a wealth of natural and man-made features. Local field work has naturally always featured in the undergraduate and postgraduate work. Additionally, however, field excursions have been organised, initially to other parts of the British Isles, and in more recent years to overseas locations in The Netherlands, Norway, France, Germany, Spain, Italy, Yugoslavia, Greece, Majorca and Tunisia. The Department was a pioneer here in adapting package tours in the off-peak season as a base for field excursions.

The Department was also consistently represented on, or actually organised some of, the inter-continental excursions promoted through the Geographical Association and its branches during the period 1964–1972. During the summer vacation of 1964 there was a notable trans-Atlantic field study tour covering parts of Eastern Canada, the eastern United States and the West Indies with 112 participants. This was followed in 1966 by a Tropical Summer School for over 100 participants based on the University in San Juan Puerto Rico in the West Indies. In 1968 a smaller group of 70 undertook a 2,000 mile 'safari' from Mombasa, Kenya to Fort Portal and the Mountains of the Moon in Uganda. In 1970 a party of 150 geography teachers and lecturers participated in a trans-continental field study tour across Canada commencing in Montreal and terminating in Vancouver. The success of this venture led to a further visit with 150 participants to Western Canada and Western U.S.A. in the summer of 1972. Regrettably currency and other economic difficulties brought this activity to a halt thereafter.

Mention should also be made of the use which has been made of Departmental and College facilities by visiting field groups. The Department has pioneered package deals in Swansea which gave visiting geographical parties not only accommodation and meals in the Halls of Residence and College House but also working facilities in the Department. Well over 200 parties have been catered for during the Easter and Summer vacations of the last decade and if we add the number of 'Journeys through Geography' rail visitors (also serviced by members of the Department) no less than 10,000 visiting pupils and students of geography have been based on the department for field work during the last decade. Although serving a wider community, staff contributions to this kind of activity are clearly valuable for recruitment possibilities.

Entrances to Natural Sciences Buildings, East and West, in which the Department of Geography is principally housed.

Space does not permit a detailed analysis of the research interests and publications of members of staff in the Department. The full details are, however, available for those interested in the annual reports of the College. We can only record here that several hundred research papers in a wide variety of topics have been published by the academic staff during the first twenty-five years along with well over 30 books and atlases (listed in table 2).

The mid-seventies has also seen the formalisation, through the Inter-University Council, of the previously mentioned 'link' with Khartoum. Arrangements have now been made for a regular exchange of staff and postgraduate students. Exchanges to date auger well for the future and an ambitious research programme is being developed. The Department also has a large number of unofficial links with departments of Geography in Canada and Australia. These have arisen through members of staff as a result of exchanges, study leave and participation in activities such as lecture tours and summer schools. These links have been valuable in placing postgraduate students from the Department, with the result that Swansea is now well represented amongst the academic staffs of departments of Geography in the Commonwealth.

Table 2
Books and related contributions published by members of staff during the period 1954–1978

W. G. V. Balchin	Cornwall: A Volume in the Making of the English Landscape Series, Hodder and Stoughton, 1955.
W. G. V. Balchin	Geography and Man. Advisory Editor. A three volume World Survey, The New Era Publishing Company 1955.
D. H. Maling	The Falkland Islands (with M. B. R. Cawkell and E. M. Cawkell) London, 1960.
C. Tomlinson	Survey Instruments and Techniques, Estates Gazette, 1963.
G. Manners	The Geography of Energy, Hutchinson, 1964.
G. Manners	South Wales in the Sixties, Pergamon, 1964.
H. J. R. Henderson	Africa and the Islands (with R. J. Harrison Church, J. I. Clarke and P. J. Clarke) Longmans Green 1964.
E. M. Bridges	The Soils and Land Use of the District of North Derby, Memoir of the Soil Survey of England and Wales, the Agricultural Research Council, Harpenden, 1966.
K. J. Hilton	The Lower Swansea Valley Project, Longmans, 1967. (Contributions from W. G. V. Balchin, E. M. Bridges, D. C. Ledger, D. H. Maling and J. Oliver).
W. G. V. Balchin	Cornwall: The Geographical Association, 1967.
D. H. Maling	Geology of the South Orkney Islands (with D. Matthews) Falklands Islands Dependencies Survey Scientific Report No. 25, H.M.S.O. 1967.
W. G. V. Balchin	Geography: An Outline for the Intending Student (Editor and three chapters) Routledge and Kegan Paul, 1970.
E. M. Bridges	World Soils, Cambridge University Press, 1970.
W. K. D. Davies	Urban Essays: Studies in the Geography of Wales (Joint Editor with H. Carter) Longmans 1970.
W. G. V. Balchin	Swansea and its Region: A Scientific Survey for the British Association Meeting in Swansea 1971, Editor. (Contributions from G. E. Groom, J. Oliver, D. M. Harding, E. M. Bridges, S. H. Cousens, H. R. J. Davies, D. T. Herbert, H. J. R. Henderson, G. Humphrys, J. A. Edwards and W. G. V. Balchin.)
C. J. Thomas	Major Suburban Shopping Centres: Atlas and Statistical Handbook (with D. Thorpe and P. T. Kivell) Manchester Business School, 1971.
D. M. Harding	A recreational and Amenity study of the Llyn Brianne Area, West Glamorgan Water Board, 1972.
G. Humphrys	Industrial Britain: South Wales, David and Charles, 1972.

L. Symons	Russian Agriculture: A Geographic Survey, G. Bell and Sons, 1972.
D. T. Herbert	Urban Geography: A Social Perspective, David and Charles, 1972.
H. R. J. Davies	Tropical Africa: An Atlas for Rural Development, University of Wales Press, 1973.
D. H. Maling	Coordinate Systems and Map Projections, George Philip, 1973.
A. H. Perry	Synoptic Climatology (with R. G. Barry) Methuen 1973.
L. Symons	Geography of the British Isles: Agriculture, Hicks Smith, 1973.
H. R. J. Davies	An Advanced Geography of Africa (with J. I. Clarke et al) Hulton, 1975.
A. H. Perry	Weather Maps (with V. C. Perry), Oliver and Boyd 1975.
L. Symons	Russian Transport: an Historical and Geographical Survey (with C. White), Bell, 1975.
A. H. Perry	Weather and Climate (with V. C. Perry) Longmans, Ireland, 1975.
H. R. J. Davies	Town and Country in North Central State of Nigeria, Ahmadu Bello University Press 1976.
D. T. Herbert	Social Areas in Cities: Vol. 1 Spatial Processes and Form. (Editor with R. J. Johnston) John Wiley, 1976.
D. T. Herbert	Social Areas in Cities: Vol. 2 Spatial Perspectives on Problems and Policies. (Editor with R. J. Johnston) John Wiley 1976.
A. H. Perry	Geographical Field Studies in Ireland (with V. C. Perry) Educational Co. of Ireland, 1977.
A. H. Perry	The Ocean-Atmosphere System (with M. J. Walker) Longmans, 1977.
E. M. Bridges	Problems of a Small Estuary (editor with A. Nelson-Smith), University College of Swansea, 1977.
A. H. Perry	Weather and Climate for West African Schools Nigeria, 1977.
A. H. Perry	Statistical Diagrams in Geography (with V. C. Perry) Educational Company of Ireland, 1977.
D. T. Herbert	Geography and the Urban Environment (Editor with R. J. Johnston) Vol. 1 John Wiley, 1978.

Geography in Swansea currently registers over 600 students each session for its various courses in all four faculties in College. Its registrations in the Faculty of Science and the Faculty of Economic and Social Studies often exceed all other departments in these two Faculties; it is normally the third largest in the Faculty of Arts and contributes service courses to the Faculty of Applied Science. Over 100 students are prepared for graduation each year and there is a postgraduate school of around 20, the academic staff currently numbers 27 supported by a secretarial and technical staff of 11. What began 'in a cupboard under the stairs' of Singleton Abbey has grown to be the largest department in the College and one of the largest departments of Geography in the United Kingdom. Many of its former students now occupy positions of responsibility in universities, technical colleges, schools, the civil service, local government and industry both at home and overseas. Its staff and postgraduate students have established a reputation for the Department in the world of Geography where it has pioneered many ideas ranging from academic innovations to the planning and equipping of a geography department, to graduate cartographers, map librarians and administrative assistants, as well as novel field excursions.

Geography at Swansea thus enters its Silver Jubilee year as an independent department with a reputation, staff and material resources which auger well for the future despite present difficulties. There is ample scope for further development, more particularly in the Faculty of Economic and Social Studies and the Faculty of Applied Science. New methods of collecting and analysing data, remote sensing, greater precision afforded by quantitative techniques, the development of computer-graphics, new conceptual frameworks of thought, the recognition of graphicacy as a communication skill as important as literacy, numeracy and articulacy, the revival of interest in land-use studies, and the acceptance of a geographical approach to the solution of social and economic problems: all these and more imply that Geography is entering the 1980s with new and expanding horizons.

BIBLIOGRAPHY OF W. G. V. BALCHIN

1937   The Erosion Surfaces of North Cornwall
Geographical Journal Vol XC No 1 July 1937 pp 52–63
Field surveys and maps for 'The Culbin Sands and Burghead Bay' by J. A. Steers
Geographical Journal Vol XC No 6 December 1937 pp 498–528

1938   The Chalk Water Table South-east of Cambridge (with W. V. Lewis)
Handbook for the British Association for the Advancement of Science meeting in Cambridge 1938 pp 20–24
Field surveys and maps for 'Minor Changes in Shingle Spits' by J. A. Steers
International Geographical Congress Amsterdam 1938

1939   Field surveys and maps for 'Sand and Shingle Formations in Cardigan Bay' by J. A. Steers
Geographical Journal Vol XCIV No 3 September 1939 pp 209–227
Geomorphological contributions in 'Nivation and Corrie Erosion in West Spitsbergen'
Longyear City Spitsbergen: Mining Coal at 78° North (with Norman Pye)
Geographical Journal Vol XCIV No 6 December 1939 pp 447–465

1940   Past Sea Levels at Dungeness (with W. V. Lewis)
Geographical Journal Vol XCVI No 4 October 1940 pp 258–285

1941   The Raised Features of Billefjord and Sassenfjord, West Spitsbergen
Geographical Journal Vol XCVII No 6 June 1941 pp 364–376
Longyear City Spitsbergen: Mining Coal at 78° North (with Norman Pye)
Chambers's Journal November 1941 pp 689–691

1942   Map Making in Wartime
B.B.C. talk published in The Listener 14th January 1943

1943   The Sargasso, Strangest Sea in the World
B.B.C. talk published in The Listener 10th June 1943

1944   Deserts of the British Isles
Chambers's Journal February 1944 pp 62–64
Cartography and the Universities (with Norman Pye)
Nature 1st July 1944
Wartime Information (with Norman Pye)
Letter to The Times 6th January 1944
The Swastika
Folklore Vol LV December 1944 pp 167–168

1945   The Construction of Distribution Maps (with W. V. Lewis)
Geography No 149 Vol XXX Pt 3 September 1945 pp 86–92

1946   The Geomorphology of the North Cornish Coast
Transactions of the Royal Geological Society of Cornwall Vol XVII Pt 6 1946 pp 317–334
Training Areas
Letter to The Times 30th November 1946

1947   Forecasting the Weather
Letter to The Times 5th April 1947
Air Maps
Empire Survey Review Vol IX No 66 1947 pp 138–147
A Micro-Climatological Investigation of Bath and the Surrounding District (with Norman Pye)
Quarterly Journal of the Royal Meteorological Society Vol 73 No 317–318 July–October 1947 pp 297–334
Air Transport and Geography
Royal Geographical Society December 147 pp 23
Geography and Man (Advisory Editor of a three volume world survey)
New Era Publishing Co Ltd

1948   Local Rainfall Variations in Bath and the Surrounding District (with Norman Pye)
Quarterly Journal of the Royal Meteorological Society Vol 74 No 321–322 July–October 1948 pp 361–378
Local Climatic Studies for Schools
Geography No 161 Vol XXXIII Pt 3 September 1948 pp 128–136
The Danger of Smog
Letter in The Times 6th November 1948
Parenthood and Taxation
Letter to The Times 9th December 1948
Reprinted under the title Taxation Favours Childless Couples Economic Digest February 1949 p 253

1949   Recent Advances in the Study of Micro-Climatology
British Science News Vol 2 No 21 pp 271–274
Climate and Weather Exercises (with A. W. Richards)
Harrap 1949 80 pp
G.S.G.S Maps and H.D. Charts
Geography No 163 Vol XXXIV Pt 1 March 1949 pp 37–39
Man as a factor in recent climatic change
Contribution to a Symposium 'Post Glacial Climatic Change' Quarterly Journal of the Royal Meteorological Society No 324 Vol 75 April 1949 pp 181–182

1950   Maps for the Tourist
Letter to The Times 1st July 1950
Observations on Local Temperature Variations and Plant Responses (with Norman Pye)
Journal of Ecology Vol 38 No 2 November 1950 pp 345–353
Temperature and Humidity Variations in an Urban Area of Diversified Relief (with Norman Pye)
Journal of the Manchester Geographical Society 1949–50 pp 1–22
About 50 articles, maps and diagrams contributed to Chambers's Encyclopaedia

1951   The Geographical Association
The Times Educational Supplement 12th January 1951
Monthly Return Magic
Letter to The Times 30th March 1951
The Representation of True to Scale Linear Values on Map Projections
Geography No 172 Vol XXXVI Pt 2 May 1951 pp 120–124
Cartographic Portrayal by Geographers
Indian Geographical Journal Silver Jubilee Souvenir Volume 1951 pp 141–147

1952   Practical and Experimental Geography (with A. W. Richards)
Methuen 1952 136 pp
Economy of Fuel
Letter to The Times 21st March 1952

Erosion Surfaces of Exmoor and Adjacent Areas
Geographical Journal Vol CXVIII Pt 4 December 1952 pp 453–476
The Evidence for Late Tertiary Eustatic Changes of Sea Level in Western Europe
Proceedings of the VIIIth General Assembly of the International Geographical Congress at Washington U.S.A. 1952 pp 296–300

1953   Books for Freshmen
Letter to The Times 1st January 1953
Desert Landforms
Filmstrip Common Ground Ltd June 1953
The Drought in the Southwestern United States (with Norman Pye)
Weather Vol 8 No 8 August 1953 pp 233–236
River Floods in Great Britain
Nature Vol 172 15th August 1953 p 263
Flood Control and Water Conservation
Nature Vol 172 7th November 1953 p 823

1954   The Geographical Association
Nature Vol 173 16th January 1954 p 99
Mountain Building
Filmstrip Common Ground Ltd February 1954
The Choice of Map Projections
Empire Survey Review No 92 Vol XII 1954 pp 263–276
Recent Economic Trends in Arizona (with Norman Pye)
Geographical Journal Vol CXX Pt 2 June 1954 pp 156–173
Coastal Flooding in Britain
Nature Vol 174 31st July 1954 p 193
Development and Utilisation of Water Resources
Nature Vol 174 31st July 1954 p 213
Reprinted in the Journal of the Institution of Water Engineers Vol 9 No 1 February 1955 pp 17–18
Cornwall – Making of the English Landscape Series (ed. W. G. Hoskins)
Hodder and Stoughton 1954 128 pp

1955   The Geographical Association
Nature Vol 175 29th January 1955 p 198
Research in Geography
Inaugural Lecture University College of Swansea February 1955
Financial Aids to Geographical Research
Royal Geographical Society March 1955
Recent Advances in the Study of Micro-Climatology
Journal of the Institution of Water Engineers Vol 9 May 1955
The Water Problem in Great Britain
Nature Vol 176 17th December 1955 pp 1133–1134
Climate and Culture in Southern Arizona (with Norman Pye)
Weather Vol X No 12 December 1955 pp 399–404
Piedmont Profiles in the Arid Cycle (with Norman Pye)
Proceedings of the Geologists Association Vol 66 Pt 3 1955 pp 167–181
Geography and Man (Advisory Editor of a three volume world survey)
New Era Publishing Co Ltd

1956   The Sea Coast
Filmstrip Common Ground Ltd January 1956
Water Resources of Great Britain
Nature No 4498 Vol 177 p 75
Water in the Future
The Observer 27th May 1958

Water and the National Economy
River Boards Association Yearbook 1956 pp 1–14
Bookless Students
The Observer 7th October 1956

1957   The Nation's Water Supply. An address given to the annual conference of the Geographical Association and subsequently printed in –
The Contract Journal 17th January 1957
Water and Water Engineering No 732 Vol 61 February 1957
Journal of the National Farmers' Union April 1957
Geography No 197 Vol XLII Pt 3 July 1957 pp 149–159
Hydrological Research
Water and Water Engineering No 734 Vol 61 April 1957
Water in Britain
The Times 24th June 1957
Dangerous Waters
The Times Educational Supplement No 2201 26th July 1957
Water Resources in Great Britain
Nature No 4579 Vol 180 pp 223–224
Britain's Water Supply Problem
Water and Water Engineering No 737 Vol 61 July 1957
Map Projections in History
Impulse No 2 September 1957 pp 9–13

1958   Weathering and Mass Wasting (with A. M. Coleman)
Filmstrip Common Ground Ltd February 1958
A Water Use Survey
Water and Water Engineering No 746 Vol 62 April 1958
Seventy Years of Geography
The Times Educational Supplement No 2237 4th April 1958
Professors under Pressure
The Economist 12th July 1958 pp 108–109
The Purification of Saline Water
The New Scientist No 103 Vol 4 6th November 1958
A Water Use Survey
Geographical Journal Vol CXXIV Pt 4 December 1958 pp 476–493

1959   University Expansion in Great Britain
The New Scientist No 121 Vol 5 12th March 1959
Water Supply and Demand in Great Britain
Nature No 4688 Vol 184 pp BA 18– BA 20
Reprinted in Excerpta Medica, Amsterdam
The Origin and Development of Surface Depressions in the Mendip Hills (with A. M. Coleman)
Proceedings of the Geologists Associations Vol 70 Pt 4 1959 pp 291–309

1960   River Studies in Nigeria
Nature No 4709 Vol 185 p 274
Atlases Today
Geographical Magazine No 11 Vol XXXII April 1960 pp 554–563
A Nineteenth Century Pedestrian Excursion
Empire Survey Review No 116 Vol XV April 1960 pp 285–286
New Academic Structures – Planning for Emergent Universities
The Times Educational Supplement 24th June 1960 p 353
The World and Water
Vickers Magazine Summer 1960 pp 32–36
Water Resources in the United States
Nature No 4737 Vol 187 pp 562–564

The Mammoth Task of Mapping Britain
Evening Post Swansea 17th October 1960

1961　Hydrology in Great Britain
Nature No 4761 Vol 189 pp 278–279
New Universities
The Times Educational Supplement No 2390 10th March 1961
Water Resources in Wales
Nature No 4784 Vol 191 pp 135–136
Water Conservation in Great Britain
Nature No 4787 Vol 191 pp 421–423
Water Resources of the United States
Nature No 4787 Vol 191 pp 444–446
A New Campus Community Concept
The Times Educational Supplement No 2421 13th October 1961

1962　Geography – A Chapter in 'After the VIth'
Advisory Centre for Education 1962
Britain's Water Problem
Nature No 4822 Vol 193 pp 1244–1245
Bold Action Needed on Universities
The Times 3rd April 1962
Irrigation in Great Britain
Nature No 4842 Vol 195 pp 656–657
Recent Trends in Physical Geography
The Times Educational Supplement No 2459 6th July 1962
Reprinted in Education South Africa Vol LXXII No 9 September 1962

1964　The Denudation Chronology of South West England
Chapter in 'Present Views on Some Aspects of the Geology of Cornwall and Devon'
150th Anniversary Volume of the Royal Geological Society of Cornwall 1964 pp 267–281
Hydrology
Chapter in 'The British Isles' Published by Nelson for the International Geographical Congress London 1964 Edited by J. W. Watson and J. B. Sissons pp 74–90
Land and Water Use in the United States
Nature No 4941 Vol 203 p 113

1965　Sixteen articles jointly with A. M. Coleman on geographical aspects of Eastern Canada, Eastern U.S.A. and Puerto Rico
Panorama Vol XI 1965 Geographical Association
Puerto Rico (with A. M. Coleman)
Geography Vol L Pt 3 July 1965 pp 274–286
Graphicacy Should be the Fourth Ace in the Pack (with A. M. Coleman)
The Times Educational Supplement No 2633 5th November 1965 p 947
Subsequently reprinted in –
The School of Graphic Design, London
The Cartographer, Toronto Vol 3 No 1 June 1966 pp 185–195
World Education Markets Inc, New York
School Education Quarterly Melbourne

1966　Geography in Canadian Universities (with A. M. Coleman)
Nature No 5027 Vol 209 pp 960–963
Careers for Geographers
Geography Vol LI Pt 2 April 1966 pp 133–134
Canadian University Geography Departments (with A. M. Coleman)
Geographical Journal Vol 132 Pt 2 June 1966 pp 324–326

The Consultative Machinery of the Ordnance Survey (with A. M. Coleman)
The Cartographer, Canada Vol 3 No 1 June 1966 pp 48–51
A British Cartographic Investigation (with A. M. Coleman)
The Cartographer, Canada Vol 3 No 2 December 1966

1967   Cornwall in the 'Landscape through Maps' Series Edited by K. C. Edwards
Geographical Association 1967 40 pp
Water Policy in the United States
Geographical Journal Vol 133 Pt 4 December 1967 pp 514–516
Cartography and Computers (with A. M. Coleman)
The Cartographer, Canada Vol 4 No 2 December 1967 pp 120–127
The Metric System and the British Ordnance Survey (with A. M. Coleman)
The Cartographer, Canada Vol. 4 No 2 December 1967

1968   Water Conservation in 'Mind Alive'
Hutchinson

1969   Recent Advances in British Cartography
Canadian Cartographer Vol 6 No 1 June 1969 pp 65–69

1970   Geography – An Outline for the Intending Student (Editor and three Chapters)
Routledge and Kegan Paul Ltd 1970 196 pp
Puerto Rico (with A. M. Coleman)
Filmstrip Common Ground Ltd 1970

1971   Swansea and its Region – A Scientific Survey for the British Association for the Advancement of Science meeting in Swansea 1971 – Editor and two Chapters
University College of Swansea 1971 392 pp

1972   Graphicacy – Presidential Address to the Geographical Association
Geography Vol LVII Pt 3 July 1972 pp 185–195
Inspiration in Maps and Plans
Geographical Magazine Vol XLIV No 11 p 742
Grafisk Fremstilling
Kulturgeografi, Aarhus Vol 118 1972
Graphicacy (with Walter Leimgruber)
Regio Basiliensius, Basle Heft XIII/1+2 1972
Natural and Made-Made Disasters – Strategies for Survival
Presidential Address to Section E of the British Association for the Advancement of Science Leicester Meeting 1972

1973   Progress in Graphicacy (with A. M. Coleman)
The Times Educational Supplement 11th May 1973
Regional Surveys of the British Association for the Advancement of Science
Geography Vol 58 Pt 3 July 1973 pp 237–241
Natural and Man-Made Disasters
Geoforum Vol 13 1973 pp 83–84
Graphicacy (with A. M. Coleman) in 'Perspectives in Geographical Education'
Oliver and Boyd 1973

1974   An Institute of Cornish Studies
Geographical Journal Vol 140 Pt 1 February 1974 pp 173–174
Graphicacy
Bulletin of the Illinois Geographical Society Vol XVI No 2 December 1974
Computer Controlled Laser Graphic Mapping
Canadian Cartographer Vol 11 No 2 December 1974 pp 183–185
The New Ordnance Survey 1:50,000 Map Series of Great Britain
Canadian Cartographer Vol 11 No 2 December 1974 pp 181–183
Geography and University Entrance
Swansea Geographer Vol 12 1974 pp 1–3

1975   Vancouver
Panorama Thanet Geographical Association Vol 14 1975
Geography in Swansea 1920–1975
Swansea Geographer Vol 13 1975 pp i–iii
Recycling our Resources
Horizon, King's College London Vol 24 1975 pp 6–17
Structure and Landforms (with A. M. Coleman)
Filmstrip Common Ground Ltd 1975
Arid Landscapes (with A. M. Coleman)
Filmstrip Common Ground Ltd 1975
Limestone and Karst (with A. M. Coleman)
Filmstrip Common Ground Ltd 1975
Glaciated Landscapes (with A. M. Coleman)
Filmstrip Common Ground Ltd 1975

1976   Graphicacy
American Cartographer Vol 3 No 1 April 1976 pp 33–38
Adjustment to Natural Hazards in the United Kingdom
Foresight Vol 2 1976 pp 2–17

1977   Inflation Hits the Ordnance Survey
The Times Educational Supplement 25 March 1977 p 42
Replacing the Three R's with the Four Aces
The Times 19th April 1977 p 12
Ice in the Landscape (with A. M. Coleman)
Filmstrip Common Ground Ltd 1977
Copyright and Designs Law
Geographical Journal Vol 143 Pt 3 November 1977 p 502

1978   The Sea Coast (with A. M. Coleman)
Filmstrip Common Ground Ltd 1978
Graficacia
Geografia, Brasil Vol 3 No 5 April 1978 pp 1–13
Careers for Geographers
Geographical Journal Vol 144 Pt 2 July 1977 pp 288–292

1979   Earth Movements and Continental Drift (with A. M. Coleman)
Filmstrip Common Ground Ltd

AN EXTRACT FROM THE B.B.C. RADIO PROGRAMME 'THE WORLD GOES BY' OF 23rd DECEMBER, 1942

W. G. V. BALCHIN INTERVIEWED BY FREDDIE GRISEWOOD

GRISEWOOD: Now for something about a section of the 'backroom boys' who are not in the news and probably never will be, but whose work is vital to the fighting services – the people who produce our maps and charts. Mr. W. G. V. Balchin, who is an expert in this field is here to speak about this.

BALCHIN: Each of the services maintains a section responsible for this job. The Royal Navy and the Merchant Navy look to the hydrographic department of the Admiralty which was set up 150 years ago and is probably the least known of our publishing authorities. It issues and keeps corrected some 4,000 separate charts covering all the oceans and coasts of the world, and every year over a million copies are printed. Much of the information changes rapidly and the charts are continually being corrected. Immediate dangers – such as sunken wrecks and many others – are notified to users by the daily issues of Admiralty Notices to Mariners.

GRISEWOOD: How does the Admiralty get material for these notices? I suppose from Ship's Captains, Coastguards and so on?

BALCHIN: Well, it comes in from a variety of sources. In peace time the Navy has 8 ships doing surveying work. Some of them in the far corners of the world. Dominion and other Government Survey Departments, Harbour Authorities and so on, send in material. The collection of charts and maps held by the Department is probably the largest and most valuable in the world. It has been estimated to number nearly a quarter of a million, among them are some nearly 300 years old including many fine specimens drawn on skin. I need hardly say that the production of charts is immensely responsible work for it's on these charts that the navigating officer of any ship relies. A rock misplaced may mean disaster, the loss of a tramp steamer or a 10 million pound battleship, so the hydrographic department has one objective over and above everything else – and that is accuracy. Calculations, a drawing, plotting, engraving, and lithography, must give a final result correct to the nearest hundredth of an inch.

The War Office has a somewhat similar organisation to supply the Army with maps. Some idea of the importance of this work can be gathered from the published fact that in the last war over 32 million maps were supplied to the Army. 32 million. The survey section of the Royal Engineers carries out survey work in the field, and when theatres of war change rapidly their work is exceedingly arduous and responsible. Often of course, existing maps can be used, additional war information being added on the spot. But often fighting is going on in unmapped areas. This means a rapid topographical survey on the spot, as for example, in the East African campaign. In recent years in order to keep pace with the speed of modern war there's been a development of mobile map printing units, which can if necessary accompany the main body of troops.

The Royal Air Force depends for its supplies on the map section of the Air Ministry. The Special needs of airmen demand specially prepared maps which help them to identify prominent landmarks; vivid colours are used to bring out high ground, railways, roads, woods and water.

And then what about the Home Guard, and those units of the Army charged with protecting these islands. The Ordnance survey is the natural source for their maps. It isn't insular pride but a plain statement of fact to say that there is no other country in the world so well surveyed as the United Kingdom. The whole country has now been covered by some 15,000 sheets, on a scale of 6 inches to one mile. These put together would cover an area roughly the size of a football pitch. All important districts are also covered on a scale of 25 inches to one mile. Well these are the major national agencies which produce maps and charts. Since the war began of course, they've had many unusual problems to deal with. The map makers have had to contend with air raids and evacuation for example, including the removal of whole printing works almost overnight. Urgent demands have been invariably met. Even before the war we were well in advance of the Germans in the science of map and chart making. We need have little fear that we are still not keeping ahead of them.

THE RAISED FEATURES OF BILLEFJORD AND SASSENFJORD WEST SPITSBERGEN

W. G. V. BALCHIN

THE Cambridge Spitsbergen Expedition of 1938, with its base at the head of Billefjord, enabled the writer to make a study of what can best be described as a great field laboratory of raised beaches and associated features. It is an area rich in both erosional and constructional forms: raised wave-cut platforms, raised cliffs and shingle beaches, in places up to 300 feet above sea-level, being present except where scree cones have on steeper slopes occasionally obliterated the features. The absence of any detailed work on the area and the ease with which past shorelines may in places be traced, suggested that an intensive study with mapping and levelling might throw light both on the formation of shingle ridges in a region slowly emerging from a glacial period and also upon the "isostatic" recovery of the district. Plane-table mapping was carried out on a scale of 4 inches to 1 mile and numerous lines of tacheometric levels were run. In the following pages it is hoped to give a general account of the existing features, suggestions as to their mode of origin, and finally a brief discussion of the relative changes of level which have taken place as indicated by the levelling.

The region is largely dominated by a series of rectangular mountain masses with steep escarpments, the remains of a dissected plateau some 3000 feet in height. The escarpments, although modified by corrie erosion, have in many cases a buttressed appearance which bears striking resemblance to forms associated with the cycle of arid erosion. In the north the topography is largely obscured by the New Friesland ice-cap, but over most of Dickson Land and Bünsow Land permanent snow is not extensive and apart from the glaciers which come from the ice-cap the main glaciation consists of snow patches and corrie glaciers. The glaciers all show evidence of retreat and wide U-shaped valleys are common.

The rocks of the region are mainly of Permo-Carboniferous age, and over most of the area the limestone and gypsum beds dip gently to the south at 2–5 degrees. Underlying them is a pre-Devonian metamorphic complex. Between the mountain masses lie wide valleys, in many cases arms of the sea, with a general rectangular pattern. A. M. Peach suggested [1] that these valleys were the product of pre-glacial river erosion and that they were drowned by a pre-glacial inundation. On the coastal lowlands however occasional outcrops afford clear evidence of considerable downthrow and show that the physiography has to some extent been determined by block faulting. This suggests that in any study involving isostatic recovery the approach should in the first instance be local rather than regional, and offers a more logical explanation of the wide and rectangular patterned valleys with their steep flanking escarpments. The Campbell range is thus interpreted as a miniature block mountain with fault scarps.

On the east side of Billefjord, Carboniferous limestone and gypsum beds

---

[1] A. M. Peach, "Pre-glacial platform and raised beaches of Prince Charles Foreland," *Trans. Geol. Soc.* Edinburgh, 1915.

predominate, but to the north the southerly dip produces increasing exposures of the underlying pre-Devonian. On the west side in Dickson Land the Old Red Sandstone is the lowest bed seen, but near the coast both the Lower and Upper Carboniferous are well developed and the Culm beds of yellow sandstone form a marked feature. In Mimer valley the Permo-Carboniferous, here consisting of black shales and cherts, is again found and covers most of the area to the south.

The coastal plain skirting the escarpments is rarely more than 1 mile wide and is made up almost entirely of raised marine deposits, the latter being derived from the local formations outlined above.

The factors mainly affecting the growth of shingle ridges [1] are firstly the supply of material and secondly the strength, duration, fetch, and direction of the wind. In Billefjord and Sassenfjord great quantities of fluvio-glacial material are carried seawards during the summer melting period and shingle complexes tend to arise where streams debouch on to the coastal plain. The absence of vegetation, and intense frost action breaking down the Carboniferous beds, together with the power of the streams, all combine to ensure a plentiful supply of material. Extensive fan or delta distributaries indicate that material is being supplied at a faster rate than can be dispersed by normal marine processes. Such material is almost always of a coarse and heavy character, although a finer type is transported and the streams are normally milky with suspended solids and rock flour. When conditions in Billefjord were calm the water of the Ekholm river could be traced seawards by the suspended solids. The air photograph (Plate 1) shows this and the drift to the north. The sudden and frequent summer flooding induces a steep gradient to base level and may account for the absence of sandy accumulations.

Wind observations have been kept at Green Harbour some 60 miles southwest of Billefjord. These show the predominant direction of the wind in summer to be north-east, and throughout the year from south and south-east. The summer alone concerns us since shingle ridge formation can only occur during this ice-free period. Observations on sixty-five days from late June to early September 1938 revealed that in Billefjord, the chief wind directions were N. 13, N.E. 5, E.N.E. 7, E. 4, S.S.W. 15, S.W. 7. These observations agree with those of the Oxford University Expedition in 1933,[2] the only other summer records available for Billefjord. The disagreement with Green Harbour may be ascribed to the mountains, the winds tend to blow up and down the fjords. Thus S.S.W. and north winds will be of consequence here in the evolution of coastal forms. The northerly winds from the New Friesland ice-cap were the strongest, and this was emphasized when our party was detained on Gips Hook for five days unable to launch the boat owing to the very heavy seas. But the south-westerly winds have a greater fetch, and this, with the ocean swell which enters Isfjord and approaches from the south-west, produces a dominant beach-drift to the north.

Two additional factors are important. Fluctuations of land and sea have altered the level at which marine processes have worked, and shingle formation can proceed only when the fjord is ice-free. According to records at

[1] W. V. Lewis, "Evolution of shoreline curves," *Proc. Geol. Assoc.*, 1938.
[2] A. R. Glen, "Oxford University Spitsbergen Expedition 1933," *Geogr. J.*, 1934.

Advent Bay the winter freeze up has not been so long in recent years. Nevertheless isolated patches of ice-foot were noted in early July: it has been suggested by many glaciologists that the ice-foot itself is an erosive agent so the few examples seen were kept under observation. In this district however the ice-foot, like the snow patches and very probably for the same reason (see below), seems to have little or no erosive power. No evidence was found to alter the view that summer wave action is, and has been, the dominant factor.

This is in direct contrast with some of the early observations on the raised shingle and beaches of Spitsbergen. Thus we find Garwood and Gregory with the following suggestions:

> "Between the main raised beach lines occur numerous smaller wavy ridges, which often resemble the ridges between plough furrows. A few days' observation on shore supplied a simple explanation of their mode of origin. At the end of June the shore of Ice Fjord was bounded by a belt of Fast ice; as it melted, a channel of water was formed between it and the shore. When the temperature fell to freezing point, this water being practically quite fresh, was frozen. Owing to the resistance of the ice belt, the newly formed ice could expand only on the landward side; as the young ice presses against the shore, it pushes the beach material before it into ridges." [1]

Even bar formation and beach drift is ascribed to ice:

> "As the ice grinds along the shore it pushes the beach material eastward, until it has formed a bar which juts out for a third of the distance across the bay." [1]

By 1921 however the observations of Wordie,[2] Tyrell,[3] and others had ascribed to these coastal features an origin more in line with modern ideas.

The raised features (Fig. 1)

The coast falls into four broad divisions. Raised shingle complexes and associated marine levels dominate; next come raised wave-cut platforms; over the remainder there is little or no coastal plain and the scarp slopes either descend direct to the sea or are covered with modern scree cones.

Raised platforms.—These are best developed at the junction of Sassenfjord and Billefjord, where the Gåsöyane (Anser Islands) are undoubtedly fragments of a raised platform of marine erosion (Plate 6). The islands rise to a maximum height of 65 feet and have a general slope to the south-west, the resistant dolerite of which they are composed probably accounting for their preservation. Glacial striae with two main directions of N.N.E. and E.S.E. were noted from the lower levels and seem to be the result of ice from Billefjord and Sassenfjord. Post-glacial icebergs could hardly have produced both the extensive striae and the ice-smoothed surfaces, and there can be little doubt that most of this platform is of pre-glacial age.

The coastal plain of the adjacent mainland from Anser Bay to Gips Bay is similarly a plain of marine denudation emerging directly from the sea. The

[1] E. J. Garwood and J. W. Gregory, "Glacial geology of Spitsbergen," *Q.J.G.S.*, 1898, pp. 214–215.
[2] J. M. Wordie, "Present day conditions in Spitsbergen," *Geogr. J.*, 58 (1921) 42–43.
[3] G. W. Tyrell, "Glaciers of Spitsbergen," *Geol. Soc. Glasgow*, vol. xvii.

Phot. Norges Svalbard og Ishavs-Undersøkelser

1   Cape Ekholm

2. *Modern cliff in raised shingle north of Cape Scott (to right) Billefjord. Raised shoreline A to left*

3. *Raised shingle and tilted shorelines, eastern Billefjord looking north from Phantom Point*

4. *Raised shingle with polygons, Cape Ekholm. Shorelines B and D in middle distance*

platform rises gently inland reaching in three-quarters of a mile a height of 308 feet at the base of Mount Jean: here there are fragments of an old cliff. Glacial striae occur on this platform but are common only on the lower portion, and this suggests that the upper part is possibly of a very late or post-glacial age. The formation of the platform in dolerite would appear to account for the preservation of the pre-glacial platform and also for the absence of other wave-cut features showing temporary sea-levels. For to the east, in the less resistant Carboniferous rocks, the pre-glacial platform has disappeared and a platform at a lower level has taken its place. In the dolerite the relative change of sea-level merely seems to have extended the pre-glacial platform into higher levels.

A very scanty shingle deposit on the platform occasionally takes the form of beach ridges, but material tends to drift away from here either into Sassenfjord or Billefjord, and a bare rock platform devoid of deposits is more characteristic. Gips Hook bears testimony to the force of the northerly waves, for a cliff 40 feet high has been cut in the dolerite. With the gradual appearance of the platform these cliffs are raised above wave action and a further section of the platform becomes subjected to the cutting process: this accounts for the $1\frac{1}{2}$ mile stretch of cliff, some 40–50 feet high, which extends from Gips Hook to the foot of Mount Jean. On first examination this appears to be a tilted erosional cliff related to one marine stillstand; actually it is a succession of innumerable ancient "Gips Hooks" related to many marine levels. There is one exact reproduction of the modern coastline in the elevated part (Map B). The angle formed by this cliff and the foot of the Cowan Range becomes a trap for sediments, mainly of local derivation, and a fine series of shingle ridges at successively lower levels and with a general northerly orientation fills the angle.

On the western side of Billefjord, south of Skans Bay and opposite to the Gåsöyane, is a further exposure of a wave-cut platform. It stretches intermittently to the south of Dickson Land and rises inland until terminated by a raised marine cliff some 100 feet high. No glacial striae were found, but rock exposures are few owing to an extensive growth of vegetation. A correlation of this platform with the Gips Hook platform seems possible, from its position and a similar formation in dolerite. The pre-glacial platform would also appear to underlie some of the recent deposits, for rock exposures were noted from the Ekholm Valley, whilst on the foreshore at Cape Scott recent wave action has uncovered a smoothed rock surface with some glacial striae.

The raised shingle complexes make an assemblage of features which can be described as magnificent, and shingle beaches in perfect preservation are raised in places over 300 feet above sea-level. Three main groups may be distinguished: Billefjord, Gips Bay, and Bjöna Haven.

In eastern Billefjord (Map A, Plate 1) an extensive development of raised features fringes the Campbell Mountains and Cowan Range, and extends for 10 miles from Cape Napier to below Phantom Point (Skrymtodden), comprising almost the whole coastal plain. A relative change of level has taken place during the formation and marine processes have worked at successively lower levels. Shingle ridges have been built up on the rising front. But during periodic stillstands, longshore drift and consequent erosion appear to have been dominant, and cliffs were cut in the old raised shingle ridges. With continued elevation the cliffs have been raised above wave action and mark past shorelines; the coast now resembles a series of steps rising landwards to a height, in places, of 250 feet. Movements have not however been uniform and the steps are generally tilted, with a gradient to the north. Streams have cut deep narrow V-shaped valleys across them, whilst the cones of larger glacial streams obliterate some of the raised features: nevertheless the latter, as the map shows, are dominant.

As indicated by Johnson [1] interpretation and correlation should preferably be made on the basis of ancient marine levels or shorelines, and these can be deduced with accuracy only from erosional features. Along the eastern shores of Billefjord, cliff fragments, although known to be tilted, are so extensive that each shoreline can be traced with ease. Six such major episodes may be distinguished (A, B, C, D, E, F, of which F is the modern: Map A), mostly with erosional cliffs of 20 feet upwards (Plate 2). Minor variations occur locally and seem related to slight differences in wind direction during the formation of the shingle ridges; these have been mapped but should not be confused with the major cliffed features. Lines of tacheometric levels were run at intervals along the coast to determine the heights of the raised shorelines. From these determinations the tilts can be calculated. (See below.)

The shingle, of which the ridge pattern is still largely preserved on each step, is fairly uniform in size, being up to 2 inches in diameter throughout. In the higher levels it has been subject to frost action and the typically rounded beach pebble is replaced by angular and sub-angular forms. By digging in the shingle rounded pebbles were always found ultimately, the depth at which this occurred increasing with the elevation.

Stone polygons occur in places but are not widespread, and even when they are superimposed on the ridges the ridge pattern can normally be distinguished (Plate 4). The infrequence of polygons on the ridges suggests either that they take very long to form or that the proportion of fine material and water plays a very large part in their origin, for the shingle, acting like a sieve, does not retain the melt-water. A more recent example of the stability of the shingle is found in Gips Valley, where tractor marks, footprints, etc., made by the Scottish Spitsbergen Syndicate twenty years ago are in a perfect state of preservation.

Solifluction has occasionally destroyed all evidence of ridging, most markedly on the upper steps and less frequently at the base of the marine-cut cliffs. It is remarkable that the unconsolidated shingle cliffs should retain their form so long. They must not be confused with notching produced by longitudinal snow patches,[2] they are definitely of marine origin, as the beach ridges which run up to their base conclusively prove. The porosity of the shingle seems to prevent snow-patch erosion, whilst the absence of finer sediments to act as a lubricant retards solifluction.

[1] D. Johnson, "The correlation of ancient marine levels," C. R. Congress, Intern. Geogr., Paris, 1931.
[2] W. V. Lewis, "Snow-patch erosion in Iceland," *Geogr. J.*, August 1939. L. H. McCabe, "Nivation and corrie erosion in West Spitsbergen," *ibid.*, December 1939.

The distance from crest to crest of the ridges varies from 3 to 5 feet and is fairly constant. Few storm beaches were seen. The ridges are largely unvegetated, but hollows may carry *Saxifraga oppositifolia*, *Dryas octopetala*, and *Cetraria sp.*, with in moister areas *Hypnum uncinatum* (*var. plumulosum*) and *Salix polaris*. Very large included boulders of foreign origin occasionally occur, and are considered to be erratics ice borne from New Friesland, deposited when icebergs from the Nordenskiöld glacier have been stranded on the shore. This process was often observed while we were mapping the ridges.

Turning now to modern conditions: a succession of melt-water streams from the southerly facing slopes ensures a plentiful supply of material; the orientation of the coast being N.N.E. the dominant S.S.W. influence gives rise to a northerly drift [1] and a tendency for the coast to swing out to face the direction of the dominant wave approach.[2] The stone fans deposited by the streams tend to encourage the latter and largely determine the point at which the change takes place. The result is a series of miniature cuspate forelands: Cape Scott for instance is a duplicate of Cape Ekholm.

An interesting illustration of the effect of fetch is seen from Fig. 1; dotted lines have been drawn perpendicular to the trend of the *modern* northerly orientated beaches along the east side of Billefjord. These lines tend to swing round as one passes from Cape Napier to Anser Bay, and the increasing effect of the fjord is felt. The present supplies a key to the past in helping to account for the northerly orientation of almost all the preserved elevated ridges. Erosion during stillstands produced cliffs in the shingle and the S.S.W. facing shores have suffered at the expense of the northerly, where accumulation probably continued to a later date.

The maps indicate the wealth and variety of shore features in the area, but at Cape Ekholm there are several features especially worthy of mention. In the absence of vegetation this region may be likened to a full-scale earth-sculpture tank. It has a series of raised beaches, cliffs, and associated fluvial rejuvenation features: the latter represented by the "cone in cone" structures of the fans and by river terraces which are well developed near the narrow rock constriction christened the Iron Gorge. Three large lakes were mapped south of this gorge, and from the map might appear to lie in an old distributary of the river Ekholm. The existence however of a series of shingle ridges in good preservation between and 100 feet above two of them indicates that the lakes do not lie on an old distributary and have different origins. Geological evidence suggests a minor fault along which recent movement has taken place. The middle lake has an underground outlet and solution in the underlying limestone may be a contributary factor. The small lakes at Bruce City and elsewhere all appear to be the result of depressions produced by thrown-up shingle embankments. The moisture is derived from the winter snow and the permanently frozen ground holds up its dispersal.

[1] Quite apart from the evidence of the shingle the coast is littered with a most amazing collection of driftwood, from barrels and cabin doors to Siberian logs. These increased in number northwards despite the use for fuel by past expeditions staying at Bruce City.

[2] See W. V. Lewis, "Evolution of shoreline curves," *Proc. Geol. Assoc.*, 1938.

South of Cape Scott and near Phantom Point the deep V-shaped valleys cut right through shingle to present-day sea-level; but in the Ekholm Valley, especially east of the Iron Gorge, the shingle appears to form but a thin covering to a rock platform. The latter is probably of pre-glacial age, but no striae were found on the few exposures noted. Eastwards the material grades into a fluvio-glacial deposit of the Ekholm, related to a much earlier sea-level (probably B). Close to Cape Ekholm, itself are several raised capes, which repeat the characteristics of the present cape.

To the north of Cape Ekholm a modern cliff some 8o feet high cut in the raised shingle ridges, gives an excellent cross section of the ridges (Plate 8). This reveals definite bedding of a fine-coarse-fine sequence which can be traced upwards, at a constant angle of 27°, to the shingle undulations of the surface. Measurements on the modern beaches reveal a slope which increases from 5° to 27°. The latter appears to be the angle of rest and is only found near the crest of the ridge. It is suggested that in this case at Cape Ekholm the material accumulated in deep water and has accordingly assumed the angle of rest. The alternation of fine and coarse sediments may be either a seasonal feature or related to the frequency of storms coupled with the supply of material. Similar conditions were noted on the north-facing slope of the Gips valley complex. It is worthy of note because I think no mention of false bedding of this kind, which could be very misleading, has appeared in print.

The second major shingle-complex lies between the Aitken and Usher ranges at the southern end of Gips valley covering an area of some 3 miles by 4 (Map B, Plate 7). There is little doubt that in early post-glacial time Gips valley formed an inlet of Isfjord, parallel and similar to Billefjord and Templefjord; for apart from the height of the raised features at the foot of the Aitken and Usher ranges (which were levelled and found to be 252 feet and 233 feet respectively), wave-cut markings are traceable northwards in Gips valley. Into this inlet, somewhat narrower than its associates, fluvio-glacial material has likewise been poured. At the entrance two fans have formed and wave action has built an imposing series of shingle ridges. This in time doubtless blocked the inlet, and if it were not actually turned into a lake the effective winds were cut off. No shingle ridges were found farther inland than the foot of the Aitken range; to the north, all ridges have been obliterated, if they ever existed. Since no ridge patterns appear to have been cut through by the river Gip it seems improbable that the southern end of Gips valley was ever blocked to form a freshwater lake higher than the mean sea-level of the time. The large lakes shown on Mathieson's map of 1919 are not true lakes but rather flat marshy areas liable to flood when excessive melting occurs, and through which the river Gip flows in a braided fashion.

The eastern part of the valley and bay has a south-westerly aspect and faces a great stretch of water to the entrance of Isfjord. This has been of great importance, for material from the Aitken fan has drifted northwards and has been built up there into a series of shingle ridges. It will be understood that the fan has come into existence only with the successive emergence of the area; in the first place material was very probably deposited in much the same way as is now seen in the younger fans of Billefjord. The highest point show-

6. *Gips Hook and Gåsöyane Islands, a raised marine platform*

5. *Bjöna Haven and Templefjord from point m on Map C. Von Post glacier in distance*

7. *Gips valley from Mount Aitken (2,000 ft). Map B.*

8. Section through raised shingle ridges, Cape Ekholm

9. Rejuvenated valley above Aitken Gorge, Gips valley

10. Scree and fan coast of Cowan Range, Billefjord

ing evidence of marine action on this side is a wave-cut cliff 252 feet above present sea-level. Ridge development becomes predominant westwards from Lake Lillian which has an elevation of 217 feet. Each ridge is at a slightly lower level, and a section across the area has a convex form suggesting that the latter part of the emergence has taken place more rapidly.

The shingle ridges at first flanked the foot of the Aitken range but have since swung round to face south-west; this has been achieved only in recent times and as a result of the upper parts being cut off from wave action by the emergence and growth of the fans, which now almost meet. Shingle development has since been confined to an area to the south. Northwards, before this had happened, the southerly winds had less influence and the ridges are orientated to the north-east, facing straight up Gips valley from which direction the dominant winds would come.

Whilst the area to the east of the outlet of the river Gip has a simple pattern of parallel storm ridges (the largest in the whole area) the region to the west which lies in the lee of Gips Hook and the Anser platform is very complex. The lower parts were more responsive to southerly winds from Sassenfjord, but the higher parts were being built before the complex north of the Aitken fan or the fan itself had arisen, and while Gips valley was still an inlet of Sassenfjord. Hence many of the ridges have a north-easterly orientation and some may even be traced on the top of Salisbury Crags at 330 feet.

The gradual differential uplift (the south rising more quickly), the growth of the shingle ridges and fans, the appearance of the Anser platform, and the gradual disappearance of the sea from Gips valley, are largely responsible for the present topography.

The raised wave-cut cliffs are similarly complex. They are plentiful in the unconsolidated shingle and in harder rock outcrops. The series of parallel cliffs to the east of the river Gip are of marine origin and have not been produced by lateral river erosion as one might suppose. They consist of a series of steps, with truncated shingle ridges and included ponds forming the flats, as on the coast of Billefjord. Some cliffs cut in the unconsolidated shingle decrease in height up the valley and pass into ridges: a change in the direction of the dominant wind, as has recently taken place in Björna Haven (see below), would seem to account for this.

On Fig. 1 the sequence of the cliffs is indicated: since the area is known to have been tilted it has not been possible to correlate the shorelines of the Gips Bay area with those of Billefjord, nor the two sides of the valley, although eight major cliffings or shorelines can be distinguished, one above the other, on both sides. We had no time for much levelling here. Gips valley itself should receive detailed study, for much additional light will doubtless be shed on the nature of the region's recovery from the glacial period. River rejuvenation is proved in the terraces cut by the Gip and in the gorges at the apices of the two stone fans (Plate 9).

Eastwards of the Temple range is the cuspate foreland of Björna Haven (Map C, Plate 5). The foreland proper has two distinct parts: that to the south of the major cliff *mn* is a series of truncated laterals orientated towards the south-east, with major groupings demarcated by minor cliffs. These appear to be the product of a south-easterly drift along the foot of the Temple range building shingle ridges facing the south-west; but continued drift has led to a recession of the coastline and only the truncated laterals (related to the south-easterly winds) now remain. These ridges are not much above sea-level, and are probably very recent.

The second part, north of the large cliff *mn*, is a concentric series of major unvegetated shingle ridges falling gradually from 120 feet to present sea-level and facing the full extent of Templefjord to the north-east. The growth of the fan from the Sindeballe range, and the spit which the southerly drift has produced, now protects Bjöna Haven from the full force of the north-easterly winds down Templefjord, and the dominant winds are for the time being from the east. In an effort to readjust the coastline to the new conditions erosion has commenced near Cape Bjöna and the material drifts north to accumulate near the hut. Hence there is a recession near the point, and accumulation follows in the bay as the coastline swings round to face more easterly. Raised marine-cut cliffs are not common, one whose base is 140 feet above sea-level lies to the south-west of the stone fan's apex. The latter has terraces and some interesting rejuvenation forms.

Raised wave-cut features.—Raised cliffs occur near Bruce Hut and Cape Schoultz on the east side of Templefjord, and these, as in the cases already cited, rise to the south. Raised shingle deposits, but heavily eroded, are found north of Cape Rudmose in Petunia Bay. On the west of Billefjord wave-cut etchings were observed on the lower flanks of Mount Pyramid, at the Trappers Hut, and south of Skans Bay. If the latter area is seen from the fjord or from Anser Bay a dip to the south appears instead of the customary northerly trend. Closer examination reveals that this apparent anomaly is due to wave-cut etchings being confined to the harder bands of rock which, as discussed earlier, dip to the south. Wave action has merely served to emphasize bedding, and from a distance isolated cliff fragments appear to join and give a false impression of continuity. In Skans Bay raised cliffs cut in shingle conformed to the general rule. But the coast of Dickson Land is not generally a region of accumulation, very little shingle was noted and no drift-wood.

Scree cone and fan coasts.—Elsewhere, apart from the Nordenskiöld and Von Post glacier fronts, the coast is either precipitous, as for example the Temple range, or built up of scree cones which descend steeply to the sea, as in Dickson Land, the Cowan range, etc. (Plate 10).

The evidence of the included fauna

Little was added by the expedition to the already existing knowledge of the fauna to be found in the raised beaches,[1] but past collections have almost invariably been localized by height. A word of warning is here necessary, for considerable tilting may, as in this case, have taken place. The height of the fauna in such circumstances can be no criterion of its age and past marine

[1] C. S. Elton and D. Baden-Powell, "Raised beach fossils from Spitsbergen," *Geol. Mag.*, LXVIII, 1931.

shorelines as evidenced by destructional features such as cliffs and benches should preferably form the basis of correlation. Collections were therefore made with reference to the various raised shorelines bearing in mind the possibility that some light might be thrown upon climatic change. In making such collections various factors tend to diminish the accuracy. The more delicate fauna naturally breaks up under the conditions of deposition, whilst frost action renders collecting on the upper exposed surfaces difficult, comminution having proceeded at a rapid rate. The possibility of modern shells being transported by birds, and fauna being carried downwards by stream action must also be borne in mind. To offset these difficulties collections were made from near the top of various narrow V-shaped valleys cut by melt-water streams in the unconsolidated shingle. Representative groups were taken from the beaches formed between the periodic stillstands in Billefjord, and the fossils found were as follows:

	Before A	A—B	C—D	D—E	Modern.
Mytilus edulis (Linn.)	X	X	X	X	
Chlamys islandica (Müll.) ..	X	X			X
Astarte borealis (Chem.) ..	X	X	X	X	X
Astarte sp.			X		
Cyprina islandica arctica (Linn.)		X	X		
Mya truncata (Linn.)	X	X	X		X
Saxicava arctica (Linn.) ..	X	X			X
Calcareous algae Lithothamnium glaciale					X
Margarites helicina and grønlandica					X
Whale bones			X		

Mytilus edulis inhabits those areas in the tidal zone free from sea-ice and is not found in Spitsbergen to-day. Examples from the modern beach level were undoubtedly derived washings. Its occurrence in the raised beach deposits suggests that the conditions of the formation of sea-ice were different from those of the present day and warmer conditions are indicated.

Astarte borealis was the commonest mollusc from all the deposits. Employing Jensen's method,[1] the living specimens have a length/height ratio of from 75 to 83 per cent. with an average of 78·6 per cent. The samples collected from the upper raised beaches (above A, A—B, C—D) show ratios of 85 per cent., indicating a warmer sea. Specimens from between D and E gave ratios of 96-99 per cent., indicating considerably warmer conditions, this shape being equivalent to the warm form of *Astarte montagui* (Dillwyn).

Cyprina islandica is a species now extinct in Spitsbergen and is characteristic of warmer waters; it is not a common mollusc and has only been recorded on three previous occasions.

The chief conclusion emerging from the analysis points to the formation of all the raised features under more genial conditions than prevail at the present. Whilst the evidence of *Astarte borealis* suggests especially warm conditions (for these latitudes) in the period immediately following upon the

[1] A. S. Jensen, 'Results of the Ingolf expedition,' Lamellibranchiata, 1912.

stillstand represented by the shoreline D. The significance of this will be emphasized later. Finally, in the absence of any definite faunal demarcation between deposits and in the present state of our knowledge, it would appear unwise to attempt a correlation of the beaches based upon faunal content.

The raised shorelines of eastern Billefjord

Tacheometric lines of levels were run perpendicular to the coast at approximately equal distances from Cape Napier to Phantom Point. Heights were initially referred to local high-water mark and tidal observations carried out at the base camp enabled a correction to approximate mean sea-level to be made. The lines are shown on Map A. Sections have since been drawn along each line and from these it is possible to ascertain the height above mean sea-level of the base of each marine-cut cliff crossed by the line. The height and position of the basal points being known, one can draw a section along the coast to illustrate the displacement each shoreline has undergone. The continuity of the raised cliffs (Map A) enables the respective points lying on each shoreline to be joined with confidence and these all appear to lie without exception on straight lines. This suggests a uniform recovery with no actual differential warping. The method is shown in Fig. 2, and this, if allowance be made for the vertical exaggeration, is in effect a view of the shorelines of teasern Billefjord as seen from Dickson Land. The tilts of the shorelines to the southern horizon have been calculated, and along the section chosen are as follows: A 53'; B 29'; C 21'; D 20'; E 4'; F 0' (modern level). (Plate 3.)

The uniform rise in sea-level (a eustatic movement) which is considered to have followed the termination of the glacial period in consequence of the melting of the ice-caps must undoubtedly ante-date level A, for all these raised features are found in shingle and fairly warm summer conditions must have prevailed before a supply of material for the beaches, and the forces to produce them would become available. This is borne out by the faunal evidence which indicates more genial conditions than exist to-day. This strongly suggests that the tilted shorelines have been produced for the major part by the isostatic recovery of the region, except for the change from C to D, the close parallelism of which suggests a eustatic drop. Such a parallelism could only otherwise be produced by either a uniform and very equal block uplift or alternatively an uplift over a very large area (a regional epeirogenetic shift): neither would seem feasible in this district. The magnitude of the eustatic drop is measurable by the perpendicular distance, approximately 64 feet, between the shorelines. Continuing recovery has imparted to both a subsequent tilt.

The differential recovery does not seem to have taken place about a constant axis or hinge-line, for the point of intersection of B and C is farther north than that of A and B; and the intersection of E and F is farther north than D and E. The presumed eustatic fall separates the two phases. A movement of the hinge-line northwards appears to have occurred and would naturally be expected with the progressive amelioration of the climate and the disappearance of the ice mass responsible for the original depression.

Even the small angles involved in the tilting are sufficient to produce large vertical differences of height in a short distance (53 minutes involves 813 feet in 10 miles), and since no raised features were noted at a height exceeding 350 feet it seems that recovery is essentially local rather than regional. It may possibly be partly occurring along the already existing zones of weakness in the faults mentioned above, and along which there is, in the Ekholm valley, evidence of very recent movement. The fault blocks are in all probability acting as independent units. Should this be so, correlation between Billefjord, Gips Bay, etc., would only be possible on the basis of the included faunal remains and the difficulties in this method have already been pointed out.

The apparent dip or tilt of shoreline B in azimuth 23 degrees along the eastern shore of Billefjord is 29 minutes. This shoreline rises when traced eastwards into the Ekholm valley and from the measurements made an apparent dip or tilt of 52 minutes in azimuth 295 degrees is revealed. This gives a maximum or true dip of 58 minutes in azimuth 322 degrees. This was the only level which had an easterly extension sufficiently great enough to determine with accuracy a second tilt or apparent dip, and hence from this the azimuth and magnitude of the maximum. It is possible that should the Gips valley complex be systematically levelled sufficient evidence would be available to disentangle the tilts and hence the movements, if any, of the azimuth of maximum tilting.

The evidence from the Ekholm valley adds further weight to the argument that the recovery is local, for if the tilt of level A (the highest) is continued to the west side of Billefjord it passes below sea-level before reaching the coast, yet raised features are found on this western side.

The field data indicates the existence of a pre-glacial platform of marine abrasion, much of which has now disappeared. The maximum glaciation of the Pleistocene period caused a depression of the area under the load of the ice, and when progressive amelioration of the climate released the locked-up waters of the ice-caps, the sea returned to its former level more quickly than the land. This produced either an extension or further erosion of the pre-glacial platform.

The land, slowly being relieved of its ice load, then began to experience an isostatic recovery of an intermittent character, a movement which has continued to the present day. The combination of this with marine erosion and construction is largely responsible for the extensive development of raised features. That much of this is of recent date is apparent, for genial conditions must have prevailed before the shingle complexes could have been formed, a condition which is borne out by the faunal evidence. The complexes although older than those which occur on the coasts of Britain are thus very young geologically. Their mode of origin serves to emphasize conclusions already reached in the British examples studied.

During the isostatic recovery and between levels C and D of Billefjord a eustatic fall of 64 feet seems to have taken place. From the faunal evidence it has been seen that *Astarte borealis* passes into the warm form of *Astarte montagui* after level D, thus indicating much warmer conditions. The similarity of the above sequence with parts of Fennoscandia will at once be apparent and suggests a possible correlation of the Billefjord eustatic fall with the Ancylus Lake and Submerged Forest periods of Boreal age in Europe.

The evidence also points to independent recovery by fault blocks, the movements thus being local rather than regional. This can only mean that for such areas detailed and intensive methods in research must be applied, a conclusion to be emphasized for future investigators. Each unit may prove to have its own special contribution in unravelling the problem of the post-glacial recovery of Spitsbergen.

I am especially indebted to Mr. W. B. Harland, the geologist to the expedition, who kindly undertook the identification of the faunal remains; to Mr. P. M. Pritchard, who acted as staffman throughout the levelling; and to Mr. J. M. Wordie, Mr. J. A. Steers, Mr. W. V. Lewis, and the many other friends who have helped in the final preparation of the MS.

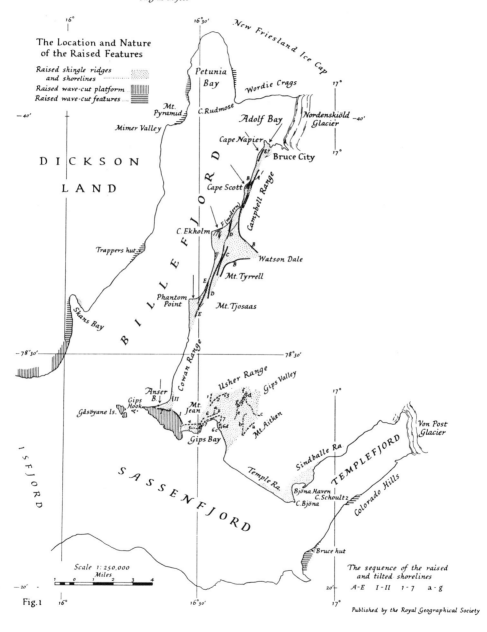

BILLEFJORD AND SASSENFJORD
SPITSBERGEN
by W.G.V. Balchin

:=:=: *Trend of shingle ridges*
——— *Raised wave-cut cliffs*
Fans and cones
4—— *Lines of instrumental levels*
R t. *River terraces*
Heights in feet

The Location and Nature
of the Raised Features

Raised shingle ridges
and shorelines
Raised wave-cut platform
Raised wave-cut features

16°   16°30'   New Friesland Ice Cap   17°

Petunia
Bay   Wordie Crags

Mt.
Pyramid   C.Rudmose   Adolf Bay   Nordenskiöld
Glacier
— 40'   —40'
Mimer Valley   Cape Napier
Bruce City   17°

D I C K S O N   Cape Scott   Campbell Range

L A N D   C. Ekholm

Trappers hut   Watson Dale

Mt. Tyrrell

Phantom
Point   Mt.Tjosaas

Skans Bay

B I L L E F J O R D

— 78°30'   78°30'

Usher Range   Gips Valley
Anser
B.   Mt.
Gips   Jean   Mt. Aitken   17°
Hook   Von Post
Gåsöyane Is.   Glacier

Cowan Range

Gips Bay

Sindballe Ra   TEMPLEFJORD

I S F J O R D   S A S S E N F J O R D   Temple Ra.   Colorado Hills
Bjöna Haven
C.Schoultz
C.Bjöna

Bruce hut

Scale 1:250,000
Miles   The sequence of the raised
and tilted shorelines
— 20'   20'   A-E   I-II   1-7   a-g

Fig.1   16°   16°30'   17°

Published by the Royal Geographical Society

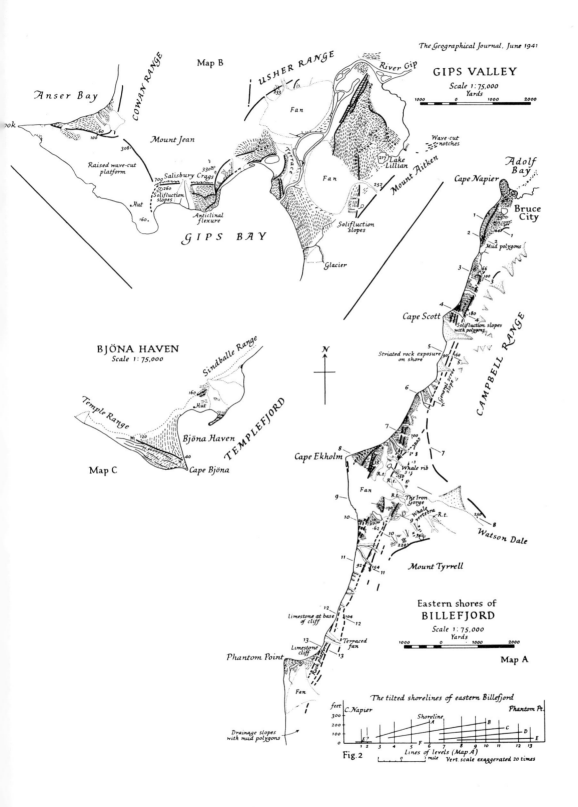

THE DENUDATION CHRONOLOGY OF SOUTH-WEST ENGLAND

W. G. V. BALCHIN

CONTENTS

I. INTRODUCTION

The physical features of South-West England can be summed up in the statement that it is a region of deep, narrow, V-shaped valleys, alternating with flat-topped interfluves which rise in step like formation inland from the surrounding coast. In this respect the peninsula stands out as unique among the physical regions of Britain. This generalization however simplifies a fascinating morphology which has resulted from a complex history of river dissection punctuated by phases of marine planation. It is the form, distribution, age and origin of the erosion surfaces, which largely constitute the flat-topped interfluves, combined with the evolution of the drainage pattern, that enables the geomorphologist to piece together the denudation chronology of the area.

Although much of the peninsula still awaits detailed morphological analysis and the majority of research workers to date have concentrated on either drainage evolution or erosion surfaces within their chosen areas we now have a sufficient number of studies to provide the main elements in the geomorphological story. Differences of opinion occur within the literature as the story unfolds, but an increasing measure of agreement seems to be emerging with continuing research. A review of our present state of knowledge falls naturally into three divisions: the erosion surfaces, the drainage evolution, and the denudation chronology which emerges when we consider the drainage in relation to the erosion surfaces.

II. THE EROSION SURFACES

Whilst the purist might argue that most morphological features consist of erosion surfaces, the term is here used in the commonly accepted sense of plateau like areas constituting geographical features which can be mapped. Such surfaces usually mark the end of sub-aerial, marine or arid cycles of erosion and often provide keys to the recognition of past base levels, (Pls. 1—4).

Erosion surfaces corresponding to long periods of still-stand in the base level are locally of a generally horizontal nature. *In extenso* however the surfaces are not flat although this is a term which is often used in descriptions. Thus the marine surface will normally be a gently inclined plane rising landwards: the

56

average submarine declivities of existing shallow seas reveal gradients of up to 20 ft. per mile, whilst off stormy coasts marine peneplanes at present in course of formation may have gradients of some 90 ft. per mile. This however is a slope of less than one degree which although capable of producing considerable height differences in short distances actually forms an apparently flat surface when subsequently exposed to human inspection.

It may be anticipated that after exposure the rear of a marine surface will be terminated in regions of resistant rocks by a steeper rise or bluff marking the position of an old cliff line. With an alteration in base level however an emergent marine surface becomes subject to sub-aerial erosion and soon begins to lose its characteristics as a result of river dissection. Evidence of the former existence of the marine surface may be found in flat topped hills and interfluves separating more or less angular V-shaped valleys. A marked acceleration in the rate of change of slope on interfluve crests will terminate the surface and bluffs may denote the position of an old cliff line. Successive bluffs at correlative heights may enable an old cliff line and hence the base level to be traced over the face of the country.

The sub-aerial surface on the other hand is not quite so simple. Even in the stage of old age a great variety of forms will be possible in the morphology and we may find a rolling relief with an amplitude of perhaps 100 ft. to 150 ft. Hence when dissected by later erosion related to lower base levels no extensive flat surfaces will be found, but rather a general accordance of summit heights with rejuvenated polycyclic valleys. When the possibility of subsequent warping or tilting is also envisaged it is clear that the separation of sub-aerial surfaces will be more difficult than with marine surfaces for there may be no convenient cliff line remnants.

Arid erosion surfaces of the pediment type constitute a third possibility. Pediments now in course of formation are usually found in piedmont zones, have slopes of from $\frac{1}{2}$ to 7 degrees, and are normally backed by mountain fronts some hundreds of feet in height rising at slopes of up to 30 degrees from the pediment. In a degraded form confusion of the pediment with the marine erosion surface might seem possible, but the scale of the features and any associated deposits usually enables a distinction to be made.

The first recorded recognition of erosion surfaces in south-west England appears to be Clement Reid's description towards the end of the last century of the narrow shelf fringing the south and west coasts of Cornwall. This shelf, being backed above 430 ft. by a steep bluff suggesting a worn down cliff line clearly seemed to be of marine origin. Further support for this hypothesis came from the marine deposits at St. Erth which appeared to be associated with the surface, although the deposits were located in a valley cut in the shelf. The included fossils led Clement Reid (1896) to postulate an early Pliocene origin but there now seems some doubt as to this dating. H. B. Milner (1922) suggests an Eocene age in view of the mode of occurrence and elevation of the deposits whilst more recently S. W. Wooldridge (1950) has shown that a late Pliocene or even later age is more likely.

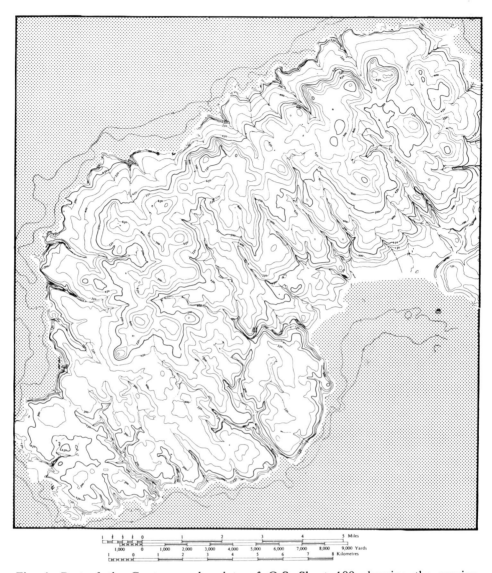

Fig. 1. Part of the Contours-only plate of O.S. Sheet 189 showing the erosion surfaces of the Penwith Peninsula. The north-west coast shows the 400 ft. surface and the conspicuous bluff which backs it at 430 ft. The broad expanse of the 400 ft. surface on the south is also revealed together with the deeply incised valleys.

58

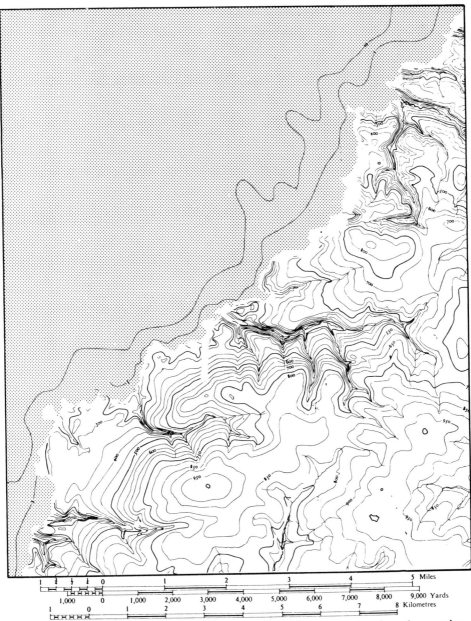

Fig. 2. Part of the Contours-only plate of O.S. Sheet 174 showing the erosion surfaces in the vicinity of Boscastle and Tintagel. Along the coast are remnants of the 400 ft. surface backed by the conspicuous bluff at 430 ft. The extract also shows parts of the 850 ft. surface and Condolden bluff at 920 ft. together with Davidstow Moor at 1,000 ft.

In 1907 Jukes-Brown described the coastal plateaux in the neighbourhood of Torquay and in 1908 G. Barrow drew attention to further erosion surfaces at 750 ft. and nearly 1000 ft. on Bodmin Moor, which were again thought to be of marine origin and probably of Miocene age, although no definite evidence for the latter suggestion was available.

In keeping with the nineteenth century British geological tradition initiated by A. C. Ramsey in Wales all these erosion surfaces were attributed to marine agencies. A completely divergent view was however put forward by the great American geomorphologist W. M. Davis in 1909: influenced by his United States background he proposed that the landscape of Devon and Cornwall could be explained by two cycles of sub-aerial denudation surrounding a monadnock. Sub-aerial origins were also suggested by L. Sawicki (1912) who after visiting Wales with W. M. Davis in 1911 subsequently travelled through Devon and Somerset with three French geographers. These divergent views were based on brief and superficial visits and they did not at the time, nor subsequently, command much support. The new ideas however might well have influenced later opinions held by Clement Reid, who, in the Newton Abbot Memoir, is inclined to invoke a sub-aerial origin for the upper Dartmoor surfaces.

Both in south-west England and elsewhere in Britain a considerable amount of contradictory evidence was, up to the outbreak of the First World War, being assembled with no clear acceptance of either point of view. Although observations continued elsewhere in Britain the next advance in the south-west did not come until the nineteen thirties since when there has been a steady flow of research papers. In 1936 C. W. F. R. Gullick suggested that further planations existed in south-west Cornwall at approximately 600 ft. and 180 ft. in addition to the already demonstrated and by then accepted level at 430 ft. In the same year J. F. N. Green (1936) further suggested that the Bodmin Moor features which Barrow had described could be traced eastwards into east Devon. Green also draws attention to the difficulty of determining with accuracy the heights of the sea level related to any particular marine erosion surface, locally complicated in the west because of the accumulation of head upon the platform.

The erosion surfaces of the south-west were also discussed in 1936 by P. Macar of Belgium. Whilst recognizing marine levels terminating at 430. 750 and 1000 ft. with a further level at 1200 ft. he introduces a somewhat discordant note by a resuscitation of the Jukes-Brown concept of local warping.

The following year a paper on the erosion surfaces of North Cornwall was published by the present writer and this included for the first time a distribution map of the already accepted surfaces together with an indication of a further lower level in the Padstow area. Attention was also drawn to the dangers of using heights for designating the surfaces since the same surface can vary in height from place to place. The proposal was made that local place names be used rather than heights. The numerous bluffs terminating the surfaces were also mapped for the first time and this data along with the distribution of the surfaces enabled a map of the earlier coastlines to be reconstructed. No warping was revealed by this analysis and there seemed little doubt that in this part of Cornwall all the recognized surfaces were of marine origin. The sequence which emerged was as follows:

Davidstow	circa 1,000 ft.
Condolden	base level at 920 ft., height range from 920—850 ft.
Treswallock	base level at 820 ft., height range from 820—600 ft.
Trevena	base level at 430 ft., height range from 430—300 ft.
Rosken	base level at 285 ft., height range from 285—240 ft.

On the basis of Clement Reid's and Barrow's dating the Rosken and Trevena surfaces were placed in the Pliocene whilst the upper surfaces were thought to be of Miocene age.

In 1938 there came a notable paper from S. E. Hollingworth in which a purely statistical approach to the problem was made by means of altimetric frequency curves covering the higher ground of western England and Wales. Devon and Cornwall are considered separately and the results of the statistical investigations correlate closely with the field information as then recorded. The Trevena (430 ft.), Treswallock (280 ft.) and Davidstow (1,000 ft.) planations emerged very clearly from the analysis but in addition the curves revealed the possibility of further surfaces at intermediate altitudes.

By this time the multiplicity of levels which were appearing not only in south-west England but elsewhere in Britain and on the Continent began to be viewed with suspicion in some quarters. The evidence was however clearly pointing towards a widespread and substantial eustatic shift of sea level in post Alpine time and this being so the development of both sub-aerial and sub-marine erosion surfaces at a wide variety of levels according to the length of the still-stands, local lithological conditions etc. was only to be expected. The magnitude of the changes appeared very large and many geologists found difficulty in accepting the idea, for the solution of one problem was it seemed merely leading to the creation of another.

Subsequent detailed studies have however tended to confirm this thesis. N J. G. Pounds in 1939 dealt with the Lizard area and J. F. N. Green followed in 1941 with a description of the high platforms of East Devon distinguishing at least six erosion surfaces in the height range between 440—920 ft. These stages were all considered to be of marine origin and Miocene to Pliocene in age. In a further paper in 1949 Green examines the River Dart area and traces at least eight levels between 430 and 1150 ft. which are again all thought to be of Mio-Pliocene origin. At about the same time S. W. Wooldridge (1950) reviewed the origin and geographical significance of the upland plains of Britain as a whole and in this notable contribution we find south-west England discussed in relation to the rest of the country.

A detailed analysis of the Exmoor region by the present writer followed in 1952 and this also revealed a staircase of levels, separated by bluffs interpreted as the worn down remnants of earlier clifflines, ranging up towards an elevation of 1225 ft. Above this height there appeared to be undulating traces of an early

Tertiary sub-aerial peneplain together with a suspicion of remnants of a sub-Cretaceous peneplain in the summit regions. The sequence which emerged from the analysis was as follows:

Summit 'Surface'	Remnants
Exmoor Surface	Sub-aerial peneplain above 1250 ft.
Lynton Surface	base level at 1225 ft., height range 1225—1000 ft.
Molland Surface	base level at 925 ft., height range 925— 850 ft.
Anstey Surface	base level at 825 ft., height range 825— 700 ft.
Buckland Surface	base level at 675 ft., height range 675— 500 ft.
Georgeham Surface	base level at 425 ft., height range 425— 300 ft.
Instow Surface	base level at 280 ft., height range 280— 200 ft.

Detailed distribution maps of the erosion surface remnants were also presented in support of the text. The sequence agreed with much that had already been observed elsewhere in the south-west.

In the same year N. Stephens investigated the erosion cycles of South West Devon and produced similar evidence of a staircase of levels, his conclusions in summary form being:

Above 1100 ft.	Broad expanses of undulating mature slopes, but no clear divisions possible.
1100—1000 ft. surface	Probably composite, in part marine, in part large valley facets. Well developed around the Dartmoor periphery.
840— 750 ft. surface	A marine abrasion surface. Widespread throughout the area. Bounded by bluffs at both upper and lower limits.
680— 550 ft. surface	Sub-aerially modified seaward end of the preceding marine surface.
430— 350 ft. surface	A marine abrasion surface. Well marked and indicative of a long still-stand.
320— 300 ft. surface	Sub-aerially modified seaward end of the preceding marine surface.
280— 250 ft. 210 ft. surface 190— 160 ft.	A series of marine abrasion surfaces cut during the retreat of the sea from the 430 ft. level.

Both Balchin (1952) and Stephens (1952) recognized the importance of the sub-aerial modification of emergent marine surfaces and also the possibility of sub-marine trimming of pre-existing sub-aerial surfaces.

More recently further detailed studies on erosion surfaces have been undertaken on Bodmin Moor by M. R. Weller (1959), in North Devon by Miss M. A. Arber (1960), in the Kerrier Peninsula by G. Fryer (1957-1958, published 1960) and in North-west Devon by M. J. Bradshaw (1961). The first two studies follow earlier approaches and largely agree with previous work. Weller supports the view that the 1000 ft. Bodmin surface is marine in origin but he thinks that

Barrow's next lower surface can be divided into two sub-aerial phases. He devotes considerable attention, for the first time in print, to the conspicuous remnants of a shoreline at 650-675 ft. on the south side of Bodmin Moor and this emerges from his analysis as a major phase in the denudation chronology. It is significant that a conspicuous feature at this level is also found on Exmoor (Balchin 1952), on Dartmoor (Stephens 1952), throughout the coastal regions of Wales (Brown 1957) and in south-east England (Wooldridge and Linton 1939). Below this important base level evidence was found of two further major still-stands at 430 ft. and 180 ft. In North Devon Miss Arber continues the major staircase of surfaces noted on Exmood (Balchin 1952) downwards with two further stages below the Instow (280 ft.) level. These are the Hele (150—100 ft.) and Croyde (approximately 50 ft.). Both these surfaces are restricted in area, they cut and therefore postdate the periglacial deposits of head and with them we begin to pass into the raised beaches of the glacial period.

M. J. Bradshaw's (1961) very detailed study of a restricted area of north-west Devon reveals the importance of the pre-submergence landscape in the present day topography. He agrees with previous researchers that a major marine incursion up to the 690 ft. level took place, with a subsequent withdrawal punctuated by still-stands at 650, 570, 520, 480, 430. 350 and 290 ft. Bradshaw accumulates however a considerable amount of evidence throughout his description of this part of Devon pointing to the re-occupancy of a pre-existing drainage system with re-emergence.

The conclusions of G. Fryer (1960) introduce a somewhat discordant note into the story. In his investigation of the land forms of Kerrier he rejects the marine hypothesis apart from the 430 ft. transgression and argues in favour of the sub-aerial denudation of a single extensive surface which he claims as a pediplain dating from Triassic time. This thesis echoes views put forward by O. T. Jones (1951) for Wales. It represents the third possibility, already mentioned in our introduction, of explaining erosion surfaces: but one which in south-west England as a whole raises almost as many problems as it solves and which so far has found few supporters. At present the majority of the evidence points to a eustatic marine hypothesis with emergent surfaces being subjected to sub-aerial modification, and rejuvenation affecting the rivers after each marine regression.

As this chapter was being written an account of the geomorphology of southern Dartmoor was published by A. R. Orme (1964). The polygenetic and polycyclic origins of the landforms in southern Dartmoor and the adjacent plateau country are described and four principal planation surfaces are distinguished at the higher levels. An early Tertiary peneplain from 1,620 - 1,520 ft. is flanked by a less well developed 1,375 - 1,050 ft. surface which probably post-dates the mid-Tertiary earth movements. Below these are late Tertiary surfaces at 1,000 - 875 ft. and 820 - 730 ft. Orme suggests a sub-aerial origin for these upper surfaces but introduces a new note into the literature by discussing the possibility of a form of pediplanation under warm humid conditions. Below these elevations the late Tertiary landscape is thought to have been drowned to a height of approximately 700 ft. by an early

Pleistocene marine transgression. The subsequent regression was punctuated by stillstands at 690, 600, 550, 460, 400, 327, 150, 126, 25, 14 and – 150 ft. within the area studied by Orme.

The task of assembling all these studies into a detailed geomorphological map for the whole of south-west England has yet to be attempted. It will not be an easy task for the identification of erosion surface fragments and the determination of their origin is a subjective exercise leaving much room for discussion. That surfaces exist there can be no doubt, but a divergency of opinion clearly exists as to the number and the origin of the features. These divergences however need not occasion alarm, for clearly at any particular still-stand we have both a sub-aerial and submarine surface in course of production: and if sufficient time elapses and a eustatic fall next occurs then the geomorphologist should be able to trace a sub-aerial surface grading down into a submarine surface. But since the exposed submarine surface will itself be open to sub-aerial attack it will clearly tend to disappear and its preservation will depend on the local resistance of the rocks. A variety of conditions will hence be possible and the intrusion of a sub-aerial surface into a sequence of submarine surfaces, or vice versa is quite possible. For correlative purposes the really important criterion in all cases is the identification of the associated base levels.

Dating the surfaces is also problematical. Only two lines of evidence exist —structural information and superficial deposits, neither of which are often conclusive. Unwarped surfaces must clearly post-date major orogenic movements such as the Alpine and this somewhat narrows possibilities for marine surfaces in the south-west. Sub-aerial surfaces will clearly be difficult to date in any circumstances, but marine surfaces with deposits offer some basis. Unfortunately few deposits have come to light on the marine surfaces in south-west England. Indeed despite the strong morphological evidence suggesting a marine origin for the majority of the erosion surfaces there is a remarkable absence of clearly correlative marine deposits.

Sands and gravels have been found at Polcrebo (500 ft.), Trenhale (430 ft.), Crousa Common (360 ft.) and St. Agnes (375 ft.) at various times and whilst quite probably of marine origin they are of little help for dating purposes as no included fossils have come to light. The Fremington and Filleigh clays of north-west Devon are likely to prove to be alluvial infillings of an earlier river valley. Probably the only significant deposits in the west are those at St. Erth and Orleigh Court. The deposits at St. Erth are fossiliferous and undoubtedly marine but unfortunately have complications in that they occur within a valley cut in the erosion surface. Originally identified towards the end of the last century and placed in the Older Pliocene by Clement Reid these deposits have been a key factor in early efforts at dating the lower surfaces in Cornwall. Wooldridge has suggested however that both the St. Erth deposits and the dating need re-examination in the light of new geological data. The discovery of Red Crag fauna in the Netley Heath beds (which rest on the undoubted 600 ft. marine bench of south-east England) and the decision of the International Geological Congress of 1948 to redraw the Pliocene/

Pleistocene boundary such that the Red Crag now falls within the Pleistocene, suggests that some, if not all, of the 'Pliocene' features of south-west England must now be regarded as early Pleistocene.

The second significant deposit is that at Orleigh Court which stretches, on the Georgeham surface, from Orleigh Mill to Yeo Bridge near Bideford. It consists of a superficial sand and flint cover extending for some three quarters by a quarter of a mile. The postwar Geological Survey's Regional Handbook describes the deposit as an outlier of Greensand—"the most westerly limit of the Cretaceous". The author, however, appears to have overlooked a paper by Inkerman Rogers and Brian Simpson (1937) which gives a petrological analysis of the deposits. The regional handbook seems to echo an early suggestion made by De la Beche in his classical report. A later opinion was given by W. A. F. Ussher (1879) who suggested that the deposit was probably a " re-assorted Cretaceous material, perhaps a Tertiary gravel" rather than Greensand in situ. P. G. H. Boswell in 1923 ascribed the deposit to the Eocene but Milner in the discussion of this paper favoured a Pliocene age. Rogers and Simpson considered that it must be a derived deposit of at least post-Eocene age and that it was probably laid down on part of the 400 ft. platform. It is very significant that the deposit extends up to, but not beyond, the 400 ft. contour, and that it is very near to the 430 ft. bluff. This flint gravel appears to have been originally a beach deposit analogous to the flint gravel beaches which occur at the modern sea-level in Padstow Bay, Mount's Bay and Gunwalloe.

The most recent consideration of superficial deposits comes from R. S. Waters (1960) with references to East Devon, West Dorset and South Somerset. Here we pass out of the Palaeozoic zone into a region dominated by an upland plateau of Cretaceous rocks comparatively rich in superficial deposits. Waters has managed to show that these consist of two types. West of a dividing line which runs north-south near Axminster 'typical' Clay with flints and chert occurs, but east of this line and at lower levels there is found in addition to the clay with flint patches of well rounded gravels in a sandy matrix. These contain unmistakable beach cobbles of flint with beach-hammered and chatter marked flints. Waters interpretation of these deposits does not entirely fit the general consensus of opinion regarding denudation chronology in south-west England but his identification of marine deposits is of considerable interest to those supporting the marine hypothesis.

The lack of marine deposits has sometimes been advanced by sub-aerial protaganists as a serious weakness in the submarine argument. Recently, however, aqualung divers have shown that deposits on the west coast of Cornwall are confined to a very narrow beach zone and that a bare rock platform is soon reached. If past offshore conditions on the staircase of platforms resembled those of the present wave cut abrasion platform, it is not difficult to account for the absence of deposits on the relatively narrow submarine shelves which are now exposed. It must further be remembered that there was no large adjacent land mass in south-west England upon which substantial debris carrying rivers could arise.

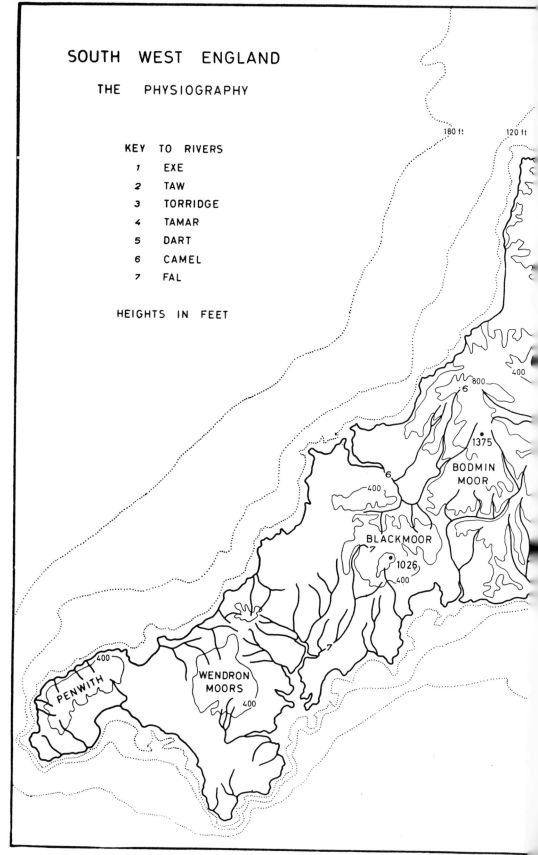

Fig. 3. Physiographic Map of South-West England.

EXMOOR

• 1707

BRENDON
HILLS

BLACKDOWN
HILLS

• 930

DARTMOOR

2039 •

60 ft

120 ft

180 ft

60 ft

0   10   20

MILES

III. THE EVOLUTION OF THE DRAINAGE PATTERN

In contrast to the growing volume of literature on erosion surfaces in south-west England there have been few attempts to analyse the drainage system and its evolution. One of the earliest studies was by A. W. Clayden in his History of Devonshire Scenery (1906). Although he perceived certain drainage reversals in north-west Devon much of his work must now be regarded as superceded. An interesting paper on river gorges in Devon and Cornwall by H. Dewey (1916) introduced the concept of extended consequent drainage upon emergent coastal platforms accompanied by rejuvenation as a result of lowered base levels. Later contributions have until recently been largely incidental to erosion surface enquiries. Even J. F. N. Green's History of the River Dart (1949) largely becomees an account of the erosion surfaces and terraces associated with the river.

In 1951 R. S. Waters examined the drainage evolution of south-west Devon in detail and like Dewey in north Cornwall (1916) came to the conclusion that the majority of the rivers are extended consequents upon emergent platforms which have received successive waves of rejuvenation. The drainage pattern was considered to have developed since the early Miocene and westerly flowing streams were thought to have grown at the expense of easterly flowing. The general direction taken by each small stream was determined mainly by the seaward slope of the successively emergent late Pliocene and early Pleistocene strand flats. No simple relationship of the drainage pattern with the geology could be traced.

These studies were of restricted localities however and the peninsula as a whole was not reconsidered until S. W. Wooldridge (1954) drew attention to a number of fundamental facts in the drainage pattern that provide clues for the denudation chronology. The main water parting, which can be traced for some 250 miles through Devon and Cornwall, throws light on the competition between north and south flowing drainage. A number of cols on this line suggest river piracy and much adjustment. (Fig. 3.) Three of these cols are of major significance. In the far west an original southward drainage has been reversed in the Hayle-Marazion depression. To the north east of this reversal the peculiar looped course of the Camel suggests reversal on an even larger scale. At Red Moor a broad gap at about 450 ft. probably represents the old drainage line of the upper Camel southwards to Lostwithiel and the present Fowey estuary. Northwards the imminent capture of the headstream of the Tamar by the Bude Haven drainage repeats the pattern and when complete will closely imitate the great Camel loop.

These features also throw light on the remarkable course of the Torridge. This river rises near Hartland and flows south-eastwards for twelve miles parallel to the Tamar. The high ground of Dartmoor blocks the continuation of this line and the original flow might well have been eastwards to the Exe drainage. The lower Torridge from Hatherleigh to Bideford Bay flows north-westwards and is either of much more recent origin or the reversed descendent of a stream formerly flowing south-east. The line of the Taw continued in that of the Yeo may also mark the line of a former stream flowing south-eastwards to join an ancestor of the Creedy.

68

The Exe and its tributaries also rise close to the northern coast and these too exhibit a south-east trend, but eastwards a series of captures has broken the continuity of similar southward flowing streams. The Batherm has beheaded the Loman and the upper Tone has been diverted eastwards by a subsequent tributary of the Parrett. This capture is analogous to that of the Bray by the Taw. Wooldridge suggests that it has originated by a simple adjustment to structure in the ready excavation of the Triassic rocks.

Considering the rivers as whole Wooldridge suggested that the evidence points to the existence of a former drainage to the south or south-east of which the Exe and the Tamar remain as substantial witnesses. Elsewhere reversal of drainage in the headstreams has occurred which suggests that originally the peninsular water parting was probably located well beyond the present north and west coast. All this implies an 'initial surface' sloping south. But there is also another element which implies an original easterly slope. This shows in the rivers of Dartmoor and Exmoor.

More recently detailed drainage studies have been made of the Lyn system by Scott Simpson (1953), the Exe River by C. Kidson (1962) and the Dart system by D. Brunsden (1963). The River Lyn is notable for its rejuvenation history and for the series of four captures by coastal erosion which throw light on much that has happened elsewhere on the Cornish coast. The Exe valley, according to Kidson's detailed levelling of the longitudinal profile, reveals nine major control stages of which two, the Westermill (690 ft.) and Nethercote (330 ft.) are significant. A major marine transgression seems to have marked both of these base levels. The evidence from the Exe valley supports the generally held thesis of a falling, albeit oscillatory, base level producing both erosion surfaces and river rejuvenations.

A similar but even more complicated story has been worked out on the River Dart by D. Brunsden. Seventeen stages are claimed of which the upper six are within the moorland area and the lower eleven in the coastal zone below 690 ft. The lower surfaces are dominantly submarine in origin but Brunsden favours sub-aerial origins for the upper surfaces. The summit peneplain from 1900—1500 ft. is thought to be tilted and hence of early Tertiary age, but none of the lower features show signs of warping and are hence considered to be post Alpine. A major change in the landscape is again detected above and below the 690 ft. level. The earliest drainage pattern recognizable on Dartmoor is thought to have been eastward and to have produced the early Tertiary peneplain. With the uplift and southerly tilting of this surface the drainage was rejuvenated and the south flowing tributaries extended themselves into the northern moor and the north flowing streams were suppressed. The eastward drainage was rejuvenated at the intermediate stage but the pattern was interrupted by the transgressive 690 ft. sea. Following the retreat of the shore during Pleistocene time the drainage was extended across the intermittently emerging sea floor and superimposed across the east-west lineaments in the Palaeozoic rocks.

IV. THE DENUDATION CHRONOLOGY

A point has now been reached where the varied evidence provided by the erosion surfaces, superficial deposits, drainage patterns and river profiles may be reviewed in an effort to provide a summary denudation chronology for south-west England. The total of the data now recorded provides material more appropriate to a Ph.D. thesis than to a short chapter, but in either case the broad outlines of the denudation chronology can be distinguished and despite differences of opinion on detail there is a notable and increasing measure of agreement on the main sequence.

One early geological episode which has influenced the present morphology was the pre-Triassic faulting (Thomas 1940) which led to the formation of basin-like depressions in which Triassic conglomerates and red sandstones were laid down. Certain of these faults and other new ones moved some hundreds of feet in late Triassic time and again to a miner extent in post-Liassic time. This produced a block fault system in some areas, e.g. eastern Exmoor. Although subsequently buried to a greater or lesser extent by Mesozoic deposits the faulting where it existed has influenced dissection during Tertiary time and in parts the topography could be regarded as partly exhumed. Such faulting must clearly have disrupted any Triassic peneplain that may have existed and much doubt is thereby cast on the pediment thesis.

Evidence from the geological deposits now ceases and the story can only be continued by reference to erosional features. It seems clear from the entrenched meanders of the Barle, Exe and other rivers on Exmoor (Balchin, 1952) that the drainage pattern has in the higher reaches of certain rivers been superimposed. This could only have occurred from a Cretaceous cover, for the Palaeozoic rocks are known to have been exposed in Eocene time. J. F. N. Green (1949) advanced a somewhat similar suggestion for Dartmoor but in terms of an Eocene planation with a cover of Eocene sediments. This dating however does not fit the known Eocene deposits of southern England which become coarser and more gravelly as they are traced from Hampshire into Dorset, and both the Reading beds and lower Bagshot sands may be shown to pass westwards into true sub-angular river gravels. The constituents of the gravels clearly indicate the exposure of Palaeozoic and Permian rocks further west.

Of the possible Cretaceous cover of Exmoor no trace now remains and we can only point to the so called 'summit surface' which, with a gentle slope of seven minutes of a degree to the east, runs approximately into the level at which Cretaceous deposits occur in southern England. This strongly suggests that in the 'summit surface' we may have fragmentary traces of a sub-Cretaceous surface.

With the retreat of the sea from the west sub-aerial agencies immediately began the task of removing the cover and by mid-Eocene time this appears to have been largely completed. But in the process the river system had in part been let down onto the Palaeozoic rocks. There is reason to suppose that this cycle of sub-aerial erosion extended through the Eocene period into the Oligocene and achieved a fairly advanced stage of maturity, traces of which are now left in the

Exmoor surface (Balchin 1952) high above the direct influence of the marine transgressions which came later.

The topography of the early Tertiary sub-aerial cycle was next modified by two agencies. In the first place there now seems agreement (Hollingworth 1938) that the late Oligocene and early Miocene folding associated with the Alpine orogeny extended to some degree into Devon and Cornwall. Secondly there is clear evidence of a widespread submergence of the greater part of the area, which as has been seen, is now dominated by a series of platforms or narrow shelves fringing all the high ground. Most authors submit that none of these features show any conspicuous signs of warping so that the agreed influence of the Alpine movements enables us to fix a limit to the age of the surfaces. Throughout south-west England research workers agree that the plateau like erosion surfaces below the 690 ft. level are primarily of marine origin but above this level opinion is divided between sub-aerial and submarine agencies. Doubtless some of the difficulty in interpretation is related to the later sub-aerial modification of earlier submarine surfaces, and also to the submarine trimming of pre-existing sub-aerial surfaces.

Whatever the explanation for a particular local feature there seems little doubt that there was a falling base level from late Miocene time onwards which was interrupted by a major transgression at approximately the 675+ ft. level in the early Pleistocene (according to recent dating). Subsequent to this transgression there seems to have been a gradual re-emergence of the region punctuated by still-stands of the main base level of which that at the 430 ft. stage is the most pronounced. The multiplicity of levels and surfaces that characterise the literature is at first confusing, but also understandable, since we are apparently dealing with eustatic shifts of sea level which would not necessarily leave the same record everywhere, although of course a prolonged still-stand should be easily traceable. This is indeed so in the case of the 430 and 675 ft. levels.

It is in these major oscillations of the base level that we may seek explanations for some of the more puzzling drainage reversals, river captures and the like. With the re-emergence of the land from the sea some rivers will doubtless have re-occupied such traces of their old courses as still existed but others will have fashioned new valleys. In many cases it is possible to distinguish both pre-platform and post-platform valley types. Rejuvenation has clearly influenced the great majority of the river courses as the polycyclic longitudinal and transverse profiles show. We cannot however explain the whole drainage pattern on the basis of extended streams consequent upon the slope of the emergent platforms. Elements of the early Tertiary sub-aerial surface were not completely erased by the marine transgressions and this palimpsest of an earlier period has clearly influenced many of the river courses. In some areas this control, as we have seen, can be traced back still earlier to superimposition from a Cretaceous cover. Other valleys have been formed by ancient coastal waterfalls which have migrated back inland. All these facts plus the possibility of oscillations in the lowering of the base level, adjustment to structure and river capture must be taken into account when unravelling the denudation chronology of any particular river.

REFERENCES

ARBER, E. A. N. 1912. The Coast Scenery of North Devon. London (Dent).

ARBER, MURIEL A. 1960. Pleistocene Sea Levels in North Devon. *Proc. Geol. Ass., Lond.*, **71,** 169-176.

BALCHIN, W. G. V. 1937. The Erosion Surfaces of North Cornwall. *Geog. Journ.* **90,** 52-63.

—— 1946. The Geomorphology of the North Cornish Coast. *Trans. R. geol. Soc. Cornwall*, **17,** 317-344.

—— 1952. The Erosion Surfaces of Exmoor and Adjacent Areas. *Geog. Journ.,* **118,** 453-476.

—— 1952. The Evidence for Late Tertiary Eustatic Changes of Sea Level in Western Europe. Proc. *8th General Assembly and 17th Congress of Int. Geog. Union, Washington*, 296-300.

BARROW, G. 1908. The High Level Platforms of Bodmin Moor and their relation to the deposits of stream tin and Wolfram. *Quart. J. geol. Soc., Lond.* **64,** 384-400.

BOSWELL, P. G. H. 1923. Petrography of the Cretaceous and Tertiary Outliers of the West of England. *Quart. J. geol. Soc., Lond.* **79,** 205-230.

BRADSHAW, M. J. 1961. Aspects of the Geomorphology of North West Devon. *M.A. Thesis of the University of London* (unpublished).

BROWN, E. H. 1957. The Physique of Wales. *Geog. Journ.,* **123,** 208-230.

BRUNSDEN, D. 1963. The Denudation Chronology of the River Dart. *Trans. Inst. Brit. Geog.,* **32,** 49-63.

—— KIDSON, C., ORME, A. R. and WATERS, R. S. 1964. Denudation Chronology of Parts of South-Western England. *Field Studies,* **2,** 115-132.

CLAYDEN, A. W. 1906. The History of Devonshire Scenery. J. G. Commin Exeter and Chatto and Windus.

DEWEY, H. 1916. On the Origins of some river gorges in Cornwall and Devon. *Quart. J. geol. Soc., Lond.,* **72,** 63-76.

—— 1948. *British Regional Geology of South-West England.* Geol. Surv. U.K.

FRYER, G. 1958. Evolution of the Land Forms of Kerrier. *Trans. R. geol. Soc. Corn.,* **19,** 122-153.

GREEN, J. F. N. 1936. The Terraces of Southernmost England. *Quart. J. geol. Soc., Lond.,* **92,** 58-88.

—— 1941. The High Platforms of East Devon. *Proc. Geol. Ass., Lond.,* **52,** 36-52.

—— 1949. The History of the River Dart, Devon. *Proc. Geol. Ass., Lond.,* **60,** 105-124.

GUILCHER, A. 1949. Aspects et problèmes morphologiques du massif de Devon-Cornwall comparées à ceux d'Armorique. *Rev. Géo, Alp.,* **37,** 689-717.

GULLICK, C. W. F. R. 1936. A Physiographic Survey of West Cornwall. *Trans. R. geol. Soc. Cornwall,* **16,** 380.

HENDRIKS, E. M. L. 1923. The Physiography of South West Cornwall, the distribution of the chalk flints and the origin of the gravels of Crousa Down. *Geol. Mag.,* **60,** 21-31.

HOLLINGWORTH, S. E. 1939. The Recognition and Correlation of High Level Erosion Surfaces in Britain. *Quart. J. geol. Soc., Lond.,* **94,** 55-79.

JONES, O. T. 1930. Some Episodes in the Geological History of the Bristol Channel Region. Presidential Address to *Section C of the British Association, Bristol, 1930.* 57-82.

—— 1951. The Drainage systems of Wales and the Adjacent Areas: *Quart. J. geol. Soc., Lond.,* **107,** 201-225.

JUKES-BROWN, A. J. 1907. The Age and Origin of the Plateaux around Torquay. *Quart. J. geol. Soc., Lond.*, **63**, 106-123.

KIDSON, C. 1962. The Denudation Chronology of the River Exe. *Trans. Inst. Brit. Geog.*, **31**, 43-46.

MACAR, P. 1936. Quelques remarques sur la Géomorphologie des Cornouailles et du Sud de Devonshire. *Bull. Soc. Géol. Belg.*, **60**, 152-168.

MILNER, H. B. 1922. The Nature and Origin of the Piocene deposits of the County of Cornwall. *Quart. J. geol. Soc., Lond.*, **78**, 348-377.

NORTH, F. J. 1929. *The Evolution of the Bristol Channel*. National Museum of Wales, Cardiff.

ORME, A. R. 1961. The geomorphology of the South Hams. *Ph.D. Thesis of the University of Birmingham* (unpublished).

—— 1964. The geomorphology of Southern Dartmoor, pages 31-72 of Dartmoor Essays, *The Devonshire Association for the Advancement of Science, Literature and Art*.

PICKARD, R. 1946. High Level Gravels in East and North Devon. *Trans. Devon Ass.*, **78**, 207-228.

POUNDS, N. J. G. 1939. The Helford Depression and the 200 ft. Platform. *Trans. R. Corn. Poly. Soc.*, **9**, 33-37.

—— 1945. Notes on the Geomorphology of the area to the west of Falmouth. *Trans. R. Corn. Poly. Soc.*, **11**, 13-20.

REID, C. 1896. The Pliocene Rocks of Britain. *Mem. geol. Surv. U.K.*

—— 1913. The Geology of the Country around Newton Abbot. *Mem. geol. Surv. U.K.*

ROGERS, INKERMAN and SIMPSON, B. 1937. The Flint Gravel Deposit of Orleigh Court, Buckland Brewer, North Devon. *Geol. Mag.*, **74**, 309-316.

SAWICKI, L. 1912. Die Einebungsflächen in Wales and Devon. *C.R. Soc. Sci. Varsovie*, **5**, 123-134.

SIMPSON, SCOTT. 1953. The Development of the Lyn Drainage System and its relation to the Origin of the Coast between Combe Martin and Porlock. *Proc. Geol. Ass., Lond.*, **64**, 14-23.

STEPHENS, N. 1952. Erosion Cycles in South West Devon. *M.Sc. Thesis of the University of Bristol* (unpublished).

THOMAS, A. N. 1940. The Triassic Rocks of North West Somerset. *Proc. Geol. Ass., Lond.*, **51**, 1-43.

USSHER, W. A. E. 1878. The Chronological Value of the Pleistocene Deposits of Devon. *Quart. J. geol. Soc., Lond.*, **34**, 449-458.

—— 1879. On the Deposits of Petrockstow, in Devon. *Trans. Devon Ass.*, **11**, 422-428.

WATERS, R. S. 1951. Some Aspects of the Denudation Chronology of S.W. Devon. *M.A. Thesis of the University of Reading* (unpublished).

—— 1960. The bearing of the superficial deposits on the age and origin of the upland plain of East Devon, West Dorset and South Somerset. *Trans. Inst. Brit. Geog.*, **28**, 89-97.

WELLER, M. R. 1959. A Contribution to the Geomorphology of Bodmin Moor and Adjacent Districts. *M.A. Thesis of the University of London* (unpublished).

—— 1960. Erosion Surfaces of Bodmin Moor. *Trans. R. geol. Soc. Corn.*, **19**, pt. 3, 233-242.

WOOLDRIDGE, S. W. 1950. The Upland Plains of Britain. Presidential Address to Section E British Association Birmingham 1950. *Adv. Science*, **7**, no. 26. 162-175.

—— 1954. The Physique of the South West. *Geography*, **39**, 231-261.

—— and LINTON, D. L. 1939. Structure, Surface and Drainage in South East England. *Trans. Inst. Brit. Geog.*, **10,** 1-124.

PLATE 1

With acknowledgements to Aerofilms and Aero Pictorial Ltd.

Deeply incised valleys in the 400 ft. marine erosion surface near Polperro.

PLATE 2

With acknowledgements to Aerofilms, Ltd.

Lamorna Cove, the '400' ft. platform of marine abrasion in the Penwith peninsula.

PLATE 3

Kelsey Head from Holywell near Newquay. Part of the lower 200 ft. marine erosion surface.

With acknowledgements to "The Times"

PLATE 4

Logan Rock near Porthcurno, the coastal platform of marine abrasion near Land's End.

With acknowledgements to Aerofilms and Aero Pictorial Ltd.

Piedmont profiles in the arid cycle

by W. G. V. BALCHIN and N. PYE

Received 4 November 1953; read 2 July 1954

CONTENTS

ABSTRACT: The paper discusses the origin of piedmont profiles in the arid cycle of erosion, with particular reference to the Sonora and Mohave Deserts of Arizona and California. The various physiographic elements may be divided into those produced by erosion and those produced by the accumulation of the eroded material. In the former group fall the retreating mountain front, the pediment and the river terrace, whilst the latter includes the bahada, the peripediment (alluvial zone) and the playa. The relative importance of each of these two groups determines the resulting piedmont profile. At least sixteen combinations appear possible but some are more common than others, and the evidence gathered suggests that landscape forms developed under semi-arid to arid conditions are much more responsive to minor changes in lithology and/or climate. It follows that different combinations of the profile elements may co-exist within short distances, and that detailed explanations are only locally applicable. Herein, it is thought, may lie the key to many opposing points of view regarding the origin of certain features; more especially the rock-cut surface or pediment.

1. INTRODUCTION

THE PHYSIOGRAPHIC features of deserts are very varied, but a broad distinction may be made between the great plains and plateaux of the African and Australian areas and the succession of arid, mountain-girt basins of parts of Africa, Asia and North America. It is in the latter area that landscape forms peculiar to the arid cycle have especially developed; more particularly in those localities adjacent to the mountains, i.e. in the piedmont zones. Here the mountains often stand out from the adjacent plains with startling abruptness. From a distance the hill slopes appear remarkably steep, rising precipitously to jagged peaks and forming the *sierra* type of mountain range. Closer inspection reveals that the plain itself rises in a gentle slope to the mountain foot, but there is then an abrupt change in the mountain gradients without any transition zone of intermediate slope, or any region of low foothills. It is evident that the dominant processes responsible for the formation of the mountain slopes must differ considerably from those responsible for the plains. The mountain slopes are sometimes gashed by gullies down which intermittent streams tumble in torrential courses to lower levels. When these streams reach the plain their velocities are checked and transporting powers reduced, with the result that their loads are deposited in fan-shaped accumulations. Each fan results from a single mountain stream and normally this divides radially from the apex of the fan. The load is thus distributed, and in the course of time adjacent fans may join to form a continuous alluvial deposit, or *bahada*, flanking the mountain foot.

Further examination shows that the plain itself may present either an erosional or an alluvial aspect. Bare planed rock surfaces, which have been variously referred to as *pediments, rock pediments* or *sub-aerial benches*, may form an important element in the piedmont zone. These may stretch away from the mountain foot, eventually disappearing beneath gently sloping plains of alluvial accumulation sometimes referred to as *graded piedmont slopes*. These in turn may pass into either a dead flat plain or *playa* associated with a basin of interior drainage, or into the dissections of a through-flowing river.

There thus exists a fundamental difference between the smooth graded profiles associated with the humid cycle, and the sectioned profiles, with angular junctions, typical of the arid cycle. Some seventy years have now passed since Gilbert first touched upon these differences, and during this time identical features have been described from a variety of arid areas ranging from Arizona, California, Utah, Colorado and New Mexico in the United States to Chile, Mongolia, Australia and many parts of Africa. It seems clear that these landscape forms in mountain areas are concomitant with arid conditions. Along with many purely descriptive accounts there have also appeared hypothetical works in which theories have been advanced to account for the origin of these features. The planed rock surface has probably given rise to most controversy and rival schools of thought have variously suggested that the origin is to be found in the recession of the mountain front by weathering processes (Lawson, 1915; Bryan, 1936; Davis, 1930); or that the feature results from lateral corrasion by ephemeral streams operating in a zone between degradation in the mountains and aggradation in the plains (Gilbert, 1877; Johnson, 1931; Blackwelder, 1931; Howard, 1942); others have looked to special processes such as sheetflood erosion (McGee, 1897) or sheetwash erosion (Rich, 1935) which are known to operate under arid conditions. The angle between the mountains and the plains, together with the nature of the retreat of the mountain slope, has also given rise to discussion. Deductions can be made from some of the theories that, so far as the present authors could ascertain, had not been fully tested in the field, and it was with this object in view that a small expedition was organised in 1952 to visit the Sonora and Mohave deserts of Arizona and California.

In the Sonoran Desert there are nearly a hundred isolated mountain ranges, varying from five to ten miles in width, and rising from five to six thousand feet above debris-filled basins some twenty-five to thirty miles in extent. The mountains consist of granite, gneiss and other crystalline rocks, in places capped by lava flows, and they have the typical fault-block form common throughout the Basin and Range province. In the piedmont zones we find the canyons, fans, bahadas, pediments, and alluvial zones already mentioned. Whilst interior drainage to enclosed basins or bolsons occurs, it is by no means universal, and in many parts there are through-flowing (although intermittent) rivers such as the Gila, Salt, San Pedro and Santa Cruz. Combined with the fact that much of the area has slopes on which water might run directly to the sea, were there enough rain, it is perhaps more correct to say that this is largely an area of exterior drainage.

For this reason, therefore, attention was also directed to the Mohave Desert of Southern California. This, with somewhat similar topography and climatic conditions, is characterised by interior drainage. Smaller ranges of mountains, more widely dispersed, here demarcate extensive infilled bolsons, the centres of which are marked by soda lakes, borax lakes, and dry lakes. This is a region of rising base levels, whereas much of the Arizonan desert area is now controlled by a falling base level. During the course of the expedition, field observations and slope measurements were made throughout these areas and over several thousand miles of territory.

2. THE LONGITUDINAL PROFILE[1]

(a) **The mountain slopes** in the region studied ranged from 25° to almost 90° from the horizontal, and in all cases rose abruptly from the adjacent morphological feature. Whatever the angle, there is a distinct tendency for it to remain almost the same until the crest of the slope is reached. There is also a correlation between the angle of slope and the type of rock; isolated hills, mountain slopes and canyon walls cut in the same rock all tend to assume slopes of the same angle under arid conditions, and it seems quite evident that with unimpeded removal of the weathered debris these slopes retreat parallel to themselves. The actual slope which forms is controlled by the resistance to weathering and by the physical properties of the rock. The nature of any jointing in the rock is very significant, for this is largely the factor deciding the sizes of the blocks which may be detached from the rock face. The resistance of these blocks to disintegration, together with their size and number, materially affects the angle of rest and usually decides the slope for a particular rock. Whilst theoretically any

[1] Profiles taken approximately normal to the run of the mountain front.

angle becomes a possibility, in actual practice one usually finds either a precipitous clean-faced slope, approaching the vertical, and related to widely-jointed rocks, or boulder-strewn slopes ranging between 25° and 45° which are related to more closely-jointed rocks (Plate 5, A). Certain types of granite, gneiss, some massive lava flows and fine-grained porphyritic rocks give rise to precipitous slopes, and here recession takes place either by prolonged uniform surface disintegration, or by undermining at the base of the more resistant rocks. The presence or absence of talus depends on the relative rates of weathering and removal. The more normal granite (e.g. Sacaton Mountains, Arizona) (Plate 5, B), gneiss (Santa Catalina Mountains, Arizona) and lava (Tucson Mountains, Arizona) weathers into a boulder-strewn slope of 30–50°, interrupted by occasional cliffs related to the more resistant rocks. The spacing of the jointing controls the size of the boulders and these may vary from less than a foot to several feet in diameter: hence normally fine-grained granites and gneisses, with closely-spaced joints, will give rise to gentler mountain slopes than the coarse-grained types. The rate of change on all these slopes must be very slow indeed in the absence of any violent water action. Shreve, for instance, cites cases of *palo verde* (the greenstick tree) up to 400 years old growing between the boulders and so placed that little or no movement can have taken place in the tree's lifetime.

But disintegration does continue, the bedrock decaying along the joints and the occasional rain washing away the fine fragments. From time to time boulders are set in motion down the slope and perhaps break to pieces *en route*. By these processes the mountain front slowly retreats, while maintaining its angle of slope. Whether talus or material is found at the mountain foot depends on the local balance of forces between the prevailing climatic conditions and the rock resistance.

(b) **The bahada** form arises in the piedmont zone, where the rainfall is sufficient to produce streams rather than rain wash, and it is the counterpart of canyon cutting at higher levels. The gradient of the individual fan is intimately related to the size of the incision at the rear. Short precipitous gullies on the mountain front pass into steeply graded fans in the piedmont zone, slopes of up to 20° being noted. Large canyons which have deeply dissected the mountain area merge into broad fans of very small gradient. In these cases slopes will normally be less than 7° and may be as low as 1°. The alluvial fans of the Santa Catalina Mountains, near Tucson, Arizona, have a radial extent of some four miles and slopes of 5° in the steepest parts, dropping to 2° in the lower parts. It is the larger and less steep fans that coalesce into the bahada to form extensive gently sloping plains which, from a distance, may be confused with the pediment. Although there are superficial similarities to the pediment, a close examination soon reveals the bahada's true nature. It is built up to some thickness with poorly-

PLATE 5

B. Granitic boulder-strewn slopes giving place abruptly to pediment with thin veneer of fine-grained sediment. Sacaton Mountains, Arizona

A. Peripediment reaching to waste-mantled mountain front with precipitous summit slopes. Sharp angular junctions. Mescal Peak south-west of Tombstone, Arizona

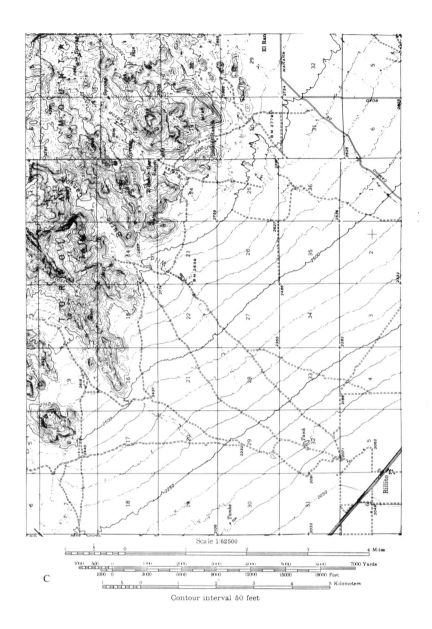

Scale 1:62500

1000 500 1000 2000 3000 4000 5000 6000 7000 Yards

1000 0 3000 6000 9000 12000 15000 18000 Feet

1 .5 0 1 2 3 4 5 Kilometers

C

Contour interval 50 feet

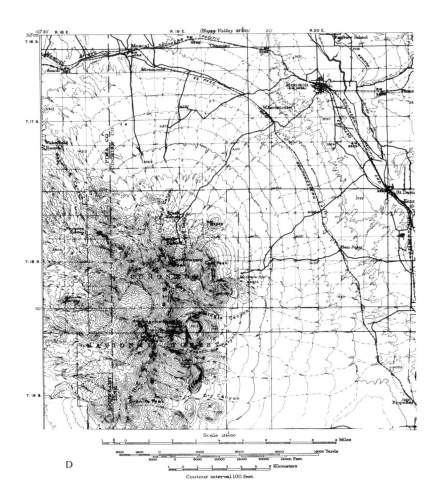

Scale 1:126000

3000 1500 0 3000 6000 9000 12000 Yards

5000 0 5000 10000 15000 20000 25000 Feet

1 0 1 2 3 4 5 6 Kilometers

Contour interval 100 feet

D

stratified detritus and large included boulders deposited under torrential conditions; sections reveal that near the surface each layer is almost parallel to the particular fan surface. The composition is such that many are, in fact, rock debris fans rather than 'alluvial' fans in the conventional sense of the word (Plate 6, A). The longitudinal profile is definitely a shallow concave curve, with the concavity upwards, and the gradient increasing steadily towards the mountain front. The feature masks the mountain front and forms a zone of aggradation along its foot. The base of the bahada is normally revealed by a clear junction angle with the next morphological element in the sequence except in those cases where gradients of 1°, or less, obtain.

(c) **The pediment,** at upper levels, has probably been confused by many with the mature low gradient bahada, and at lower levels with the alluvial zone (Fig. 1), but the pediment proper is very different from either because it consists of a gently inclined planed rock surface which rises to the foot of the mountain front and cuts indifferently across rocks of varying lithology and structure (Plate 6, B; Plate 5, C, D). The gradients all fall within the range $\frac{1}{2}$°–7°. Whilst the differences in slope are slight, they often appear to be correlative with other factors. Slopes opposite to large canyons are commonly more gentle than those opposite to small canyons, whilst the pediment which runs to the foot of the mountain front has usually a slightly higher gradient than the areas opposite to the canyons.[1] It was also noted that rocks weathering into a coarse debris (e.g. Baboquivari Mountains) give rise to slightly steeper pediment slopes than those which break up into a fine debris (e.g. the Sacaton Mountains); whilst rocks such as andesite lava (e.g. near Ajo), which weather to large resistant blocks, fail to yield any pediment forms at all. Differences in slope rarely exceeded one or two degrees, and were often imperceptible to the eye, but the trend does throw some light on the origin of the pediment. It is clear that stream size and lithological factors must not be overlooked.

Confusion with the other landscape forms has undoubtedly arisen because, in places, the pediment is often overspread with a thin veneer of gravelly detritus which may conceal much, if not all, of the rock surface. A further difficulty arises in that the pediment disappears beneath the next feature—the graded alluvial zone, in most cases—and rarely seems to attain any great width. The longitudinal profile of the visible section is frequently of a uniform gradient and thus contributes little towards a solution of its origin. For if it is a water-eroded feature, i.e. related to either lateral corrasion (Johnson, 1931, 1932a; Gilbert, 1877; Blackwelder, 1931a; Howard, 1942), sheet-flooding (McGee, 1897) or sheetwash (Rich, 1935), its profile should show a concave tendency; whilst if it is due to the normal

[1] Contrary to the theoretical deduction of J. L. Rich (1935).

recession of the mountain front with a rising base level (Lawson, 1915; Bryan, 1925) its profile should show a convex tendency.

In the present investigation various attempts were made to trace with an auger the sub-alluvial rock floor of buried pediments in the Sierrita and Tortolita Mountains, near Tucson, but the gravelly nature of the detritus made it impossible to determine the depth of the rock surface with any degree of accuracy. Experience showed that this method could only be used in the very fine deposits well away from the mountain front, but here the depth of the detritus was considerably beyond the range of the normal auger. Well and ground water-borings are however sometimes of great value in giving an indication of the depth of the detritus, although they rarely reveal the actual rock floor as the borings are normally stopped as soon as water is reached. Now, however, a great deal of evidence has been collected by the Ground Water Division of the United States Geological Survey and in many areas this definitely points to an increased rate of accumulation outwards from the mountain front, and suggests that the sub-alluvial rock floor is probably convex upwards, as Lawson supposed (1915). This particular aspect of the problem could probably be resolved by sample seismic surveys which may well be made before very long in view of the growing economic significance of ground water supplies, coupled with the problem of falling water table levels in these areas.[1]

If the term pediment be confined to the exposed and visible portion of the rock surface, then the areal extent and incidence of the feature is probably very much less in both the Sonoran and Mohave areas than previous writers have estimated. McGee thought that some two-fifths of the Sonora Desert region consisted of pediment plains but the 1952 traverses did not reveal any very extensive exposure of bare piedmont erosion surfaces, and those that were noted, more especially in the Tortolita, Baboquivari and Sierrita Mountains, together with the Ajo region, presented a very hummocky surface and were by no means as smooth as might have been expected from the literature. These pediments were runnelled and were clearly being influenced by stream-flood action. Dissections of up to fifteen to twenty feet in depth were by no means uncommon, although from a distance smooth skyline profiles were often simulated. A regular smooth planated rock surface may be a rarity, in fact, but a smooth surface profile often occurs at lower levels when the rock has a cover of alluvial deposits. What is not yet clear is the permissible depth of the veneer that a rock plain may have and still remain a true pediment, rather than becoming a true sub-alluvial rock bench. One criterion which might eventually prove useful is the depth of scour of the intermittent stream action (Howard, 1942; Tator, 1952a).

[1] See W. G. V. Balchin & N. Pye, 1953. The Drought in the South-Western United States. *Weather*, Royal Meteorological Society, London, 8, 223–6.,

PLATE 6

A. Section through bahada zone, Santa Rita Mountains, south of Tucson, Arizona

B. Rock pediment of the Sierrita Mountains south-west of Tucson, Arizona

C. Rejuvenated peripediment in the Gila River valley near Safford, Arizona

(d) **The alluvial zone** succeeds the true pediment as the next element in the sectioned profile. The surface slope of the first part is normally less than five degrees, and may fall as low as fifteen minutes of arc (e.g. south of Tucson on the flanks of the Sierrita Mountains). The skyline longitudinal profile does not reveal the junction, which is a zone rather than a line, and this can only be found by traversing the ground. Many previous writers have described pediments with alluvial covers up to several hundred feet in thickness, although most talk in terms of a 'thin veneer' without specifying the actual depth. We feel that a distinction should be made between the rock surface which has a really thin veneer but is still within the range of sub-aerial weathering agencies, and hence still subject to change, and the rock surface which is buried beneath a thicker alluvial cover and hence protected from further change. It would seem logical to restrict the use of the term pediment to the former case and to use the phrase sub-alluvial bench for the latter.

That part of the alluvial zone above the 'bench' which continues the slope of, and grades into, the pediment is of constructional rather than degradational origin, and should be distinguished from the pediment. As it is peripheral to the pediment, and often superficially similar, Howard's term *peripediment* (1942) might usefully be confined in future to this feature, and in fact seems to be so used in Child's work (1948) on the Little Colorado Region. The combined pediment and peripediment may then be described as a *pediplane* (Howard, 1942). With this distinction the depth of the detritus on the pediment would be restricted to the depth of scour of any intermittent stream action. This would normally be measured in inches, although exceptionally it might be measurable in feet (Fig. 1).

Usually the upper parts of the peripediments in the Sonora and Mohave

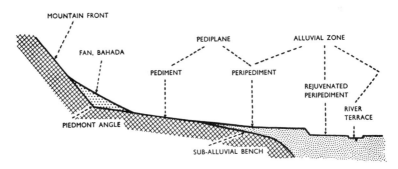

Fig. 1. Elements in the Piedmont Profile

89

Deserts are composed of detritus which is poorly sorted and which frequently resembles deposits of a torrential character. But this is probably due to the occasional sheetflood and streamflood which sweeps down and across the pediment, carrying all before it, until with decreasing speed first the coarse and then the fine load is dropped. Downslope on the peripediment, however, the material is better sorted, becomes much smaller in size, and eventually passes into a fine deposit, especially in the granite areas (e.g. The Sacaton Mountains). The surface often shows the effect of an occasional sheetwash but the shallow shifting channels caused by stream flooding are clearly in evidence, and it is along these that the vegetation will often be found to be growing. Normally the thickness of the alluvial deposits seems to increase downslope and well-borings, together with occasional dissections, reveal depths of up to 200 ft. Beyond this amount there may be a sudden increase to several hundred, and sometimes more than a thousand, feet of sediment, marking the infilling of a fault-trough or basin (e.g. the Tucson bolson). Conditions such as these indicate a past history of rising base levels, and are well illustrated in the Mohave Desert (e.g. between Amboy and Barstow). The peripediment may be terminated by another similar feature descending from an opposite piedmont slope, or by a through-flowing river, or by a playa. In all cases the line of demarcation is clear and distinct. Even with the playa, although the slope may change from something less than one degree to zero, the change is clearly shown by the sudden cessation of the scanty vegetation. The gleaming white perfectly flat playas of the Mohave desert (e.g. Rogers Dry Lake, Soda Lake, etc.) carry salt, soda and borax deposits, which, together with the intermittent inundations, effectively eliminate most, if not all, types of vegetation. Morphologically these are areas of rising base-levels.

Elsewhere, however, intermittent streams or through-flowing rivers may terminate the peripediment. The intermittent streams can co-exist with a rising base-level but the through-flowing continuous river may give either a relatively stable base-level, or may show rejuvenations with a consequential dissection of deposits which have accumulated under different conditions. The latter is commonly found in southern Arizona where successive rejuvenations of the rivers have dissected the peripediment, and also in places the pediment. Along the Santa Cruz, San Pedro and Gila Rivers up to four marked stages, cut in loose or poorly-consolidated material, can be distinguished, and these rise from the present floodplain in a series of clear-cut steps. But whilst the lowest step is a flat floored floodplain terminated by a river-cut cliff, the higher stages have slopes similar to the peripediment, and are terminated by bluffs apparently retreating parallel to themselves. These appear to be rather special forms, initiated by river action, but developed further under the prevailing semi-arid conditions. They may be regarded as rejuvenated peripediments and would merit a more detailed study and survey than time permitted in the present investigation (Plate 6, C).[1]

All the possible elements in the longitudinal profile have now been described but the actual profile which results in any locality will depend on the particular combination of the elements prevailing in that area. The boulder-strewn mountain front may give place to the rock pediment and then pass into the alluvial zone (Fig. 2, A) as in the Sierrita Mountains. In other localities (e.g. the Sacaton Mountains) the alluvial zone extends to the base of the mountain front and completely masks the pediment (Fig. 2, B), or the presumed pediment, in the absence of information from well-borings. Elsewhere the mountain front may be mantled by a well-developed bahada which gives place to the pediment, and then the peripediment (Fig. 2, C), but this condition did not seem characteristic of the areas visited in 1952. The situation shown in Fig. 2, D, where the bahada passes directly into the alluvial zone without exposure of the pediment (e.g. the Santa Rita Mountains in Arizona and near Amboy in the Mohave Desert) was much more prevalent.

We have already seen that the peripediment may be terminated in the lower parts in four different ways. With a rising base-level either two adjacent peripediments will make a simple junction or the central area will be occupied by a playa or dry lake. With a falling base-level the junction will either be occupied by a simple or a rejuvenated river system. Since any of the four possibilities sketched in the preceding paragraph may be combined with any of the four peripediment terminations there are, theoretically, at least sixteen different profiles possible, any one of which may arise depending on the balance of past and present morphological processes at work in a particular locality.

3. THE TRANSVERSE PROFILE[2]

An examination of the transverse profile of each of the morphological elements distinguished so far reveals certain characteristics which contribute to an understanding of their formation. The simple mountain front normally presents a uniform or 'level' profile, apart from those parts which have been gullied or canyoned. The bahada has an undulatory transverse profile, since it is made up of a series of coalescing fans. With steeply graded fans these undulations will be very conspicuous, but in the mature low gradient bahada they may well be imperceptible.

When the pediment is considered, however, we find that the theorists

[1] Similar features have been described and mapped in the San Acacia area of New Mexico by C. S. Denny (1941), four 'pediment terraces' being distinguished, and in the Upper Rio Puerco Valley of New Mexico by Kirk Bryan & F. T. McCann (1936), where two 'pediments' and two river terraces are described.

[2] A direction approximately parallel to the run of the mountain front.

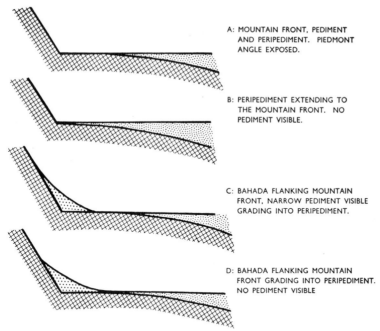

A: MOUNTAIN FRONT, PEDIMENT AND PERIPEDIMENT. PIEDMONT ANGLE EXPOSED.

B: PERIPEDIMENT EXTENDING TO THE MOUNTAIN FRONT. NO PEDIMENT VISIBLE.

C: BAHADA FLANKING MOUNTAIN FRONT, NARROW PEDIMENT VISIBLE GRADING INTO PERIPEDIMENT.

D: BAHADA FLANKING MOUNTAIN FRONT GRADING INTO PERIPEDIMENT. NO PEDIMENT VISIBLE

Fig. 2. Profiles in the Piedmont Zone

postulate the existence of three possible conditions: essentially level; upwardly convex or upwardly concave transverse profiles. Sheetwash and sheetflood action would, it is held, produce a level transverse profile; lateral planation by streams radiating out from canyons cut in the mountain front are said by Johnson (1932a) and Howard (1942) to be capable of producing rock fans with an upwardly convex transverse profile. If, however, the emphasis is placed upon stream-flood erosion (Davis, 1938), then the profile becomes undulatory and upwardly concave in the neighbourhood of the streams, since any form of integrated drainage will require a general concavity. Examination of the transverse profiles should therefore provide some indication of the mode of origin of the pediment. Apart from the special case of the Gibson Arroyo fan already noted by Gilluly (1937), no clear case of a rock fan was discovered in the areas visited in 1952, and Johnson's claim that the Sierrita Mountains had examples could not be substantiated. Both Field (1935) and Blackwelder (1931a) have also looked for, but failed to find, in the Colorado region the theoretical rock fans deduced by Johnson. In southern Arizona the transverse profile of the pediment is often almost level, except in the dissected areas or opposite to major canyons in the mountain front, and it then becomes trough-shaped, e.g. near Ajo (Gilluly). In the Mohave Desert level transverse profiles seem to prevail.

Across the peripediment, and of course on the playa, level transverse profiles are also found, except for minor undulations in the peripediment related to stream-flood courses. Where a through-flowing river such as the Santa Cruz or San Pedro, has lowered the base-level, however, both the peripediment and the pediment may be heavily dissected. Headward erosion along the minor gullies which develop on the sides of the major drainage lines may cut up the peripediment into a maze of small hills. A great deal of the plain lands of southern Arizona are now characterised by this type of bad land topography, and it greatly increases the difficulty of their utilisation (Plate 6, C).

In addition to the dissection which is clearly related to the lowering of the base-level by a through-flowing stream, there are also cases of dissection of the upper peripediment and the pediment where a rising base-level exists, e.g. the Altar Valley south-west of Tucson. Although water rarely occupies these trenches, the dissection would seem to imply a trend towards heavier rainfall, producing streamflood action rather than sheetwash and rill action.

4. THE PIEDMONT ANGLE

One important characteristic of semi-arid to arid topography is the abruptness with which the mountains stand out from the plains. This rarely occurs in the humid cycle of erosion and this particular aspect of the morphology is clearly characteristic of the arid cycle. The junction is especially marked in the absence of the bahada zone (which in places may have buried the true angle; Fig. 2, C & D) and it has been variously referred to as a 'knickpoint' (Field, 1935) or 'knick' (Bryan, 1925; Johnson, 1931, 1932a). Its very common occurrence, however, suggests that 'piedmont angle' might be a more suitable term. The angle results from the juxtaposition of the slope of the mountain front, and that of the pediment or peripediment, and is marked by a dramatic change in the character of the material which rests upon the bedrock of the two components. The gravity-controlled slope of the mountain front, strewn with large and heavy boulders, gives place suddenly to the much smaller material of the pediment, or to fine-grained sediment of the peripediment. Here the slope is controlled by water action, the gradient being the minimum slope on which the supplied debris can be transported (Lawson, 1915; Davis, 1930). The presence of a sharp piedmont angle implies that the weathered material from the mountain front is being removed from its foot as fast as it is produced, and, further, that this removal must take place largely by sheet or rill action rather than by stream action. These considerations apply particularly to the outward-facing mountain front, and exclude the possibility of the angle being produced by lateral corrasion of streams, as in Johnson's rock fan concept. No evidence in support of Johnson's approach was discovered in the field, but sharp angles may be produced in the initial stages of a mountain embayment by lateral stream action. This has also been noted by Howard (1942) in the Sacaton Mountains.

The piedmont angle is most conspicuous and the process most effective when rocks with widely-spaced joints weather without intermediate gradings into large boulders and fine-grained debris: the granite and granite-gneiss of the Sacaton Mountains produce perhaps the best examples (Plate 5, B). The angle is less dramatic, and may in fact be replaced by a concave curve, where weathering into a variety of sizes takes place, e.g. the volcanic Tucson Mountains. The angle of dip in stratified rocks is also a controlling factor, horizontally-bedded rocks clearly favouring a sharp angle whereas strata dipping against the pediment may tend to form a concave profile (e.g. west of Tombstone).

The piedmont angle not only occurs at the mountain foot but is also characteristic of the residual masses which sometimes rise above the pediment or peripediment-like nunataks above an ice cap. These are undoubtedly the remains of ridges which have formed from mountain embayments and have then been further attacked from the sides. These must inevitably grow smaller in size until they are eventually consumed by retreating slopes. The angle between the mountain slope and the plain slope is once again attributable to the two different controlling agencies—gravity on the steeper slopes, and water on the gentler slopes.

5. THE PEDIMENT PROBLEM

It seems from the evidence gathered that similar rocks occurring under similar conditions, and acted upon by similar climatic conditions, will produce the same combination of forms, but slightly different rocks under similar climatic conditions, or similar rocks under slightly different climatic conditions, will give rise to a variety of combinations. Herein may lie the key to the reconciliation of many opposing points of view about the origin of the rock-cut surface or pediment.

This feature appears to be the natural result of the parallel retreat of steep slopes (mainly mountain slopes, but minor slopes are also possible) which occur under arid conditions with the unimpeded removal of weathered material. The pediment is a zone across which the weathered material from the 'front' is transported, and the gradient is the minimum slope on which the material can be moved by the available forces. The slope must inevitably rise towards the mountain front as the front retreats, in order that the removal of debris may continue. The removal is effected very largely by sheetflood, sheetwash, streamflood and rill action, and apart from streamfloods these processes appear to have but a limited erosive effect on the rock surface. For its proper development, therefore, the pediment requires a finely-adjusted balance between the rate of weathering on the mountain front and the rate of removal of the debris: this will be determined by the interplay of the lithological and climatological factors. 'Process' in the cycle of events may also to some extent be dependent on the 'age' reached.

Excessive weathering leads to an accumulation at the mountain foot temporarily burying the piedmont angle and the pediment, whilst excessive rainfall accelerates canyon cutting and produces bahadas, partly burying and partly dissecting by streamfloods the pediment and peripediment. The latter conditions seem to have influenced a great deal of southern Arizona of recent geological date.

The alluvial zone sometimes extends to the piedmont angle and the pediment disappears from view. This is more likely to occur in the early stages of the cycle when there is a greater surface area of mountain front contributing its weathered detritus to a restricted area of aggradation. Under these conditions Lawson's upwardly convex profile (1915) should arise (probably by a series of minute steps). But with maturity a diminishing mountain front contributes a decreasing load to an increasing surface area so that the pediment emerges and grows in size, although at the same time it may exhibit signs of slow burial by a rising alluvial zone. Theoretically the gradient at this stage could be quite uniform but will probably trend to a shallow upwardly concave curve. In the ultimate stage the mountain disappears completely as two retreating, but opposite fronts, coalesce, leaving behind a slightly convex shaped eminence with an occasional nubbin—well illustrated by the Cima Dome in the Mohave Desert.

Although some measure of unanimity regarding the basic principles of semi-arid landscape formation may now be in sight, many aspects of the problem remain open. Large areas in which this type of landscape occurs still remain topographically unmapped—the remarks and opinions of the early writers are in fact largely based on visual impressions, and these can be very misleading on occasions. But topographic maps, although helpful, do not provide all the desired data. Information regarding the size, distribution and areal extent of the various morphological elements can only be obtained by *morphological* mapping, and at present such maps exist for but very limited areas near Ajo in Arizona (Gilluly, 1937), in the Little Colorado region, Arizona (Childs, 1948) and the Moreno Valley of New Mexico (Ray & Smith, 1941).

Accurate information is also lacking on the depth and exact nature of the sub-alluvial bench: here seismic surveys are probably necessary to provide the required data. There is also more need for quantitative observations regarding those semi-arid processes which do not operate under humid conditions. Here, controlled field observations over a period of time, and perhaps laboratory experiments, might yield additional data on the nature and effect of sheetflood, sheetwash and rill action in relation to lithological differences in grain size.

ACKNOWLEDGMENTS

The above paper arises from an expedition undertaken by the authors into the Sonora and Mohave Deserts of Arizona and California in 1952. Financial assistance was received from the Universities of London and Manchester, the Royal Society and the Royal Geographical Society, and also the Fulbright Authorities. This assistance is gratefully acknowledged.

REFERENCES

C. P. BERKEY & F. K. MORRIS. 1927. Geology of Mongolia, natural history of Central Asia. New York. **2**, 323–51.

BLACKWELDER, E. 1931. The lowering of playas by deflation. *Amer. J. Sci.*, **21**, 140–4.

————. 1931a. Desert plains, *J. Geol.*, **39**, 133–40.

BRADLEY, W. H. 1936. Geology of the north flank of the Uinta Mountains. *Prof. Pap.* 185–I, *U.S. geol. Surv.*, 145–72.

————. 1940. Pediments and pedestals in miniature. *J. Geomorph.*, **3**, 244–55.

BRYAN, KIRK. 1925. The Papago Country, Arizona. *Wat. Supply Pap. U.S. geol. Surv.* 499.

————. 1926. Pedestal rocks formed by differential erosion, *Bull. U.S. geol. Surv.* 790 A, 1–15.

———— & F. T. MCCANN. 1936. Successive pediments and terraces of the Upper Rio Puerco, New Mexico. *J. Geol.*, **44**, 145–72.

CHILDS, O. E. 1948. Geomorphology of the Little Colorado River, Arizona. *Bull. geol. Soc. Amer.*, **59**, 353–88.

COLLIE, G. L. 1912. Plateau of British East Africa. *Bull. geol. Soc. Amer.*, **23**, 297–316.

COTTON, C. A. 1942. *Climatic accidents*, Wellington, N.Z.

DAVIS, W. M. 1930. Rock floors in arid and in humid climates. *J. Geol.*, **38**, 1–27; 136–58.

————. 1933. Granite domes of the Mohave Desert, California. *Trans. S. Diego Soc. nat. Hist.*, **7**, 211–58.

————. 1938. Sheetfloods and streamfloods. *Bull. geol. Soc. Amer.*, **49**, 1337–416.

DENNY, C. S. 1941. Quaternary geology of San Acacia Area, New Mexico. *J. Geol.*, **49**, 225–60.

FALCONER, J. D. 1911. *Geology and Geography of northern Nigeria*. London, 1–62; 194–266.

FENNEMAN, N. 1905. Geology of the Boulder District, Colorado. *Bull. U.S. geol. Surv.*, 265, 11–19.

FIELD, ROSS. 1935. Stream carved slopes and plains in desert mountains. *Amer. J. Sci.*, (5) **29**, 313–22.

FRYE, J. C. & H. T. U. SMITH. 1942. Preliminary observations on pediment-like slopes in the Central High Plains. *J. Geomorph.*, **5**, 215–21.

GILBERT, G. K. 1877. Report on the geology of the Henry Mountains, Utah. *U.S. Geol. & Geogr. Surv.*

GILLULY, JAMES. 1937. Physiography of the Ajo Region, Arizona. *Bull. geol. Soc. Amer.*, **48**, 323–47.

GLOCK, W. S. 1932. Premonitory planations in Western Colorado. *Pan-Amer. Geol.*, **57**, 29–37.

HOLMES, A. & D. A. WRAY. 1913. Mozambique, a geographical study. *Geogr. J.*, **42**, 143–52.

HOWARD, A. D. 1942. Pediments and the Pediment Pass problem. *J. Geomorph.*, **5**, 3–31; 95–136.

JOHNSON, D. W. 1931. Planes of lateral corrasion. *Science*, **73**, 174–77.

————. 1932. Rock fans of arid regions. *Amer. J. Sci.*, **23**, 389–416.

————. 1932a. Rock planes of arid regions. *Geogr. Rev.*, **22**, 656–65.

JUTSON, J. T. 1917. Erosion and resulting land forms in Subarid Western Australia, including the origin and growth of the Dry Lakes. *Geogr. J.*, **40**, 418–37.

KEYES, C. R. 1908. Rock floors of Intermont Plains of the arid region. *Bull. geol. Soc. Amer.*, **19**, 63–92.

————. 1912. Deflative scheme of the geographic cycle in an arid climate. *Bull. geol. Soc. Amer.*, **23**, 537–62.

KING, L. C. 1951. *South African scenery*. London, 2nd ed.

KING, P. B. 1930. Geology of the Glass Mountains, Texas. *Bull. Univ. Tex.*, **3038**, 12–30.

LAWSON, A. C. 1915. The Epigene Profiles of the Desert. *Bull. Dep. Geol. Univ. Calif.*, **9**, 23–48.

LEE, W. T. 1900. The origin of the debris-covered mesas of Boulder, Colorado. *J. Geol.*, **8**, 504–11.

MACKIN, J. H. 1937. Erosional history of the Big Horn Basin. *Bull. geol. Soc. Amer.*, **48**, 813–93.

McGEE, W. J. 1897. Sheetflood erosion. *Bull. geol. Soc. Amer.*, **8**, 87–112.

OGILVIE, I. H. 1905. The high altitude conoplain. *Amer. Geol.*, **36**, 27–34.

PAIGE, SIDNEY. 1912. Rock-cut surfaces in desert ranges. *J. Geol.*, **20**, 442–50.

POWERS, W. E. 1935. Physiographic history of the Upper Arkansas River Valley and Royal Gorge, Colorado. *J. Geol.*, **43**, 184–99.

RAY, L. L. & J. F. SMITH. 1941. Geology of the Moreno Valley, New Mexico. *Bull. geol. Soc. Amer.*, **52**, 177–210.

RICH, J. L. 1935. Origin and evolution of rock fans and pediments. *Bull. geol. Soc. Amer.*, **46**, 999–1024.

SAUER, C. 1930. Basin and range forms in the Chiricahua Area. *Univ. Calif. Publ. Geogr.*, **3**, 383.

SHARP, R. P. 1940. Geomorphology of the Ruby–East Humboldt Range, Nevada. *Bull. geol. Soc. Amer.*, **51**, 337–71.

STHEEMAN, H. A. 1932. *The geology of southwestern Uganda*. The Hague.

TATOR, B. A. 1952. Piedmont interstream surfaces of the Colorado Springs Region. *Bull. geol. Soc. Amer.*, **63**, 255–74.

————. 1952. Pediment characteristics and terminology. *Ann. Ass. Amer. Geogr.*, **42**, 295–317.

————. 1953. Pediment characteristics and terminology. *Ann. Ass. Amer. Geogr.*, **43**, 47–53.

TOLMAN, C. F. 1909. Erosion and Deposition in the Southern Arizona Bolson Region. *J. Geol.*, **17**, 136–63.

A MICRO-CLIMATOLOGICAL INVESTIGATION OF BATH AND THE SURROUNDING DISTRICT

By W. G. V. BALCHIN, M.A., F.R.G.S., and NORMAN PYE, B.A.

(Manuscript received October 11, 1946—read May 21, 1947)

SUMMARY

The following paper details the organisation and outlines the observations made during the micro-climatological survey of Bath and district which was undertaken between October 1944 and January 1946 with the aid of a grant from the Leverhulme Research Fellowships and the assistance of numerous voluntary observers. By outlining the methods employed and some of the difficulties encountered it is hoped to assist future research workers in this field and at the same time to provide the necessary background account for subsequent specialist papers dealing with the Bath area. A summary of some of the more interesting facts which have emerged from the investigation is also given.

INTRODUCTION

An enforced domicile in Bath whilst engaged on National Service during the early days of World War II led the authors to an appreciation of the micro-climatic differences which existed between the city and the surrounding district. These differences in local climate have indeed been sufficiently well and long recognised to form part of the local lore, although much was inevitably and of course quite erroneously attributed to the hot springs for which Bath is renowned. Daily journeys from the city area to the surrounding heights clearly revealed the susceptibility of the area to conditions of temperature inversion and associated fogs. This and other phenomena, including marked variations in the damage to fruit crops by late spring frosts and the tendency of fungi to appear more readily in some areas than others, suggested that an investigation into local climatic conditions might yield some interesting results.

The weather conditions of 1940-41, with exceptionally cold winters and freak ice storms, had evoked such local interest it was assumed there would be little difficulty in finding competent and voluntary local observers for a micro-climatological enquiry providing that the requisite instruments could be obtained. The local authorities, whilst interested in the project in view of the city's main peace-time function as a spa and curative centre, were unable to assist financially and the project remained in abeyance until June 1944, when a grant from the Leverhulme Research Fellowships enabled the work to proceed.

Much thought was then given to the exact form the survey was to take. Three methods were considered:—

(a) a mobile survey utilising whirling hygrometers and observers on cycles to cover special phenomena,

98

(*b*) the erection of meteorological stations at suitable sites with set hours of observation and maintained by voluntary observers,

(*c*) the erection of meteorological stations at suitable sites but eliminating the observer by means of self recording instruments.

Method (*a*) would yield only temperature and humidity data and presented formidable difficulties of organisation when dependent on observers who would be required to undertake observations at short notice. Method (*c*)would eliminate the need for observers on the spot and give a continuous record, but the measurements are less reliable on self recording instruments and the cost per station would be much higher by this method. It was evident that the possibility of method (*b*) being adopted would depend on the availability of voluntary observers in suitable locations, so efforts were next directed to the compilation of a list of potential assistants. Here our assumption of a widespread interest fortunately proved correct. Contacts through a variety of organisations such as *British Rainfall,* the Bath Natural History Society and the local Education Authority resulted in the offer of services from many more people than we could possibly utilise. One important advantage from this excess number was their dispersed location, permitting selection of the most suitable sites for stations in the event of adopting method (*b*).

Taking all these factors into consideration it was eventually decided to adopt method (*b*) as the basis for the investigation but supplemented by method (*c*) at selected stations.

Attention was next turned to the supply of instruments which in the middle of 1944 were far from readily obtainable. A delay of several months was involved and a major difficulty developed in our inability to obtain standard Stevenson screens; eventually it was necessary to procure a permit from the Ministry of Supply for the purchase of wood and we ourselves constructed a set of identical screens (photo 1). To simplify construction the standard Stevenson design was modified slightly, but care was taken to ensure uniformity in the screens so that observations might be strictly comparable.

By the middle of September 1944 the bulk of the instruments had been assembled, the inspection of alternative sites and the selection of observers had been completed, and it was possible to decide on the exact location of the stations and equip them after standardisation of the instruments. Bearing in mind that variations in temperature might arise as a result of different soil and vegetation cover (Cornford 1938, Brunt 1945) stations were sited throughout on grass and as far as possible on the loamy soil (rendzina) resulting from the oolitic and liassic limestones outcropping throughout most of the area. The valley bottom stations were of necessity sited on grass covered alluvium, proximity to the river being avoided. The stations were grouped in pairs to provide cover for an area in the event of an observer occasionally being out of action. This also provided a valuable check on possible personal errors in the reading of the instruments. It eventually proved possible to commence systematic readings on October 1st 1944.

To ensure that maximum and minimum temperature records were correct to the nearest degree observers were asked to estimate readings to tenths of a degree. Personal errors were few in number and fairly easy to detect, usually taking the form of a misreading by 5 or 10 degrees—a mistake that even the trained observer occasionally makes. The pairing of the stations enabled any such gross errors to be immediately detected.

PHOTO 1.—Standard screen used in the investigation.

The established stations fell into three categories. At *primary* stations, of which there were two in number, continuous records of temperature (bimetallic thermographs), humidity (hair hygrographs), and pressure (aneroid barographs), were maintained, together with a daily 9 hrs. G.M.T. observation of maximum and minimum temperatures, wet and dry bulb temperatures, rainfall, wind force and direction. At *secondary* stations, of which there were 11 in number, a daily 9 hrs. G.M.T. observation of maximum and minimum temperature, wet and dry bulb temperature, rainfall, wind force and direction was taken. At *tertiary* stations, 15 in number, a daily 9 hrs. G.M.T. observation of rainfall was made. The tertiary observers were largely recording for *British Rainfall* and kindly agreed to co-operate in the micro-climatological survey. The primary, secondary and tertiary stations are listed in the Appendix, together with their code numbers, and they are located on Fig. 1. To avoid confusion, and to simplify, it is proposed to refer to all stations by code numbers in this and subsequent papers. In addition to the stations in and around Bath observations were also obtained from Long Ashton (Bristol), Frampton Cotterell (Bristol) and Melksham, so that regional as well as local comparisons might be made.

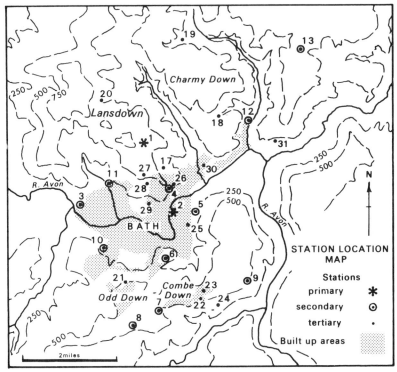

FIG. 1.—Location of observing stations. Numbers against the stations are the code numbers as listed in Appendix. Secondary stations, the symbol for which has filled up in the course of reproduction, are numbers 3 to 13.

During the organisation of the survey we had the good fortune to discover that Major H. C. Gunton, M.B.E., F.R.E.S. (who has for many years been responsible for the annual phenological report published by the Royal Meteorological Society), was temporarily resident in Bath. Major Gunton enthusiastically agreed that the scope of the research work could be usefully enlarged by organising a collateral phenological survey with observers based on the network of meteorological sites. For this, too, capable and interested observers were forthcoming and key meteorological sites were covered. The collateral study of the plant life enabled a correlation of the response of the standard plants to be made with meteorological conditions (vide Phenological Report for 1945, 1946).

For the major aspects of the survey it was decided to continue observations until 1st January 1946 to cover the phenological year October 1944-October 1945 together with the calendar year January-December 1945. In all well over fifty thousand observations were collected from probably the closest network of temperature and rainfall stations so far employed in this country.

It will be apparent that the survey was possible only through the co-operative efforts of many people. The list of meteorological stations does not cover all those who assisted; altogether something like one hundred persons have contributed in various ways to the survey and to all these our thanks are due. It is most gratifying that of those who initially volunteered, and were subsequently chosen as observers, all without exception successfully maintained fifteen months of continuous daily observations with but few breaks. We hope that our experience will encourage others to embark on co-operative investigations where reliance on voluntary assistance is necessary.

THE PHYSIOGRAPHIC SETTING

The comparatively hard Mesozoic limestones of the Inferior and Great Oolites and Forest Marble which form the mass of the Cotswold Hills have a gentle dip to the east and differential erosion has produced a scarpland topography. A great wall-like escarpment facing west and overlooking the Vale of Severn runs from Chipping Camden almost to the Mendips; in contrast there is a gentle fall eastwards down the dip slope of the rocks to an area of lower elevation largely comprised of Oxford clay. In consequence the drainage of the area is, with one exception, comparatively simple. Rivers either flow down the steep Cotswold scarp to the Severn and Bristol Channel or follow the dip slope of the Cotswolds to join the Thames; the Avon is the exception. Although beginning as a normal consequent stream down the dip slope it suddenly deviates at Malmesbury, turns south-west and follows the direction of the scarp to Bradford-on-Avon, where it turns again to flow north and west. In this section of its course the river runs against the dip of the Jurassic rocks and it has cut a deep valley through the escarpment: here in this gap we find the city of Bath. Beyond the escarpment the river flows towards Bristol over Liassic strata of a lower elevation.

This anomalous course suggests that the river Avon began its history not on the rocks at present exposed but on a regular covering of Mesozoic rocks which have long since been removed by denudation. The superimposed drainage, as it is called, then accounts for the remarkable and only gap in the Cotswold escarpment in which the city of Bath has grown. As the contours in Fig. 1 reveal, the hills around Bath attain an altitude of 650-750 feet, westwards lies the flatter Liassic country, eastward we enter a region of much more diversified topography produced by the deep incision of a series of consequent streams on the dip slope: these join the River Avon and have been able to keep pace with it in the down cutting. As a result Bath finds itself the focal point for as many as six valleys (English Combe, Weston, Swainswick, St. Catherine's, Box and Limpley Stoke). The Avon flows in the Limpley Stoke valley and itself collects the drainage of the Midford Brook and Wellow Brook. These valleys are, for the major part, deep and narrow descending from the 650-750 feet of the plateaux to less than 100 feet in the neighbourhood of Bath. The surrounding heights (Odd Down, Lansdown, Bathampton Down, Combe Down, Claverton Down, Charmy Down, etc.) are all extensive flat-topped elevations with a remarkable accordance of summit heights. They are all exposed sites and carry little tree growth.

Work previously undertaken in micro-climatology suggested that with topography such as this the area should yield some interesting results with an instrumental survey. The influence of the topography on air drainage was indeed a visible phenomenon: the surrounding Downs formed extensive cooling grounds during the night and the gentle dip to the east naturally led the cold air into the deeply incised valleys. The latter as we have seen converge on the Bath gap. Since the city of Bath is situated in the valley the area offered the additional attraction of yielding information on the interaction of urban and valley climates. Sites for the meteorological stations were chosen with this in mind: the central city area was covered by the official meteorological station in Henrietta Park (code 2) which incidentally, because of its site characteristics, cannot be considered as well situated for yielding *regional* data (c.f. Spence 1936). Other stations were established on the surrounding Downs and at the east and west ends of the city and main valley. This enabled longitudinal and cross sectional climatic profiles to be drawn.

THE OBSERVATIONS

Intending investigators in the field of local climate will find in the *Meteorological Observer's Handbook* 1942 (London, H.M. Stationery Office, 6s.) full details on the desirable environment for a site, the nature and conditions of exposure of the instruments, etc.

It is not proposed to reiterate the extensive information contained therein but rather to emphasise the following additional points which came to light as a result of the Bath survey as these may be of assistance to future workers.

Since many of the measured differences are small an accurate standardisation of the instruments must precede the distribution to the sites and in certain cases regular checks should be applied throughout the survey. The hours of observation must be uniform throughout: e.g., the monthly mean of maxima observed at 9 hrs. G.M.T. at one station cannot be compared accurately with the monthly mean at another station where the hour of observation is say 21 hrs. G.M.T. The need is even greater when dealing with minima. The necessity for strict adherence to the agreed time for observation should be impressed on observers by demonstrating the errors involved by bad timing, as for example when the temperature is changing rapidly (e.g., 9 hrs. G.M.T. in the summer months) or rain is falling, etc. A system of double checking when reading the instruments is very desirable, especially when the operation is being carried out in unpleasant conditions such as rain when there is a temptation to hasten the procedure. (See also Tinn, 1938.)

Screens in exposed situations on hilltops must be very firmly erected to prevent vibration and shaking during high winds. Minimum readings are particularly liable to be affected when the screen is not absolutely rigid. In certain cases guy ropes might even be desirable. A suitable reserve of spare and standardised instruments should be available to cover loss by damage or theft: whilst likely to be very small, this eventuality must always be taken into consideration where continuity of records is essential.

A calculating machine is a valuable adjunct in the preparation of monthly and yearly means, etc., whilst the duplication of standard forms for recording observations, together with map-diagrams for experimental plotting, is very desirable.

(a) *Maximum Temperatures*

Excluding the effect of wind disturbance the composition of the air largely determines its ability to take up heat directly by absorption and indirectly by conduction from the underlying soil. The rarity of the air at higher altitudes and the diminution of moisture and carbon dioxide results in the normal temperature lapse rate of one degree in 300 feet which is sufficiently great to affect local climates in regions of strong relief. We therefore expected, and did in fact find, that the valley sites in Bath registered consistently higher maxima than the hill top and plateaux stations. But the normal lapse rate which might be expected (about 2.5 degrees*) is exceeded throughout the year: the valley stations being some 3-4 degrees higher in winter and 5-7 degrees more in summer. This excess is largely due to the physiography—the sheltered positions in the valley bottom and the steepness of the valley sides which directs reflected insolation on to the opposite side of the valley where it impinges a second time. The greater excess occurs during fine and calm weather with cloudless skies: and as would be expected the range was found to increase during the summer months. Tinn (1938) in investigating local temperature variations in the Nottingham district has noted an excess in maxima of up to 6° F. for valley sites.

In addition to altitude, aspect was found to influence maximum temperatures. Theoretically the amount of solar radiation reaching a conical hill would be symmetrical with respect to the meridian, but the resulting temperature will be higher on a slope with a westerly exposure for two reasons: in the first place the heating of the easterly facing slope has to start from the lower temperatures of morning whereas the westerly slope is already preheated prior to receipt of the afternoon radiation; secondly, much of the morning radiation is initially expended in evaporating moisture and so is not available for temperature increase. In consequence highest temperatures may occur not where the aspect faces south but rather more to the west. This was shown up in Bath by the frequent higher maxima recorded at stations 3 and 11.

The distribution of the station sites also enables an assessment of the urban effect to be made. In winter the central city area is warmer than the surrounding country areas at similar elevation by a degree or so and exhibits the characteristic heat island within a built up area. Much is doubtless due to the increased heat generated by the city itself and the higher absorption rate permitted by the increased atmospheric pollution of winter months which also reduces outward radiation. In summer, however, the city station showed

*All temperatures are in degrees Fahrenheit.

104

lower maxima than the surrounding country sites at similar elevation to the extent of 1-2 degrees. This was an interesting confirmation of other observations that the heat island effect of winter is not necessarily continued throughout the year. Kraus (1945) instances similar variations in Vienna; much seems to depend on local circumstances and in Bath may be related partly to the greater reflection of the incoming insolation which occurs from the near white limestone of which the greater part of the city is built, and partly to the location of the city station (2) in a small park. Further, heated air will be turbulent and local variations in maxima may more easily arise. The same tendency is noticeable in the summer 9 a.m. dry bulb temperatures, considered below.

The greater local variations of the maxima occur under calm clear conditions in summer, but they do not reach the same magnitude as the variations associated with the minima and frequently under conditions of vigorous air movement little or no difference was recorded over the district—even the normal temperature lapse rate was occasionally masked. Under somewhat special conditions in winter the maxima may be affected by valley inversions. Normally these disappear before midday but in winter the lower levels may be blanketed by a thick fog cover which fails to disperse with a feeble sun and shorter day. When this occurs the hill top stations which have had bright sunny conditions record a maximum temperature several degrees higher than the valley bottoms. During the period of the investigation inversions persisted in this fashion on six days of December 1944, the hill top sites recording maxima some 5 degrees higher than the valley bottoms.

(b) *Minimum Temperatures*

The minimum temperatures which were recorded revealed two main temperature distributions either of which might prevail on any given night according to the controlling circumstances: these will be called normal and valley inversion distributions.

A clarification of the term " inversion " would appear desirable before proceeding further. It is used in two senses: (i) the meteorologist commonly refers to inversion when considering changing temperatures vertically above any given point, e.g., Johnson (1929), who has shown that nocturnal *vertical inversion* in temperature is commonly experienced most nights of the year, being intensified with calm clear conditions; (ii) the climatologist, *e.g.,* Miller (1931), uses the term inversion when describing the effects of cold air collecting in valleys and so producing lower temperatures at screen level in the bottom of the valley compared with screen level at the hill top. It will be readily seen that (a) a *valley inversion* will automatically produce a vertical inversion, but (b) a vertical inversion can occur without a valley inversion, and (c) in a region of diversified relief a valley inversion will give an accentuated vertical inversion at the valley station. It should perhaps be mentioned that on page 189 of the *Quarterly Journal* Vol. 72, April-July, 1946, Mr. W. G. V. Balchin was referring to valley inversion in discussing the Bath survey.

" Normal " distributions were found under conditions of fairly vigorous air movement, cloudy skies and high relative humidities, they were hence frequently associated with the passage of a cyclone. Under this state of affairs we find the normal temperature lapse rate which would be expected after taking into consideration the difference of altitude, thus there was usually a steady drop of about 2·5 degrees from valley floor to hill top. It should perhaps be noted that normal distributions will doubtless have included cases of vertical inversion without valley inversion, but we had no means of differentiating such occurrences.

" Valley inversion " distributions are associated with calm clear nights and low relative humidities, they are hence more frequent during anticyclonic conditions. The existence of the valley inversion has been realised for some time but few quantitative measurements have been conveniently assembled. The Bath enquiry tends to show that this state is probably more common in regions of diversified relief than has hitherto been realised and frequently occurs when even a moderate cloud cover and light winds are present. The use of monthly mean minima perhaps obscures the frequency, although some estimate may be obtained by comparing the " normal " lapse rate with the recorded mean minima for nearby stations (Manley 1946). We suggest that only a daily analysis will reveal the true nature and extent of the phenomena. On the one hand minor valley inversions may occur and yet may not be apparent in the monthly average, this was demonstrated very effectively in the summer observations in Bath. In contrast to this, major winter valley inversions may, with a 9 a.m. reading, give rise to erroneous monthly means as the effects of a very low minimum will appear twice in the list from which the average is derived. (After a very cold night the temperatures read and set at 9 a.m. will differ but little from the minima recorded: if milder conditions now arrive these same 9 a.m. readings will be observed as the minima for the succeeding 24 hours. Statistically such instances may be considered as false inversions.)

Thus even an examination of the daily record will not always reveal the exact number of occurrences, the only sound method of ascertaining this is to compare continuous thermographic records which will give the time and period during which the valley floor temperatures fell below those of the hill top. This was done for the Bath survey with the following results :—

> From 1st October 1944-1st October 1945 (phenological year) there were 233 " normal " nights and 132 " valley inversion " nights.

> From 1st January 1945-1st January 1946 (calendar year) there were 227 normal nights and 138 valley inversion nights.

The valley inversions were distributed throughout the year (see Fig. 2) and showed no marked seasonal incidence although tending to be more conspicuous in the winter months—partly due to the greater intensity permitted by the increased radiation of longer nights and the persistence of foggy conditions in the valley. The major valley inversions of winter also accounted for all the false occasions which were detected. The limited period of observation suggests an average of about six per year, mainly occurring in December.

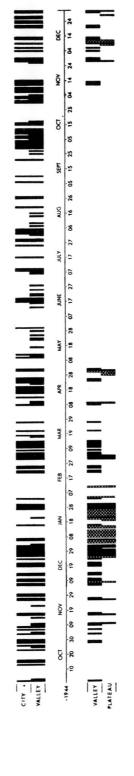

INCIDENCE OF INVERSION

INCIDENCE OF FROST

FIG. 2.—The incidence of valley inversions of temperature and the occurrence of screen frost in Bath and district from October 1944 to December 1945. Nights when screen frost occurred with no valley inversion are indicated by stippling.

Figure 2 shows, that each month contains a mixture of valley inversion and normal nights and the monthly mean is hence to a large extent fortuitous, depending not only on the number of valley inversions but also on their magnitude. The monthly means indicate the dominant characteristic, thus in winter the means are inverted on account of the larger inversions and false inversions, but not in summer, and one would not deduce the continuation of inversions throughout the year from the summer monthly mean minima, unless a mathematical analysis of the figures be undertaken. Occasionally the two effects neutralize each other and monthly mean minima are obtained which are very uniform over the whole district. It was early apparent that the monthly figures gave but little information and it was decided to separate the valley inversions from the normal and to mean each separately, with the following results:—

OCTOBER, 1944 – SEPTEMBER, 1945 (PHENOLOGICAL YEAR)

Code Numbers of Stations :	1	2	3	5	6	7	8	9	10	11	12
Average of { 132 Inversion Minima	39·9	37·7	36·1	38·5	39·4	38·6	39·5	39·2	38·5	36·8	35·1
233 Normal Minima	44·2	47·6	46·4	46·4	46·4	45·2	45·4	45·6	46·3	46·1	46·2

JANUARY, 1945 — DECEMBER, 1945 (CALENDAR YEAR)

Code Numbers of Stations :	1	2	3	5	6	7	8	9	10	11	12
Average of { 138 Inversion Minima	41·8	39·6	38·0	40·2	41·0	40·3	41·3	41·0	40·4	38·8	36·9
227 Normal Minima	44·5	47·8	46·9	46·5	46·2	45·4	45·6	45·7	46·5	46·6	46·3

For code numbers see Appendix and Fig. 1.

The mean of the normal nights reveals clear correlation with altitude, and a close agreement with the usual temperature lapse rate. The mean of the valley inversion nights shows that the valley was on an average some four degrees colder than the plateau on such nights. The phenomenon of the " warm belt " which is clearly demonstrated in some individual temperature plots is not conspicuous in the mean of the valley inversions.

The urban influence is very clearly seen in both the mean for normal and valley inversion distributions. Station 2 representing the central city area is higher than corresponding valley sites to the east and west throughout the observations. For normal conditions the retained heat of the city area keeps up the minima recorded by just over a degree and for valley inversion conditions the difference is slightly greater, some 1·5 degrees. The retained warmth of the city frequently enabled it to prevent the complete development of a valley inversion within and over the city area when the upper and lower valleys were experiencing such conditions. Careful comparison of the thermographic records shows that valley inversions were prevented in this manner on 35 nights in the phenological year and 34 nights in the calendar year; as might be expected, this is more common in the summer months when valley inversions are shallower and not so well developed with the nights being shorter. The terms shallow and deep will be used to express the height of the inversion top above the valley floor and not the temperature magnitude of the vertical inversion.

The effect of valley inversions on the distribution of screen frosts is very striking. These are plotted in detail on Fig. 2, but taking the average of the phenological and calendar years we may say that for any period of 12 months, on normal nights the hill-top sites will experience some 24 screen frosts to the valley sites average of 20, but on valley inversion nights the hill top sites only experience some 18 screen frosts to the valley's average of 55. Further, whilst the frosts in the valley on normal nights are almost confined to the three winter months of December, January and February, the frosts in the valley on valley inversion nights may occur in any month except June, July and August. This is an interesting indication that frost damage to fruit crops could be largely eliminated by improved siting of the orchards (photos 2A., 2B.).

The most extreme minima are generally recorded after a calm clear night with dry air (i.e., a low relative humidity) and snow cover. Such minima are hence associated with winter inversions. Snow forms a good radiating surface and is at the same time a poor conductor of heat from the ground underneath. The extreme minima are also associated with the greatest range of temperature differences between hill and valley sites. Thus in Bath during the snow cover of the last week of January 1945 the plateau recorded a minimum of 20° F. and the valley a minimum of 8° F.—a difference of 12° F.

These large differences were sometimes approached but never exceeded in the summer months when, despite the shorter nights, there is a big drop of temperature at night after overheating in the day and much cool air collects in the valleys.

One of the more striking visible effects of a deep valley inversion is the formation of fog. Some of the shorter autumn and winter fogs are advection fogs occurring when warm moist winds blow over colder ground; but as the temperature of the ground will be raised fairly rapidly the fogs are of short duration and rarely affect the minima recorded. The second major category of fog— radiation fog—frequently accompanies a valley inversion providing the air which collects in the valley bottom is cooled below the dew point temperature. Most valley bottoms are notoriously foggy and Bath is no exception (photos 3A., 3B.). In the fourth edition of the *Encyclopædia Britannica* published in 1810, Vol. III, p. 489, it is remarked of Bath that " as the city lies in a bottom, surrounded by very high hills, the air is constantly surcharged with damps."

The meteorologist speaks of fog when the visibility is less than 1,100 yards and of mist when less than 2,200 yards; the public commonly refers to fog when the visibility is less than 100 yards. With the meteorological definition we are not surprised to see that fog or mist will accompany well over one hundred of the yearly valley inversions experienced in the Bath area. The maximum intensity is reached in the winter period when anticyclonic conditions giving light winds and clear night skies are combined with longer nights. The air is then cooled well below the dew point and a substantial fog layer is built up. The succeeding day insolation is feeble and of short duration in winter and the fog may then fail to be dissipated during the day and persist into the next night when

PHOTO 2A.—Vegetation at Ensleigh, Lansdown (720 feet), 26th December 1944. No frost and no fog. Compare with Photo 2B.

PHOTO 2B.—Vegetation at Parade Gardens (65 feet). Inversion of 26th December 1944. Thick frost and moderate fog.

Photo 3a.—Inversion fog filling Upper Weston Valley, Bath. Kelston Round Hill rises
island fashion from the sea of mist. Compare with Photo 3b.

Photo 3b.—Upper Weston Valley, Bath, and Kelston Round Hill under normal conditions.

it becomes thicker. A remarkable example of this occurred in Bath during the last week of December 1944, when the valley was enveloped continuously in thick fog for five days, the plateau experiencing brilliant although feeble sunshine; the inversion of temperature was maintained continuously day and night throughout the entire period.

In contrast to the thick winter fogs accompanying deep inversions the mists of shallow summer inversions are but tenuous and rarely last long. Much is related to the heating required to dissipate fog at different air temperatures—a considerable rise is necessary at low temperatures, but when the air temperature is already high a further slight increase will suffice to accommodate quite dense fog. The fogs and mists in summer rapidly dissolve and in fact had not D.B.S.T. been in operation we should doubtless have missed many of the quite beautiful early morning effects following on inversions. (Six hrs. D.B.S.T. was really four hrs. G.M.T. and approximately the time of sunrise.)

A variety of interesting data was gleaned from a careful watch on fog formation and dispersal. The fog or mist of the summer valley inversions rarely reached a depth greater than 150-200 feet above the valley floor, the ceiling of the fog frequently forming the thickest part. By walking up the valley sides and rising above the fog the air mass could be observed flowing slowly down the valley; the fog or mist was on occasions observed to melt away as it flowed into the city area—a clear indication of the urban effect manifesting itself in a border-line condition. During the autumn the depth of the fog increased to some 300-400 feet and in winter the valley was frequently filled to the level of Combe Down, i.e., to the top of the southern and lower side; Lansdown, station 1, then stood out of the surrounding sea of mist, island fashion, and proceeding up the hill by the main road one invariably passed out of the fog at about the level of the Royal School (540 feet high) which corresponded with the height of Combe Down on the opposite side of the valley. This control by Combe Down resembles that of the Gstettneralm Pass described by Schmidt (1934).

The increased warmth of the city area was again frequently demonstrated during the winter fogs by a greater visibility in the centre than in the outskirts; and on one or two occasions small cumulus-like clouds were observed from Lansdown to be forming at the ceiling of the fog immediately above the centre of the city.

The construction of the valley below Bath naturally tends to encourage ponding of the cold air and fog during inversions. Ponding was also noticeable when a very light west or south-west wind prevailed: this had the double effect of assisting the flow of cold air down the dip slope of the Cotswolds into the valleys which, as we have seen, drain back towards Bath, and secondly preventing the flow of colder air westwards out on to the plain beyond the escarpment.

Under calm conditions the formation of fog or mist often occurred in the evening when trails of white mist at or near ground level could be observed slowly gravitating down the slopes to collect and stagnate in the valley (cf. Hawke 1933). This was sometimes noticed at or very near sunset and was an indication that the down-flow of cold air into the valleys begins as soon as the higher ground is losing more heat by outward radiation than it is gaining by direct insolation. The actual movement probably starts before sunset.

Temperature inversions, whether accompanied by foggy conditions or not, are of great importance, especially in winter, in a city such as Bath nestling in a valley bottom. It explains why smoke accumulates and either aggravates or forms fog on some days whilst on others the air is perfectly clear although the same amount of smoke is being produced. When not carried off horizontally by wind the smoke is dispersed upwards in convection currents formed by the accompanying hot gases; when the temperature is inverted the smoke will rise until it reaches the same air temperature and then spreads out horizontally. This was frequently observed in winter when the process greatly assisted the formation of fog. The summer was almost free from serious smoke pollution as valley inversions were shallow and less persistent and most of the smoke in Bath is derived from domestic fires which are then but little used. Bath, already a clean city by comparison with some industrial areas, could practically eliminate smoke pollution if its inhabitants could be encouraged to use smokeless fuels, though the importance of the smoke pollution emitted by the gas works in the west end of the city must not be overlooked in this connection. Because of the greater warmth and smaller relative humidity of the city area a clean atmosphere could doubtless reduce the frequency of fogs in the city below that of the surrounding country.

(c) Dry-bulb Temperatures

Observations of the dry-bulb temperatures were made at 9 hrs. G.M.T. at all primary and secondary stations with the object of providing sample instantaneous distributions over the district throughout the year, and also, by means of the accompanying wet-bulb readings, similar distributions of relative humidity (see below). Of some 450 distributions provided by the observations many coincided with the special conditions which one might otherwise have sought to record by a mobile survey.

Three factors are very evident in an examination of these observations. These are: altitude, valley inversions and the urban effect. Somewhat like the minima considered above one of two states existed, either normal, when the usual temperature lapse-rate prevailed and the hill-top stations were some 2-3 degrees lower than the valley sites, the differences being fairly consistent throughout the year, or inversionary when the temperature distribution was reversed and the valley sites were colder than the hill sites, the magnitude of the difference varying according to the season. In winter the deeper and more persistent valley inversions were nearly always strongly in evidence at 9 hrs. G.M.T. and towards the end of December there is little difference between a plot of the minima and the 9 hrs. dry bulb. In summer, however, the valley inversions rarely lasted more than two or three hours after sunrise and had disappeared before 9 hrs. G.M.T.

The city station revealed that superimposed upon these factors was the urban effect. Throughout the winter this station recorded a steady 1·5 to 2 degrees more than might have been expected for its altitude, clearly indicating that the temperature was being kept up by the generated heat and retained warmth of the city. The result was that on normal mornings the city station usually recorded some 4 degrees warmer than the surrounding plateaux. Differences after a valley inversion night depended of course on the severity of the inversion and there were clear indications that the city accelerated the break up of a reversed temperature structure.

The urban effect in summer was not, however, so marked and valley sites to the east and west frequently recorded temperatures at 9 hrs. G.M.T. slightly in excess of the city centre. This confirms in part differences already noted with the maximum temperatures (q.v.) and the 9 hrs. G.M.T. dry-bulb differences presumably arise from the same causes.

(d) Relative Humidity

Wet-bulb temperatures were observed at 9 hrs. G.M.T. along with the dry-bulb readings at all primary and secondary stations and from these the relative humidities can be calculated. Once again the resulting distribution largely depended on whether temperature distributions at 9 hrs. were normal or valley-inverted. With a normal state of affairs and a decreasing temperature with altitude, the relative humidity was found to increase with altitude over short distances. There was also an increase in relative humidity outwards from the city centre which was more marked in the winter months. A typical 9 hrs. G.M.T. relative humidity plot under normal conditions shows a central drier area, coinciding with the built-up area, with relative humidity increasing outwards in all directions and rising to the highest values on Lansdown and Combe Down. Winter humidities at this hour were around 90 per cent, summer relative humidities 75 per cent, whilst over the district the range averaged some 5-7 per cent.

As might be expected, the distributions were much modified after nights of valley inversion. If the inversion persisted in full strength until 9 hrs. G.M.T. the normal distribution of relative humidities was also found to be completely inverted, i.e., all valley sites recorded relative humidities in excess of the hill stations and under fog conditions valley recordings were more frequently 100 per cent. The city area, however, usually experienced relative humidities a little lower than the valley, and this was evidently the urban effect manifesting itself again. ·

So far as the 9 hrs. G.M.T. distribution of relative humidity is concerned the evidence suggests that the humidity is largely a reflection of the temperature and over short distances a higher temperature will mean a lower relative humidity. This further implies that over these short distances there is probably little difference in the absolute humidity content of the air. But does this condition apply throughout the day?—we have so far only considered distribution plots at 9 hrs.

A continuous record of the relative humidity was also kept at the two primary stations by means of hair hygrographs. These continuous records have provided a superabundance of data which have yet to be fully worked out. Normally the absolute humidity shows a minimum in the early hours when the temperature is low; as the temperature rises the total atmospheric content increases to a maximum during the forenoon, but then it may, and often does, decrease as the top layer of ground dries out and turbulence carries the existing atmospheric water content upwards. Hence a second minimum may be reached during the hottest part of the day. Towards evening the absolute humidity may rise again to a second maximum and then fall during the night. This doubling of the maximum and minimum is, of course, more characteristic of the summer; in winter a single night minimum and day maximum is more usual.

The relative humidity curve may be considered as a resultant of the absolute humidity and temperature curves, and since the take-up of water vapour also depends on its availability the relative humidity may be looked upon as a function of three variables producing some complicated interactions. Diurnal variation in the relative humidity is in consequence not always the inverse of the temperature variation, high temperatures do not always mean low relative humidities and so on. It is hence difficult to formulate generalisations for the factors of altitude differences and aspect differences between stations.

The urban effect, however, is fairly consistent and clearly detectable for two of the variables normally work together and the relative humidity under calm conditions then becomes more dependent on the third. In a built-up area pavements, houses, roads, etc., will greatly reduce the amount of evaporation which lowers the absolute and hence relative humidities, also towns are frequently warmer (especially in winter) and this increase further depresses the relative humidity. It is hoped to return in a later paper to this fascinating if somewhat complex problem after further examination of the continuous records.

(e) Rainfall

Information on the variation of rainfall over the district was provided by probably the densest network of stations so far to have been employed in this country—some twenty-seven stations observing within an area of twenty square miles, the majority of observers at these sites being able to supply continuous daily records throughout the entire period of the survey. Some very interesting daily, monthly and yearly distribution plots have hence been possible.

Under macro-climatic conditions altitude has long been recognised as an important factor in affecting precipitation, the windward side of a slope always has more rain than the leeward and up to a certain limit rain increases with altitude, chiefly on the windward slope. This is largely due to the forced ascent of the air on the windward slope producing adiabatic cooling, condensation and hence precipitation. It has been generally maintained (e.g., Köppen-Geiger, Handbuch der Klimatologie Vol. 1, D. Verlagsbuchhandlung Gebruder Borntraegar, Berlin, 1930) that under microclimatic conditions the elevation involved is not high enough to produce adiabatic cooling and hence excess precipitation: the emphasis has been placed on wind velocity—where the wind velocity is high little precipitation falls, hence creating a maximum on the leeward side contrary to the macro-climatic conditions.

We did not find this to be the case in Bath, where throughout the enquiry there emerged a strong correlation between altitude and precipitation. It may be that wind velocity is only dominant for a very small height difference and here the variations of precipitation are perhaps so small as to be almost negligible. The limiting zone has yet to be determined.

In Bath both monthly and annual totals showed, in general, an increasing precipitation with increasing altitude, this was somewhat remarkably and consistently revealed by a series of stations (27, 28, 29) arranged down the spur of Lansdown Road. For the calendar year 1945 the hill top sites recorded some 4-5 inches more than the valley stations 600-650 feet below: the two extremes being the city station (2) with 26·49 inches and Combe Down (22) with 32·07 inches, intermediate stations falling between these values. In keeping with these figures a greater number of " rainy days " were noted with increasing altitude, and rain was occasionally observed to be falling at high levels without reaching the valley floor.

Aspect was also a factor of considerable importance, windward-facing slopes receiving a greater precipitation. Generally these were slopes with a west or south-west aspect and the summation is of course revealed in the annual totals. But it is possible to demonstrate the significance of aspect for winds from other directions by individual day distributions.

Somewhat significantly the City's annual total (the lowest in the area) is lower than any other valley station and the urban effect again seems present: the lower relative humidities and drier conditions already noted appear sufficient to affect appreciably the total precipitation.

In addition to the major trends it is also possible to isolate particular factors for examination since daily recordings were made. Thus a wet day with persistent and strong south-west winds will show the effect of altitude and aspect; the uniform precipitation of calmer anticyclonic conditions emerges; and the precipitation resulting from an inversion fog can be isolated in the absence of further rain, etc. These and other features it is hoped to deal with in a subsequent paper on rainfall distributions.

As might be expected, daily differences between stations generally increase with a greater precipitation, and this applies particularly where wind accentuates the factors of altitude and aspect. Thus on August 21, 1945, a wet day with strong south-west winds, falls varied from ·26 to 1·40 inches giving a maximum range of 1·14 inches over the district.

Occasional showers and thunderstorms of course provide anomalous conditions (Tinn 1940) and it was sometimes possible to isolate such instances with interesting results. A thunderstorm on August 28, 1945, gave a fairly steady fall of an inch of rain along its main track, half a mile away on either side some ·78 of an inch was recorded, whilst 2-2½ miles from the main centre the precipitation was down to ·40 of an inch. Whilst factors such as altitude and aspect are constant for any particular station from year to year, thunderstorm tracks are to a large extent fortuitous, and it is apparent that large percentage variations in the annual rainfall can be produced by their absence or presence. It is questionable whether this particular factor has been sufficiently realised in some of the long-term rainfall analyses where "wet and dry" periods have been enumerated.

(f) Winds

A daily 9 hrs. G.M.T. observation of wind velocity and direction actually experienced at each site was made by all the observers at primary and secondary stations: and a careful watch on katabatic effects was also maintained by the authors.

Wind force had to be estimated by the Beaufort scale and unlike the other observations previously enumerated, the personal element is more evident. Even so there is a clear indication from the records of the effect of topography upon both direction and force. As might be expected, the regional wind is most effective on the plateau tops where it is experienced in full force: the valley bottoms are much more sheltered and the force is mostly less than half that of the hill top. Calms were quite frequent at the lower levels but rare on the plateaux. Seasonal differences were not greatly in evidence, being chiefly related to autumnal gales, which, of course, were mainly felt at higher levels.

Much also depended on the direction of the wind. Physiographically we have seen that the valley at Bath runs east-west through the wall-like escarpment of the Cotswolds; the dip slope to the east being dissected by numerous valleys all draining back to the Avon. A wind from a general easterly or westerly direction usually produced the greatest effect and force in the valley, and if the direction was sufficiently near to the trend of the valley it was mostly diverted to move along the valley—this was very evident in the high proportion of west winds recorded at station 2. This illustration of topographic control over wind direction underlines the need for a careful choice of station site when endeavouring to obtain the regional picture for forecasting. Winds from a predominantly northerly or southerly direction had least effect in the valley and if the force was low, calms were frequent in the valley bottom. A strong wind from either direction, however, would usually set up overturning in the valley and the direction and force observed at any one site largely became fortuitous. At hill-top sites in exposed positions there was of course little or no deflection of the regional wind.

Previous observations by Heywood (1933), Cornford (1938), Hawke (1933) suggested that local winds, mainly of the katabatic type, would also be in evidence in the Bath area. A careful watch was maintained by the authors and this revealed katabatic flows whenever conditions were favourable. On occasions, more especially in the winter, the movement of cold air down the valley sides could be felt quite easily, but in the main the movement is so slow that some means of rendering it visible is necessary before the wind can be detected. We were fortunate in that a medium was usually present in and around Bath. Smoke from chimneys, trains and bonfires, together with inversion fogs viewed from above, yielded some very interesting data.

The more rapid the cooling of the ground the stronger the resulting katabatic wind; snow covered slopes hence greatly assist in producing the more extreme conditions. But almost as effective as snow is grass (especially when long) and most of the fields on the hillsides and plateau in and around Bath are pasture grass.

The gentle flow of colder air into the valleys was nearly always visible, through smoke movement, on calm nights and could often be observed commencing around sunset. Usually the best indicator was a slowly smouldering bonfire with much smoke and little heat, and this if near a plateau top would reveal the downward air drainage over a considerable distance. Chimney smoke from houses dotted over the hill side and valley was of great value when the valley inversion was developing rapidly or well established, but in shallow cases the chimneys were above the level of the katabatic movement or if near the limit the warmer air from the domestic fires rose above the level of the drift.

The inversion top was often clearly demarcated in the absence of fog by rising smoke spreading out horizontally. Early morning trains up and down the valley were particularly useful in this respect for shallow summer inversions. Fully developed valley inversion fogs when viewed from the plateaux gave some illuminating examples of the movement of the cold air down valley, its occasional dispersal by the built up area, and an indication of the speed which appeared to vary from 2-6 m.p.h. The mass movement of the valley air in the morning was more turbulent than the laminar katabatic flow down the valley sides during the build up. On occasions a great wall of mist and fog was observed to flow out of the Box and Limpley Stoke valleys and envelop the lower valley—almost as if the accumulated cold air had been suddenly released in some way. The pressure and density of the colder bottom air was frequently sufficiently great for the air to flow against quite noticeable regional winds. One outstanding case from early morning revealed, by a series of dispersed chimneys, air in the valley bottom moving down valley, half way up the valley sides air was moving down into the valley, whilst near the hill top and above the inversion level there was a movement up valley in response to the regional wind. The top levels of some inversion fogs were also observed to be torn and ruffled when a light wind existed above the level of the inversion.

LOCAL CLIMATES AND HABITABILITY

It is perhaps appropriate in this more general survey to consider briefly the effect of the climatic variations, which have been distinguished, upon human living conditions.

The body normally maintains in the deeper tissues a temperature of 98·4 degrees F.; heat is continually being generated by internal metabolism and this heat is conducted away to the skin, where the temperature is lower than the deeper tissues, and there it is dissipated by various means. The feeling of pleasantness depends largely upon the maintenance of the body at the normal temperature and the efficient removal of any surplus heat.

In hot weather the loss of surplus body heat may be increased by limiting the clothing, by decreasing the air temperature, or by increasing the air movement. Conversely in cold weather heat may be prevented from escaping by wearing more clothing, by increasing the temperature, or by decreasing the air movement.

When exposed to cold the skin temperature of the normal person falls and there is an onset of shivering—involuntary muscular movements which generate heat in an attempt to make up the deficiency. When exposed to heat the efficient loss of surplus body heat is held up until the sweat glands discharge sweat which in evaporating takes heat from the body. Heat is then being lost by radiation, by convection (air currents) and by evaporation of sweat. (See Brunt 1941-43, 1943, Kraus 1945.)

We may now consider the broad climatic divisions of valley, hill and urban sites in Bath in relationship with the principles of human comfort sketched out above.

(a) *Summer*: In the greater heat of summer the human body will feel more pleasant when it is losing heat more rapidly and in consequence fares better where temperatures are lower and where there is a greater air movement. A low relative humidity will also assist more rapid evaporation. Under *normal* summer conditions the lower temperatures and greater air movement of the hill sites are more pleasing than the higher temperatures and stuffier calm conditions of the valley. It is true that relative humidities may be slightly greater at hill-top levels than in the valley bottom, but this is more than compensated for by the increased air movement. When *valley inversion* conditions prevail —confined to night periods in summer—the valley has the cooler, damper air, but when the temperature is high as in summer the increased humidity resulting from a slight fall in temperature may neutralize the reduction and create an oppressive atmosphere. The hill sites with slightly warmer but drier air plus the greater air movement are again to be preferred to the valley sites although there is perhaps less difference than for the normal day condition.

The effect of the urban climate may best be considered by making comparison with valley sites at the same altitude. Under normal temperature structures we have seen that the city may be very slightly cooler in summer but any small advantage that this gives is more than lost by the great reduction in air movement caused by the buildings. On the other hand the city is frequently better than the valley in inversions, for although temperature in this case is slightly higher than the valley the humidity is kept down and the air feels less oppressive.

Summarising for summer we therefore have :—

                                   Increasing pleasantness ⟶

Normal states: City ⟶   Valley ⟶   Hill

Valley inversion states: Valley ⟶   City   ⟶   Hill

(b) *Winter*: In winter the body will be concerned with seeking an environment where temperatures are higher and air movement reduced. Humidities should be moderate, if too high the air will be raw, if too low the air feels keen. Under *normal* conditions the higher temperature and calmer states will be provided by the valley; hill-top sites are very exposed and the strong cold winds sweeping across them make an unpleasant environment. Moreover, relative humidities are higher on hill-top sites and the air feels raw in comparison with the valley. *Valley inversion* conditions, however, reverse this picture completely. The valley now experiences lower temperatures, and cold damp air with frequent relative humidities of 100 per cent and fog. In contrast the hill tops will be basking in brilliant, if feeble, sunshine and will be warmer and calm.

Considering the urban factor and comparing with adjacent valley sites it will be remembered that in normal temperature structures the city area is warmer in winter and has a reduced air movement. It is hence a pleasanter environment. The problem becomes a little more complex when inversionary structures prevail, for whilst the greater warmth of the city helps to offset the lower temperatures and prevent the formation of fog, smoke pollution is present in winter and works against this tendency. Once the inversion is established smoke pollution tends to aggravate conditions even more and prolong the period of the fog. At present therefore the city is on balance less agreeable than the surrounding valley sites under inversionary conditions, but the position could be reversed if smoke pollution were eliminated.

Summarising for winter we have therefore:—

Increasing pleasantness———→

Normal states: Hill ——→ Valley ——→ City
Valley inversion states: City ——→ Valley ——→ Hill

Bearing in mind the proportion of normal to inversion days (about 2:1) and the greater intensity of winter inversions it is clear that on the whole hill sites emerge as the better situations, for they only suffer one defect—the raw cold winds of normal winter days. Optimum conditions probably exist where shelter can be found from these winds and locations a little below the plateau edge are perhaps ideal—such sites would coincide with the warm or thermal belt (Manley 1944) which is often found in winter inversions. It is perhaps significant that some of the better-class residential areas in Bath actually lie in this intermediate zone.

Whilst the normal individual is adaptable to these local variations and can experience them without much discomfort, one should not lose sight of the important functions of Bath as a holiday centre, place of retirement and curative spa for rheumatic disorders. For borderline cases and for those in ill-health we suggest that full regard ought to be paid to the micro-climatic factors, a subject which also has relevance to town-planning, particularly with reference to problems such as smoke pollution and the siting of future curative establishments.

APPENDIX

Code Numbers	Observer	Height in feet above M.S.L.	Position			Barograph	Thermograph	Hygrograph	Maximum	Minimum	Wet and Dry	Rainfall	Wind direction	Wind force
Primary			°	′	″									
1	Messrs. W. G. V. Balchin, N. Pye, Ensleigh, Lansdown . .	720	51 2	24 22	22 N 12 W	*	*	*	*	*	*	*	*	*
2	Central Stations													
	(i) Henrietta Park . . .	65 2	51 2	23 21	18 N 14 W	*	*	*	*	*	*	*	*	*
	(ii) Pepys Club	65 2	51 2	22 21	29 N 03 W									

Secondary

Code Numbers	Observer	Height in feet above M.S.L.	Position	Barograph	Thermograph	Hygrograph	Max mum	Minimum	Wet and Dry	Rainfall	Wind direction	Wind force
3	W. G. Rawlings, Esq., Westfield Park, Newbridge Road	60	51 23 15 N / 2 24 01 W	*			*	*	*	*		*
4	P. A. Laycock, Esq., 6, Belgrave Terrace	250	51 23 32 N / 2 21 21 W	*	*		*	*	*			
5	E. Pryer, Esq., St. Christopher's School	225	51 23 09 N / 2 20 28 W				*	*	*	*	*	*
6	P. Hambleton, Esq., City of Bath Boys' School	350	51 22 17 N / 2 21 30 W				*	*	*	*	*	*
7	P. Hambleton, Esq., 25, South Stoke Road	530	51 21 22 N / 2 21 45 W				*	*	*	*	*	*
8	E. G. W. Souster, Esq., Sulis Manor, Odd Down	560	51 21 09 N / 2 22 28 W				*	*	*	*	*	*
9	A. Griffin, Esq., Isolation Hospital	520	51 21 51 N / 2 19 10 W				*	*	*	*	*	*
10	T. Blackmore, Esq., Twerton Nurseries	220	51 22 28 N / 2 23 24 W				*	*	*	*	*	*
11	Rev. Prebendary R. W. Windsor, Weston Park	210	51 23 40 N / 2 23 10 W				*	*	*	*	*	*
12	W. Blathwayt, Esq., Eagle House, Batheaston	125	51 24 37 N / 2 19 10 W				*	*	*	*	*	*
13	R.A.F. Station, Colerne	580	51 26 20 N / 2 17 00 W				*	*	*			

Regional

Code Numbers	Observer	Height in feet above M.S.L.	Position	Barograph	Thermograph	Hygrograph	Max mum	Minimum	Wet and Dry	Rainfall	Wind direction	Wind force
14	I. Pothecary, Esq., 55, Forest Road, Melksham	136	51 22 45 N / 2 07 38 W	*			*	*	*			
15	G. E. Clothier, Esq., Research Station, Long Ashton	162	51 25 37 N / 2 40 05 W				*	*	*			
16	H. H. Harding, Esq., Frampton Cotterell, Bristol	158	51 31 57 N / 2 29 06 W				*	*	*			

Tertiary Recording rainfall only.

Code Numbers	Observer	Height in feet above M.S.L.	Position
17	Charlecombe Rsvr. Bath Waterworks	325	51 23 59 N / 2 21 33 W
18	Batheaston Resvr. Bath Waterworks	248	51 24 52 N / 2 19 57 W
19	Monkswood Resvr. Bath Waterworks	390	51 26 16 N / 2 20 53 W
20	Lansdown Station, Bath Waterworks	500	51 25 09 N / 2 23 06 W
21	D. E. Coombe, Esq. 24, Bloomfield Dr.	500	51 21 50 N / 2 22 42 W
22	Miss M. B. Clark, Combe Down	520	51 21 37 N / 2 20 29 W
23	C. Bontflower, Esq. Combe Down	520	51 21 42 N / 2 20 21 W
24	W. G. Lock, Esq. Monkton Combe	425	51 21 26 N / 2 19 54 W
25	Rev. A. B. Burney, 7, Bathwick Hill	235	51 22 47 N / 2 20 38 W
26	J. R. Sparey, Esq., Camden Road	280	51 23 36 N / 2 21 16 W
27	Miss J. McNab, Hamilton Road	530	51 23 48 N / 2 22 12 W
28	Mrs. M. I. Hicks, 7, Hermitage Rd.	410	51 23 37 N / 2 22 01 W
29	C. S. Payne, Esq., St. James's Sq.	195	51 23 23 N / 2 21 59 W
30	G. R. Marsh, Esq., Swainswick	145	51 24 02 N / 2 20 22 W
31	G. Lipscomb, Esq. Batheaston	240	51 24 26 N / 2 18 13 W

REFERENCES

Brunt, D.	1941-43	Mem. and Proc. Manchester Lit. and Phil. Soc., **85**, p. 45.
————	1943	Quart. J. R. Met. Soc., London, **69**, p. 77.
————	1945	Ibid., **71**, p. 1.
————	1946	Ibid., **72**, p. 185.
Bilham, E. G.	1938	The Climate of the British Isles. Macmillan, London.
Cornford, C. E.	1938	Quart. J. R. Met. Soc., London, **64**, p. 553.
Hawke, E. L.	1933	Ibid., **59**, p. 261, p. 401.
Heywood, G. S. P.	1933	Ibid., **59**, p. 47.
Johnson, N. K.	1929	Geophys. Mem., London, No. 46.
Kraus, E.	1945	Quart. J. R. Met. Soc., London, **71**, p. 397.
Manley, G.	1944	Geogr. J., **103**, p. 241.
————	1946	Quart. J. R. Met. Soc., London, **72**, p. 180.
Matthews, H. A.	1937	Geography, **22**, p. 87.
Miller, A. A.	1931	Climatology. Methuen, London.
Schmidt, W.	1934	Quart. J. R. Met. Soc., London, **60**, p. 345.
Spence, M. T.	1936	Ibid., **62**, p. 25.
Tinn, A. B.	1935	Ibid., **61**, p. 188.
————	1938	Ibid., **64**, p. 391.
————	1940	Ibid., **66**, p. 47.

DISCUSSION

Mr. GORDON MANLEY : I should like first to express my admiration for the persistence and thoroughness with which the authors of the paper set about the organisation of such a close network of stations, and the care they took over questions of instruments, siting, and exposure. So many people agree that this sort of work should be done and so few carry it into execution. Close surveys of this kind can be of great value. We are still too dependent on occasional surveys made of German city temperatures on summer evenings and the like and I look forward to having some more conclusions from this bulky mass of observations so painstakingly made around Bath. I have only just seen the meeting proof and therefore have few detailed criticisms to offer. I find it a little difficult to see why "vertical inversions" and "valley inversions" should be so distinguished and how you can get in the same area a vertical inversion without a valley inversion. After all if one were to count up the frequency of surface inversions at the morning ascent at Mildenhall in a flat plain I am confident that their number and intensity will be just about the same as that of the valley inversions in most places, though it can be admitted that if you take a place like Rickmansworth the local intensity, so to speak, of the valley inversion is exceptional. I see that on several quiet days in December the maxima was about 5° higher on the hill-tops than in the valleys. Not the least successful venture I have made was a Boxing Day picnic from Durham on a day of freezing fog; at 1100 feet the calm warm sunshine with an air temperature of 45° was extremely agreeable. Such days can quite often be utilised, as those who live in our more hilly districts know. One of the earliest progenitors of this society, Dr. Addison of Malvern, did some interesting local investigation in that neighbourhood in 1837. No doubt he like his ancestors for 3,000 years recognised the charms of a hillside situation.

What may well prove interesting at Bath is the incidence of frost at the various stations in relation to the area from which the cold air is derived, and also the extent of the influence of the river; also under what circumstances does the upper boundary of the valley fog begin to tilt?

The lower maxima in the city in summer are interesting. Much depends, I suspect, on the extent to which the ground is shaded, *i.e.* the size and character of the areas open to insolation. About fifty years ago I believe attention was drawn to the rather lower maxima at "Old Street" (London, E.C.) compared with the more open suburbs. Such effects do not occur at all city stations however. Kraus suggests that, comparing city and country data at Stockholm and Milan, the altitude of the sun played some part, but I doubt whether this holds in all cases. With sensitive thermometers even a small displacement of a "city" station may have appreciable effects and I doubt whether one should generalise too much from a single "town" station at Bath.

The results with regard to the lowering of the upper surface of fog over the city are very interesting. I hope it will be found possible to reproduce the illustration of this. The diagrams of incidence of rainfall are handy, and I am sure many Fellows will look forward to more. It would be helpful too if more comparisons were made between the observed phenomena and those which have from time to time been noted elsewhere.

Mr. W. H. Hogg : I agree with Mr. Manley that it is unnecessary to distinguish between the meteorological and climatological use of the term inversion.

(*Added later*). I should like to make it clear that I have no objection to the term "valley inversion" which conveniently emphasises the effect of orography on the distribution of temperature under inversion conditions. But even though the temperatures may be measured at screen level at various points along the valley bottom and slopes, if these show that there is a valley inversion, this condition is only the result of an inversion starting at the surface. Unless there is such an inversion there can be no flow of cold air down the valley sides. I do, however, think that the term " vertical inversion" is superfluous and that the phrase "a valley inversion will automatically produce a vertical inversion" is misleading.

I congratulate the authors on organising this close network of stations and collecting such a large number of important observations and think that it would be useful if more of the data could be published. I also hope that more will be seen of some of the interesting slides of rainfall distribution which had been shown at the meeting but were not in the paper. One of these slides showed how the rainfall fell off rapidly on either side of a thunderstorm track; it would be interesting to know precisely how this track was determined.

Mr. A. J. Whiten : Reference has been made to the urban effect manifesting itself in the deficiency of rainfall over the city as compared with other valley stations.

As the urban effect appears to have occasioned an increase in relative humidity, I should have expected any effect on rainfall to have been an excess rather than a deficiency.

However, I think it is unlikely that the results of urban influences on rainfall would be felt in the city itself, but more probably at some little distance to the leeward.

I have never visited Bath, but I have studied the inch ordnance sheets of the neighbourhood, and it appears to me that the causes are probably orographic, and that the deficiency would most probably occur in the hollow if the city were not there.

Being situated at the focus of a number of valleys which radiate more or less regularly from the city, it would appear that from whatever quarter the wind might blow, it would approach the city through one, or at the most, two valleys, having egress through three.

The heavier rainfall in the valleys to windward appears to me to be explainable with reference to the fact that the air moving over the surface would be constricted on entering a valley, and there would be a tendency for some to be forced upwards, in addition to the effect of that air which rode up the sides of the adjoining hills.

On debouching into the hollow about the city, this constriction would cease, and there would be a slight tendency to subsidence, which would account for the slight reduction in precipitation at this location.

The greater relative humidity of the air in the city would to some extent replenish the moisture content of the moving air, which would then pass out along the leeward valleys, and over the hills, giving more precipitation over these valleys.

Mr. W. N. McCLEAN :It is interesting to note the number of rainy days, the number of which is considerably larger at the higher rainfall sites at the higher altitudes. *"Over 0·01 inch per day"* is an artificial definition of a rainy day; and I have noticed that 0·02 inch would occur quite frequently at the higher rainfall gauge,when it was 0·01 inch at the lower rainfall gauge.

I consider that this detailed investigation of area rainfall is most valuable and helped to fill a gap in our climatological station system.

Those stations might well bring in many surrounding gauges into their rainfall records. I produced such records on the Windermere area (*Q.J.*, 66, p. 337), where there were some 20 gauges on 95 sq. miles. Such a course would enhance the value of many rain gauges, and encourage a useful decentralisation of the British Rainfall Organization.

Mr. G. A. TUNNELL :I think that the paper that has been read this evening would have been of even greater interest if diagrams of the air-flow in the area, had been given.

(*Added later*). To get accurate estimates of air-flow it would be necessary to use well-exposed surface anemometers, with perhaps low lift pilot balloons and two theodolites over the valley floor. Some very interesting information could be obtained if soundings of humidity and temperature were made over the valley and the city. The differences between the hill surface and the free air would give some indication of the moisture and radiation flow from the hillsides. I think that balloon soundings would give information concerning the slopes of inversion surfaces mentioned by Mr. Manley and the differences between valley inversions and free air inversions mentioned by Dr. Sutcliffe.

The strange phenomena of cake fungus mentioned by Mr. Pye are associated with special temperature and humidity conditions and must indicate that Bath has high temperatures associated with high humidities.

An examination of horizontal and vertical moisture gradients in conjunction with air-flow diagrams would, I think, help in explaining and forecasting the formation of fog, and indicate when high relative humidities were likely to occur. In this connection regions outside the area that are sources of moisture must exert considerable influence. For example the Bristol Channel. However in the small area under consideration the effects sought are likely to be small and very accurate observations are needed.

Major H. C. GUNTON referring to the interest and value of the paper said : I would have liked to have dealt with some phenological aspects, but, at the late hour which has been reached, must confine my remarks to a statement that details have, with the courteous concurrence of Messrs. Balchin and Pye, been included in the Phenological Reports for 1945 and 1946.

Mr. L. G. CAMERON (*communicated*) : I was interested to note that the question of aspect was mentioned, if only briefly, in the paper. It is a question which interests the agricultural meteorologist greatly and one which will demand even greater attention in the future. Mr. Balchin and Mr. Pye chose to couple wind direction with aspect. I would like it taken further and see wind velocity and rainfall intensity introduced, the whole then being considered together to produce some conception of exposure. This question of exposure is, in many cases, of fundamental importance in the choice of the best locality for the growth of certain crops. That is well known. What is perhaps not quite so easily appreciated is the fact that an unfavourable exposure can render a grazing area of little use or even make it a positive danger to cattle and sheep. Both animals can normally withstand most of the rigours of our climate but neither can endure heavy driving rain for any length of time. Obviously then, especially in hilly country, exposure must figure in the assessment of the value of any area for grazing.

I understand that this is a preliminary paper to introduce others presenting a more analytical study of the data obtained from the Bath district. I therefore want to seize this opportunity to call the authors' attention to this question of exposure in the hope that they will give it their careful consideration.

With regard to the effect of frosts on farming, it was perhaps somewhat over optimistic to suggest, as the authors have done, that frost damage to fruit crops could be largely eliminated by improved siting of orchards. Undoubtedly, greater care in the placing of orchards to avoid the cold air of the valleys would reduce the chances of damage by frost but unfortunately this is not the complete answer to the problem. Much work remains to be done on this subject before any final pronouncement can be made.

Dr. C. E. P BROOKS (*communicated*) : There are three points in this paper which seem to call for comment The first is the title : biologists and meteorologists differ in their definitions of micro-climatology but this paper does not come within either. The term "micro" suggests a very small scale, close to the ground in the air between and within the vegetation or even inside the plants. This paper is ordinary climatology appled to a limited area; it has nothing to do with micro-climatology, and to avoid misconception the title should be changed to "local climatology."

The second point is the statement (on p. 104) that the decrease of temperature with height is due in part to a corresponding decrease in the amount of moisture and carbon dioxide in the air. This has no justification as regards water-vapour; as regards carbon dioxide it is patently absurd. I am sure that even the most refined methods of measurement would fail to show any systematic decrease of CO_2 with height in a few hundred feet, and if it did, it would not be likely to have any appreciable effect on the temperature.

The third point concerns the fact that the smallest annual rainfall occurs in the city, which is attributed (on p. 116) to the effect of the built-up area itself. This is equally improbable; the real reason is that the city lies in the largest expanse of open ground. Narrow-sided valleys at little greater elevation receive in addition to the direct rainfall a part which is carried over from the high ground to windward. This is quite a well-known effect in hilly areas; the classic case is the rainfall of Seathwaite.

Apart from these points there is very little which one can say about the paper, most of which deals in rather general terms with topographical effects which are already well known from other examples. I gather that this is only an introductory statement, and that the authors have not yet completed their detailed study of the large mass of material accumulated. When this has been done, we may look forward to some very interesting results.

Mr. BALCHIN and Mr. PYE (*in reply—partly communicated*): We should like first to express our appreciation for the cordial reception which the Society has accorded to the paper and for the stimulating discussion at this evening's meeting. This acceptance of this work (which was undertaken by two professional geographers as a relaxation from war-time duties) as a climatological contribution will we hope be an encouragement to other geographers to interest themselves in a field wherein we believe their training can be of value.

A preliminary statement about the survey was considered desirable in view of the long delay which now faces most Societies in the publication of papers. The discussion has been most helpful to us and we hope that the whole paper will be of value to others able to undertake similar fieldwork. Many points have been raised, several of which perhaps call for immediate reply.

Both Mr. Gordon Manley and Mr. W. H. Hogg query our "clarification" of the use of the term inversion; this attempt to distinguish between a general inversion extending over a wider area and unrelated to minor relief forms, and the strictly localised inversion confined to the valleys, will perhaps be better understood after reading N. K. Johnson, (Geophys. Mem. Lond., No. 46, 1929). Both Dr. C. E. P. Brooks and Mr. A. J. Whiten comment on the lower rainfall in the city centre. Since this initial paper was written we have proceeded further with detailed plots of daily and monthly distributions and it is now clear that the city receives least as the surrounding hills make the city a rain shadow area for winds from nearly all directions excep ,ose from due west.

Dr. Brooks queries the use of the term "micro." The confusion of terms is unfortunate but it is not ours. Most work in this field from Germany is labelled "micro" and the word is in use in textbooks such as Climatology by Haurwitz and Austin (1944). In view of the increasing attention being given to small-scale studies by biologists we should agree with the suggestion to restrict the use of the term "micro" and employ "local" to describe surveys such as we have made (*vide* also discussion p. 188 of *Quart. J. R. Met. Soc.,* **72**).

The problem of decrease of temperature with height and the effect of moisture and carbon dioxide raised by Dr. Brooks is based on a misreading. It is clear from the text that it is not the operation of any of the factors that go to make up the general temperature lapse rate but the effect of the lapse rate *itself* that is claimed can affect the temperature in the locality with available height differences of some 650 feet.

The interest stimulated by the paper is very encouraging and it is hoped to consider many of the other suggestions made this evening in future contributions.

TEMPERATURE & HUMIDITY VARIATIONS IN AN URBAN AREA OF DIVERSIFIED RELIEF

By

W. G. V. BALCHIN and NORMAN PYE.[*]

One of the most outstanding developments in climatological thought in recent years has been a recognition of the inadequacy of the assumption that a regional pattern of climate is common to large areas. Some of the more striking effects of local climatic differences are readily discernible, as for example in the comparative earliness or lateness of plant development, the existence of frost hollows, the contrasted characteristics of adret and ubac slopes, and the varying liability to fog development. As yet, however, there are few quantitative surveys to show the magnitude of local departures from the regional macroclimate and the purpose of this paper is to present to geographers the more interesting quantitative variations in temperature and humidity that were detected in a local climatological survey carried out in and near Bath, England. Bath is a medium size city of some 80,000 inhabitants and one which, in its valley location with diversified relief in the neighbourhood, exhibits features to be found in many urban settlements.

The local climatological survey referred to was organised by the authors under the auspices of the Leverhulme Research Fellowships Foundation during the period 1944-1946. A close network of meteorological stations was established in strategic positions throughout the district. These stations fall into three categories. At primary stations, of which there were two in number, continuous records of temperature, humidity and pressure were maintained, together with a daily 9 hours GMT observation of maximum and minimum temperature, wet and dry bulb temperature, rainfall, wind force and direction. At secondary stations, of which there were 11 in number[‡], a daily 9 hours. GMT observation of maximum and minimum temperature, wet and dry bulb temperature, rainfall, wind force and direction was taken. Finally at tertiary stations, of which there were 15, a daily 9 hours GMT note of rainfall was made. Together with the climatological survey there was organised a collateral phenological survey: observations of plant growth being made in close proximity

---

[*] W.G.V. Balchin is Lecturer in Geography at King's College in the University of London, and Norman Pye is Lecturer in Geography at the University of Manchester.

[‡] At two stations the records were slightly broken, but the observations are available for most daily and monthly plots.

128

to selected meteorological stations. Altogether, some fifty thousand observations were collected from the closest network of stations ever laid down in England.

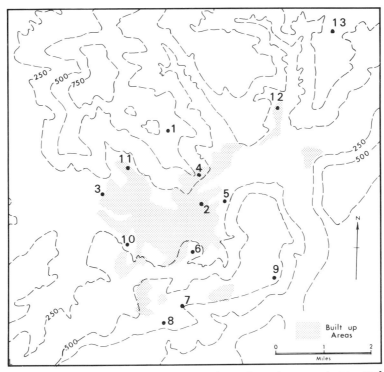

Fig. 1.—Location of Stations observing temperature and humidity.

(Numbers against the stations are the code numbers employed throughout this paper).

Papers already published elsewhere, and noted in the appendix, have dealt with the rainfall, the phenological survey, and certain meteorological aspects. The following paper presents the results of a detailed analysis of the temperature and humidity observations. The system of code numbering the stations used in previous papers has been maintained and fig. 1 shows the locations of those stations which carried out the temperature and humidity observations.

Before proceeding to the climatic aspect the physiographic situation of Bath should be noted. The city lies where the Avon cuts the remarkable and only gap in the escarpment of the Cotswold Hills; it is at a focal point where six valleys, developed on the dip slope of the escarpment, all converge (fig. 2). These valleys are deeply incised into the plateau leaving the interfluves to form the surrounding heights which exist as extensive flat

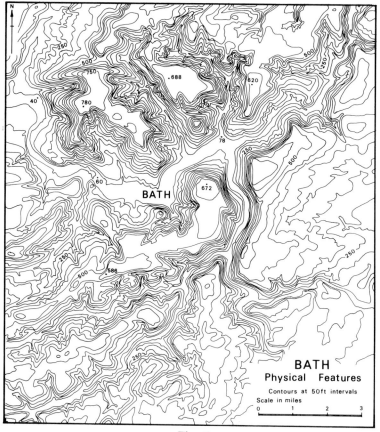

Fig. 2.

topped Downs of 650 to 750 feet above mean sea level. This physiographic situation provides the key to many of the local climatic variations, for during periods of anticyclonic calm the Downs offer extensive ground for nocturnal cooling with a consequent fall in temperature of the lower layers of the atmosphere in contact with these surfaces. There follows katabatic air drainage of the colder, and therefore heavier, air into the minor valleys whose convergence, together with the constriction of the main valley below the city, naturally tends to encourage ponding of the cold air in the Bath area.

TEMPERATURE VARIATIONS.

From the series of more than 450 daily distributions of maximum and minimum temperatures over the whole region, certain fundamentally similar patterns can be detected despite the diverse daily variations in detail and the seasonal variations in absolute value. In reducing the observations to a coherent and organised system it became clear that the patterns were related to definite types of weather. The important distinction in meteorological conditions, so far as local climatic variations were con-

130

cerned, was that between anticyclonic and other conditions. Seasonal variations are secondary influences on the fundamental patterns that are related to the major weather type. The factors producing local variations in temperature are altitude, aspect and the urban effect, and to illustrate the operation of these elements and the actual extent of variations produced within the region in

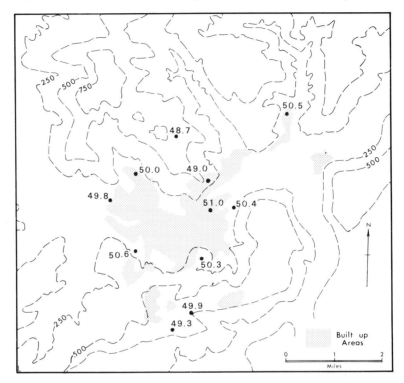

Fig. 3.—Mean maximum temperatures for November, 1944. (Illustrative of near normal conditions and urban effect).

diverse meteorological and seasonal conditions, selected daily and monthly distributions of maximum and minimum temperatures are presented.

MAXIMUM TEMPERATURES.

The month of November, 1944, was one of considerable air movement and little sunshine, and the means of the maxima (fig. 3) may be considered to represent a near normal condition with a lapse of 2.3°F. from the valley station to the plateau station as compared with the theoretical normal value of 2.5°F. derived from their difference in altitude. On the other hand in conditions of anticyclonic calm, in both winter and summer, temperature inversions easily develop by katabatic flow from the

131

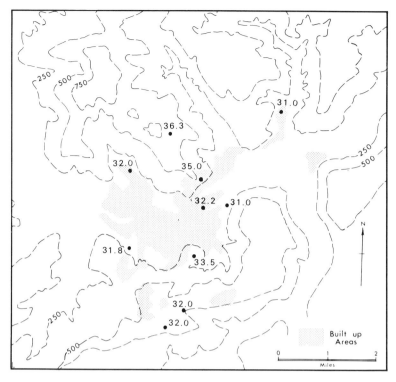

Fig. 4.—Maximum temperatures on 26th December, 1944. (Illustrative of the effect of inversion conditions during winter anticyclonic calms).

plateau into the open Avon valley.   Fig 4 shows how, under such conditions in midwinter, the maximum temperatures experienced on the plateau may be greater than those recorded in the valley.   Whilst normally Henrietta Park, station 2 (valley), has maxima exceeding those of Lansdown, station 1 (plateau), by some 2 or 3 degrees, the maximum for Lansdown was maintained above that for Henrietta Park every day from the 25th to the 29th December, the greatest difference being 5 degrees. The influence of this persistent inversion is apparent in even the monthly figures since the mean maximum for the valley bottom is but a degree higher than that for the plateau (Table I). The meteorological basis for the persistence of valley fog and its intensification by non-dispersal during the day is eloquently revealed by the thermograms for the valley and plateau stations which are seen superimposed in fig. 5.

The operation of the urban effect in producing the highest maxima in the city area is shown in fig. 3, and this relative warmth of the city was evident under all conditions and in all seasons except the summer. The existence

TABLE 1.—Monthly Mean Maximum Temperatures.
October 1944 to December 1945, inclusive.

Code Nos. of Stations	1	2	3	5	6	7	8	10	11	12
1944										
October	53.6	56.0	55.6	55.3	55.2	55.2	55.1	56.0	56.5	55.8
November	48.7	51.0	49.8	50.4	50.3	49.9	49.3	50.6	50.0	50.5
December	43.2	44.3	44.0	44.3	44.0	43.7	43.1	44.8	43.9	43.8
1945										
January	36.8	38.8	39.2	38.9	37.4	38.4	37.3	39.2	39.2	39.4
February	48.7	50.8	51.0	51.1	50.0	50.1	49.7	51.3	51.3	51.3
March	52.5	54.4	54.9	55.2	54.5	54.2	53.5	55.3	56.0	55.7
April	58.4	60.5	61.7	61.0	61.3	60.9	59.4	61.7	61.6	62.2
May	60.8	63.5	64.5	63.6	63.3	63.4	62.0	64.4	65.6	64.7
June	62.8	65.6	68.4	62.8	64.8	64.9	62.3	66.4	67.6	66.9
July	66.9	69.9	72.9	68.6	69.7	70.4	69.1	70.9	72.4	71.5
August	67.0	70.0	72.4	70.0	70.5	70.4	68.7	70.9	71.9	71.0
September	61.2	64.7	65.8	64.5	63.3	63.5	62.8	64.4	65.9	64.6
October	59.0	61.6	63.0	61.6	61.3	61.1	60.0	62.4	63.4	61.9
November	48.3	50.4	52.2	50.4	50.0	49.8	49.2	50.7	50.8	50.4
December	45.4	46.3	48.0	46.3	45.9	45.7	45.6	47.3	47.1	46.9
Mean Oct., 1944—Sept., 1945	55.1	57.5	58.4	57.1	57.0	57.1	56.0	58.0	58.5	58.1
Mean Jan., 1945—Dec., 1945	55.7	58.0	59.5	57.8	57.6	57.7	56.6	58.7	59.4	58.9

TABLE II.—Monthly Mean Minimum Temperatures,
October 1944 to December 1945, inclusive.

Code Nos. of Stations	1	2	3	5	6	7	8	10	11	12
1944										
October	42.6	44.1	43.9	43.3	44.7	42.7	43.6	43.6	42.9	42.2
November	37.8	38.8	36.8	39.1	40.1	38.4	37.9	39.0	37.5	36.7
December	34.5	34.0	33.5	34.1	34.0	34.0	34.6	34.4	33.7	32.5
1945										
January	28.2	28.5	26.7	28.5	28.6	27.8	28.0	28.7	27.5	27.3
February	38.4	40.4	39.6	39.2	40.3	38.6	38.3	39.7	38.5	39.4
March	38.8	38.6	37.7	37.7	39.7	38.4	38.6	39.1	38.0	36.3
April	41.8	42.6	40.6	41.9	42.4	40.3	41.8	42.1	41.5	40.3
May	45.0	47.0	45.9	46.7	46.4	45.3	45.9	46.4	45.5	44.8
June	48.9	51.9	49.7	50.9	49.4	49.8	50.6	50.4	49.8	49.4
July	52.8	55.2	53.0	54.3	53.6	53.0	53.6	53.6	53.1	52.7
August	52.8	54.4	52.7	53.7	53.6	53.0	53.5	52.9	52.6	51.7
September	50.5	52.6	52.1	52.5	51.1	51.2	51.6	52.1	51.7	51.3
October	46.9	47.0	46.0	46.8	47.2	46.5	47.0	46.9	46.2	44.7
November	40.5	40.5	40.0	39.4	39.9	39.8	40.6	40.6	40.4	38.6
December	36.8	37.5	37.1	36.7	36.5	35.6	36.9	37.9	37.5	35.8
Mean Oct., 1944—Sept., 1945	42.7	44.0	42.7	43.5	43.7	42.7	43.2	43.5	42.7	42.1
Mean Jan., 1945—Dec., 1945	43.5	44.7	43.4	44.0	44.1	43.3	43.9	44.2	43.5	42.7

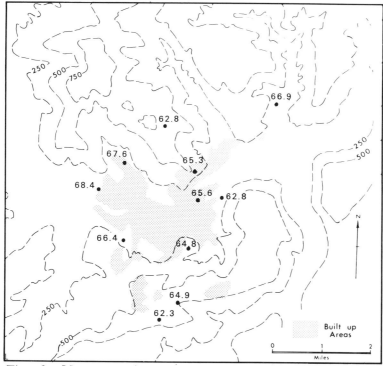

Fig. 6.—Mean maximum temperatures for June, 1945. (Illustrative of higher valley maxima but slightly lower city maxima of summer).

of this characteristic heat island within the built-up area is due to the heat generated by the city itself, the higher thermal absorption rate of buildings, reduced evaporation and the reduction of outward radiation because of the increased atmospheric pollution of winter months. The discovery that the summer maxima in the city were slightly lower than those of the surrounding country in the valley was surprising (fig. 6) but Kraus (1945) has instanced similar variations in Vienna and the thermal response of a built-up area in summer time seems to depend very much on local circumstances. In Bath the absence of a heat island within the town may be related partly to reflection from the near white limestone of which the greater part of the town is built.

In addition to altitude, aspect was found to influence maximum temperatures. Theoretically the amount of solar radiation reaching a conical hill would be symmetrical with respect to the meridian, but the resulting temperature will be higher on a slope with a westerly exposure for two reasons: in the first place the heating of the easterly facing slope has to start from the lower temperatures of morning, whereas the westerly slope is already preheated prior to receipt of the afternoon radia-

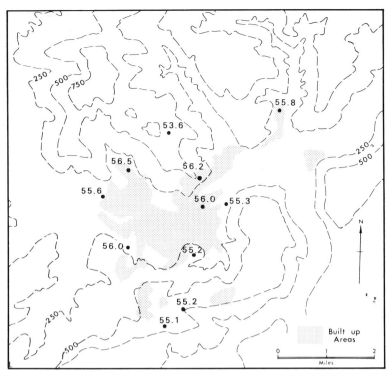

Fig. 7.—Mean maximum temperatures for October, 1944.
(Illustrates the influence of aspect).

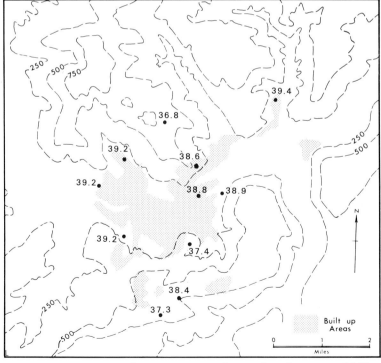

Fig. 8.—Mean maximum temperatures for January, 1945.
(Illustrates the influence of aspect).

135

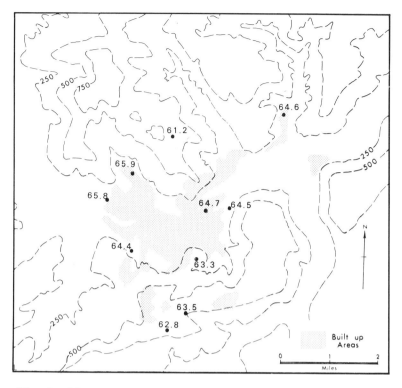

Fig. 9.—Mean maximum temperatures for September, 1945.
(Illustrates the greater excess of maxima in valley locations
with summer anticyclonic conditions).

tion; secondly, much of the morning radiation is initially
expended in evaporating moisture, and so is not available
for temperature increase.   In   consequence,   highest
temperatures may occur not where the aspect faces south,
but rather more to the west.   It is during the summer
months that aspect exerts its greatest influence, and the
importance of south-west facing slopes is brought out in
the figures for May and July, 1945 (Table 1).   The same
influence has been shown graphically in the plot of the
monthly means for October, 1944 (fig. 7.)   During   the
winter months aspect does not appear to be of such consequence, but something of its influence can be seen in the
monthly summary for January, 1945, when the south and
south-west facing stations at the western and eastern ends
of the valley record the two highest figures for the means
of the maxima temperatures (fig. 8).   With anticyclonic
conditions in summer, the valley sites, because of lower
altitude, more shelter and re-radiation, experience higher
maxima and the map for September, 1945, with a range in
the daily maxima of about 5 degrees, demonstrates this
(fig. 9).

Minimum Temperatures.

The controlling factors responsible for producing the two main minima distribution patterns seem to be (a) the presence or absence of mass movement of air over the

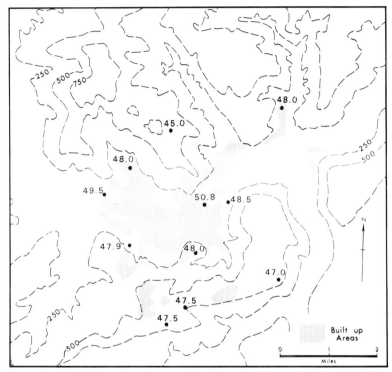

Fig. 10.—Minimum temperatures on 25th October, 1945. (Cloudy, windy conditions, giving a normal distribution modified only by the urban factor).

district, and (b) the altitude. Thus, when there is vigorous air movement the plateau has the lowest readings; but during calm periods, with much radiation at night, cold air flows into the valleys and the lowest minima occur in the valley bottoms. Fig. 10 represents a normal distribution of the minimum temperature with cloudy, windy conditions giving a normal lapse rate, modified only by the urban influence. In contrast are the inversions of these conditions which may occur at all seasons of the year, but are most marked in winter; typical of this type of minima distribution is the plot for 1st January, 1945 (fig. 11).

In addition to these full inversions of the winter time, there may be, in the summer months, an inversion of temperature between the plateau and the upper and lower ends of the valley, but not between the plateau and the centre of the city. These tendencies towards inversions

that have been precluded from full development because
of the effect of the urban area** in maintaining higher

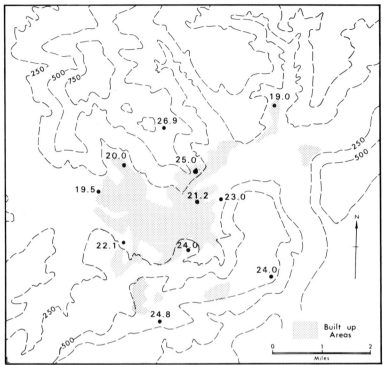

Fig. 11.—Minimum temperatures on 1st January, 1945.
(Illustrates the effect of valley temperature inversion
together with urban influence).

** Manchester covers an area more uniform in relief but
more extensively built up than Bath and affords a clear
example of the importance of the urban effect on
temperatures. The record for Oldham Road is representative of the closely built up city area; the Whitworth
Park Observatory is situated towards the outer part of
the city proper; the Burnage records relate to a southern
modern suburb, and the data from Barton airfield are
representative of temperatures on the low Manchester
Plain, well outside the built up area. Thus the comparison of these temperature data provides a fair
estimate of the extent to which man, in building his
cities, affects climate. The records of the minimum
temperatures have been investigated by Professor G.
Manley (Geog. Journ., June, 1944, pp. 254-257), and may
be summarised as follows: on quiet clear nights, Barton
is likely to have minima temperatures of between 6°
and 8° F. lower than those at Oldham Road in winter

temperatures during the night time, are represented by the conditions on 5th August, 1945 (fig. 12).   July 25th affords an example of a full inversion throughout the valley during a summer month (fig. 13).

The importance of the urban influence has been noticeable in some of the data, e.g., for 1st January, 1945 (fig. 11) and the figures for the means of the minima for November and October, 1944 (Table II), but a further example may be seen in the conditions on 13th October, 1944 (fig. 14).   Both east and west ends of the valley have

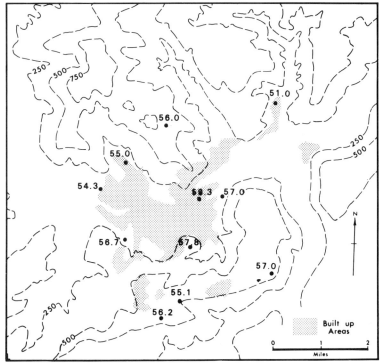

Fig. 12.—Minimum temperatures on 5th August, 1945. (Illustrating a partially developed inversion typical of the summer months. There is an inversion of temperature between the plateau and the valley extremities, but not between the plateau and the city centre because of the urban factor.)

and spring, and some 10° to 11° F. lower in summer ; Burnage, intermediate between the city and the open country, has minima temperatures between 3° and 4° F. below those at Oldham Road in winter and spring, and some 5° to 7° F. lower in summer and autumn ; Whitworth Park, nearer to the city centre, has smaller differences, its minima being usually of the order of 2°F. in winter and Spring, and 3° to 4° F. in summer and autumn.

lower minima than the centre, the built-up area appearing to keep up the temperature by about 2 degrees. The plot for 13th October, 1944 (fig. 14) and the data for the month of November, 1944, show, in addition, a feature which is often suggested, but is rarely sufficiently well marked to be brought out in the mapping, namely, the existence of a "warm belt" somewhere about the 350 feet level, a belt

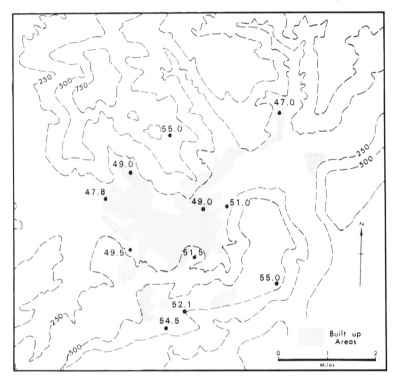

Fig. 13.—Minimum temperatures for 25th July, 1945. (Shows a fully developed summer inversion of temperature).

that escapes the cold air accumulations of the valley and also the more marked radiation and exposure of the plateau.

Fig. 15 shows that each month experiences a mixture of inversion and normal nights: the monthly mean clearly depends not only on the number but also on the magnitude of inversions. The monthly means indicate the dominant characteristic; thus in winter the means are inverted on account of the larger inversions, but not in summer, and one would not suspect the continuation of inversions throughout the year from ordinary inspection of the summer monthly mean minima.

It was early apparent that the monthly figures gave but limited information, and it was decided to separate

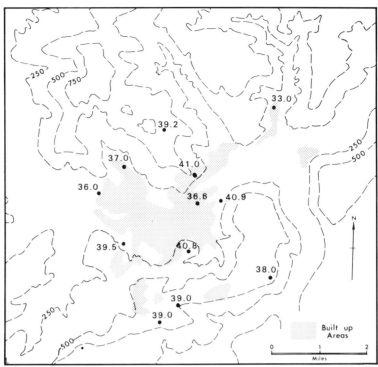

Fig. 14.—Minimum temperatures for 13th October, 1944. (Illustrates the tendency for a "warm belt" to exist at intermediate levels during the valley inversions of temperature).

the inversions from the normal and to mean each separately, with the following results:—

October, 1944—September, 1945 (Phenological Year).

Code numbers of Stations	1	2	3	5	6	7	8	9	10	11	12
132 Inversion Minima	39.9	37.7	36.1	38.5	39.4	38.6	39.5	39.2	38.5	36.8	35.1
233 Normal Minima	44.2	47.6	46.4	46.4	46.4	45.2	45.4	45.6	46.3	46.1	46.2

January, 1945—December, 1945 (Calendar Year).

138 Inversion Minima	41.8	39.6	38.0	40.2	41.0	40.3	41.3	41.0	40.4	38.8	36.9
227 Normal Minima	44.5	47.8	46.9	46.5	46.2	45.4	45.6	45.7	46.5	46.6	46.3

The mean of the normal nights reveals clear correlation with altitude, and a close agreement with the usual temperature lapse rate. The mean of the inversion nights shows that the valley was, on an average, some four degrees colder than the plateau on such nights.

The urban influence is very clearly seen in the distributions of mean minima for both normal and inversion conditions. Station 2, representing the central city area, experiences minima higher than those at the corresponding valley sites to the east and the west, Stations 3 and 12; for normal conditions the city's minima are just over a degree higher and for inversion conditions they are some two degrees higher. The retained heat of the city frequently enabled it to prevent the complete development of an inversion over the city area when the upper and lower valleys were experiencing such conditions. Comparison of the thermographic records shows that inversions were prevented in this manner on 35 nights in the phenological year, and 34 nights in the calendar year; this is more common in the summer months when inversions are not so well developed during the shorter nights.

The effect of inversions on the distribution of screen frosts is striking. These are plotted in detail on fig. 15, but representative data for a period of 12 months are that on normal nights the plateau sites experienced some 24 screen frosts to the valley sites average of 20, whereas on inversion nights the plateau sites experienced only some 18 frosts at screen level, compared with the valley's 55. Further, whilst the frosts in the valley on normal nights are confined to the three winter months of December, January and February, the frosts in the valley on inversion nights may occur in any month except June, July and August. The most extreme minima are recorded after a calm clear night with snow cover. Snow forms a good radiating surface, and is at the same time a poor conductor of heat from the ground underneath. The extreme minima are also associated with winter inversions when there is the greatest range of temperature differences between hill and valley sites. Thus in Bath during the snow cover of the last week of January, 1945, the plateau recorded a minimum of 20° F. and the valley a minimum of 8° F.— a difference of 12° F.

Inversion Fogs.

One of the more striking visible effects of an inversion is the formation of fog. Radiation fog frequently accompanies an inversion, provided the air which collects in the valley bottom is cooled below the dew point temperature. Most valley bottoms are notoriously foggy, and Bath is no exception. Fog or mist accompanied well over one hundred of the yearly inversions experienced in the Bath area. The maximum intensity is reached in the winter period when inversions are often accompanied by substantial fog layers.

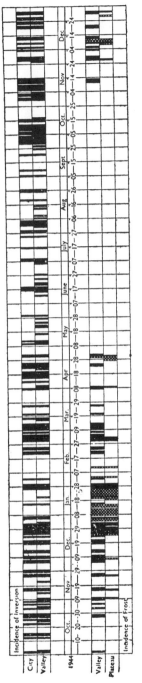

Fig. 15.—The incidence of valley inversions of temperature and the occurrence of screen frost in Bath and district from October 1944, to December 1945. Nights when screen frost occurred with no valley inversions are indicated by stippling.

143

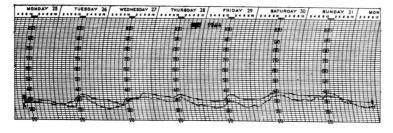

Fig. 5.
Superimposed thermographic traces for Lansdown (station 1, 720 ft., solid line) and Henrietta Park (station 2, 65 ft., broken line) for week ending 31st December, 1944 (Illustrative of a continuous period of temperature inversion).

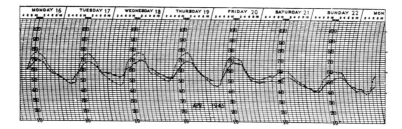

Fig. 16.
Superimposed thermograms for Lansdown (station 1, solid line) and Henrietta Park (station 2, broken line) for the week ending 22nd April, 1945. (The greater diurnal range of the valley as compared with the plateau and the crossing of the two thermograph traces are characteristic features of conditions of temperature inversion).

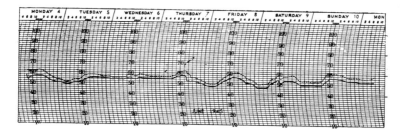

Fig. 17.
Superimposed thermograms for Lansdown (solid line) and Henrietta Park (broken line) for the week ending 10th June, 1945. (The parallelism of the traces is typical of normal conditions).

144

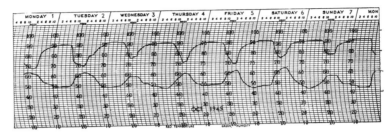

Fig. 20.

Relative humidity (upper line) and temperature (lower line) at Henrietta Park for the week-ending 7th October 1945. (Illustrates the mirror image appearance of the two traces under normal conditions).

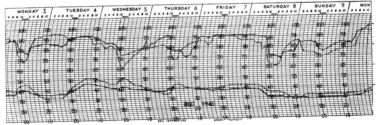

Fig. 21.

Relative humidities (upper lines) and temperatures (lower lines) for Lansdown (solid lines) and Henrietta Park (broken lines) for the week ending 9th December, 1945. (Shows the effect of both normal and inversion conditions of temperature).

With the feeble and short insolation of winter, the fog may fail to be dissipated during the day and so persist into the next night, when it becomes thicker. A remarkable example of this occurred during the last week of December, 1944, when the valley was enveloped continuously in thick fog for five days, the plateau experiencing brilliant, although feeble, sunshine; the inversion of temperature was maintained continuously day and night throughout the entire period (fig. 5).

In contrast to the thick winter fogs accompanying deep inversions, the mists of shallow summer inversions are but tenuous, rarely reach a depth more than 150—200 feet, and rapidly dissolve. During the autumn the depth of fog increased to some 300—400 feet, and in winter the valley was frequently filled to the level of the southern and lower side, the plateau to the north then standing out of the sea of fog like an island. This control of the depth of fog development by the lower side of the valley resembles that of the Gstettneralm Pass described by Schmidt (1934).

Temperature inversions, whether accompanied by foggy conditions or not, are of great importance, especially in winter, in a city such as Bath nestling in a valley bottom. It explains why smoke accumulates and either aggravates or forms fog on some days, whilst on others the air is perfectly clear although the same amount of smoke is being produced. When not carried off horizontally by wind the smoke is dispersed upwards in convection currents under normal conditions; but when the temperature is inverted the smoke will rise only until it reaches its same air temperature and then spreads out horizintally. The "smog" problems of Donora and Los Angeles have essentially the same topographical and meteorological basis as have the fogs in Bath.

Continuous Records.

In addition to the discussion on the basis of maximum and minimum temperatures, there are additional points of interest deriving from the continuous records available for the plateau and valley stations. In calm conditions in the summer time the temperature in the afternoon is higher in the valley than it is on the hills, and falls rapidly in the late afternoon, going below the hill temperature between 21 hours and 23 hours GMT. It is noticeable that temperature falls at both stations more slowly after midnight, and reaches a minimum at approximately 4 hours. It is often about 9 hours that the rising valley temperatures once more equal and then rise higher than those of the plateau station (fig. 16). In winter there are similar changes, but the diurnal range is generally not so marked.

The thermographic traces characteristic of other nights contrast with the " cross-over " of the inversion conditions in that they show a regular parallelism, the plateau trace resembling the valley trace closely in its variations, but at a level of a degree or two below that of the valley station (fig. 20.)   In rainy or cloudy weather not only the differences between the stations, but also the daily range is reduced.   An impressive result of the examination of the thermographic records was that the mean régime for the diurnal variation of temperature only applies under anticyclonic conditions.   At other times the characteristics of air masses moving over the area were dominant in the curve of diurnal variation.

LAPSE RATES.

An important conclusion to be drawn from the data for maximum and minimum temperatures is that the normal lapse rate, of approximately 1° F. for every 300 feet of ascent, assumed in free air conditions, is not applicable to temperature changes with height when the altitude is due to relief.   The topographical features themselves exert an environmental influence, and produce particular conditions of radiation and air flow which in turn react on the actual air temperatures experienced within the first few feet of air adjacent to the ground.   The mean values obtained for a calendar year strongly suggest that the average annual lapse rate encountered in such a region of diversified relief is only half the theoretical value.   This figure for the effective rate of altitudinal change of temperature compares with that suggested by Manley (1945). Thus the observed annual mean temperature for 1945 at Lansdown (station 1, height 720 feet), was 43.5° F., as compared with 44.7° F. at Henrietta Park (station 2, height 65 feet), the difference of 1.2°F. being at the rate of 1.8°F. per 1,000 feet.

Means derived from data for all days of vigorous air movement and without inversions of temperature are as follows:

TABLE III.

	J	F	M	A	M	J	Jy	A	S	O	N	D	Mean
Lansdown (720 ft.)	33.0	44.0	48.8	48.3	52.7	55.2	60.0	59.8	56.6	52.0	44.0	42.2	.49.7
Henrietta Park (65 ft.)	35.3	46.8	50.3	50.9	56.0	58.8	63.3	63.5	59.9	54.6	46.4	44.4	.52.5
Difference ..	2.3	2.8	1.5	2.6	3.3	3.6	3.3	3.7	3.3	2.6	2.4	2.2	. 2.8

The average lapse rate of 2.8° F. between the two stations for days of vigorous air movement is only slightly above the theoretical figure of 2.5° F. that would be expected from their difference in elevation.

It is evident, therefore, that in the production of an average lapse rate for all days of only 1.2° F. for the 655 feet between the valley and the plateau, there is seen the result of the influence of temperature inversions: the minimum temperatures depress the valley mean temperatures more than the factors of shelter and re-radiation can raise it by increasing the maximum temperatures.

Humidity.

Of the whole series of observations made during the local climatological survey of Bath and the surrounding district, humidity was the most troublesome element to deal with. Humidity is difficult to discuss, not only because of its greater complexity as a physical entity, but also because it is subject to relatively large casual variations. The relative humidity values over the area were collected from 9 hours GMT readings, and these provided instantaneous distributions that were useful in demonstrating

(1) the increase in relative humidity normally experienced with both altitude and distance from the city centre. The monthly mean value for April, 1945 (fig. 18) may be taken as illustrative of the fairly clear correlation of increasing relative humidity with altitude, although the urban effect of temperature increase is revealed in the existence of minimum humidities in the city area.

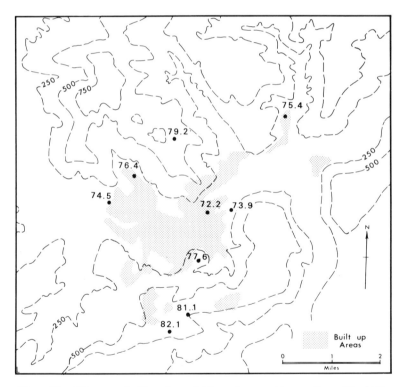

Fig. 18.—Mean relative humidity observations for 09 hrs. G.M.T. for April, 1945. (Illustrating increasing relative humidities with altitude and decreasing relative humidities with the urban effect, under normal conditions).

148

(2) the decreasing relative humidity with altitude and the approach to the city centre during conditions of temperature inversion. The 3rd February, 1945, provides an example of the inversion conditions with the relative humidity in the valley (100% at station 12) higher than that of the plateau (79% at Lansdown, station 1), and with the built-up area having the lowest value (93% at Henrietta Park, station 2), within the maxima zone in the valley.

Such single daily readings, however, are of limited value as indicators of conditions of humidity at a station during the day. Normal records of humidity are derived at climatological stations from readings of the dry and wet bulb thermometers at 9, 15 and 21 hours GMT., and it is perhaps worth noting that the hair hygrographic records during the months of September to January confirm these as the most appropriate times of observation for discovering the maximum and minimum relative humidities. The 9 hours figure represents the early morning maximum immediately before the decrease of the later morning period; the 15 hours reading, while not recording any specific phase, happens to give a statistical balance in the daily records such that the mean value obtained from the three readings approximates very closely to the mean derived from a planimetric measurement of the continuous record.

Perhaps the most striking feature of the continuous records is the remarkable constancy with which the trace for the relative humidity is an inverse of the trace for the temperature. This suggests that relative humidity is largely a reflection of the temperature, but one further factor, namely, absolute humidity, influences the relative humidity. Analysis of specimen days when the relative humidity and temperature were highly inversely correla-

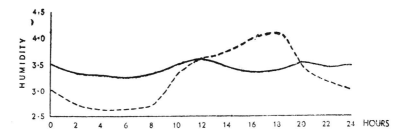

Fig. 19.—Diurnal variations in absolute humidity at Lansdown (solid line) and Henrietta Park (broken line). Based on data for days of little air movement, and absolute humidity measured in grains per cubic foot of air. The contrasted regimes during the afternoon period are related to the differences in water supply in the river valley and on the plateau).

tive showed a marked diurnal régime in the absolute humidity, and interesting differences between the régimes on the plateau and in the valley.

On the Lansdown plateau the absolute humidity is at a minimum in the early part of the morning, between 2 hours and 8 hours (fig. 19), but as the temperature rises the water content of the air increases to a maximum about mid-day; the absolute humidity then decreases during the afternoon to a secondary minimum, but rises again towards evening to a secondary maximum about 20 hours, and after midnight it gradually falls away to the early morning minimum. In the valley the régime is significantly different. Although there is again a minimum in the early part of the morning, the absolute humidity rises to a maximum about 16 hours or 18 hours, i.e., in the middle or late afternoon and soon after the warmest part of the day; thereafter the absolute humidity falls away rapidly to the early morning minimum. The secondary minimum experienced on the plateau during the hottest part of the day is explained by the drying out of the top layers of the shallow soil developed on the limestone and the upward diffusion of some of the water vapour by turbulence ; the second maximum on the plateau may be due to water vapour rising from the valley, the phase lag being a reasonable one for this. That the valley has its highest temperatures of the early or mid-afternoon associated with an increase in the absolute humidity seems to be explained by the presence of a wide, slow flowing river and a broad open alluvium floored valley in which the water table is always near to the ground surface. Here, in contrast to the plateau where the evaporation of the morning reduces the availability of water vapour in the afternoon, the valley has a continuous source of water vapour and the greater evaporation consequent upon the higher temperatures of the afternoon results in an increase in the absolute amount of atmospheric water vapour.

A comparison of relative humidities recorded at the plateau and valley stations shows that the daily régime to be expected at the valley station is for the relative humidity to remain fairly constant during the night time, and to fall rapidly after approximately 9 hours during winter months and to continue to fall until somewhere about 14 hours. After 16 hours it rises again, rapidly at first, and then more gradually, to reach the night time maximum soon after midnight (fig. 20). On the plateau the régime is essentially similar, but the rapid morning fall is later than that normal for the valley station, i.e., it begins after approximately 10 hours, and the rise to the greater relative humidies of evening begins about 15 hours, again rather earlier than is true of the valley station. On the plateau relative humidities generally run at a higher level than they do in the city, and it is a somewhat surprising fact that only a proportion of the inversion mists and fogs in the built-up area result in relative humidities higher than those in the adjoining plateau. This is undoubtedly related to the action of hygroscopic particles in promoting fog formation when relative humidities are below 100%. (Pick, 1929, 1931). Fig. 21 illustrates the temperature and relative humidity conditions at the plateau (Lansdown, shown in solid lines) and valley (Henrietta Park, shown in broken lines) stations during a week containing normal and inversion conditions. On these occasions of temperature inversion—night and morning of 3rd and 4th, morning of 6th, night and early morning of 8th and 9th—the lower temperatures of the valley were, in fact, accompanied by relative humidities higher than those on the plateau. At both hill and valley stations diurnal ranges of 20% in relative humidities can be expected during the months of September to January, and ranges of more than 30% are not uncommon even at this season.

REFERENCES.

Balchin, W. G. V. and Pye, N. .. A Micro-Climatological Investigation of Bath and the surrounding district.
Q.J.R.Met.S. Vol. 73, 1947, p. 297.

Balchin, W. G. V. and Pye, N. .. Local Rainfall Variations in Bath and the Surrounding District.
Q.J.R.Met.S. Vol. 74, 1948, p. 361.

Balchin, W. G. V. and Pye, N. .. Observations on Local Temperature Variations and Plant Responses.
J. of Ecology. Vol. 38, 1950, p. 345.

Brunt, D. .... Some Factors of Micro-Climatology
Q.J.R.Met.S. Vol. 71, 1945, p. 1.

Brunt, D. .... Some Factors of Micro-Climatology
Q.J.R.Met.S. Vol. 72, 1946, p. 185.

Hawke, E. L. .... Extreme Diurnal Ranges of Air Temperature in the British Isles
Q.J.R.Met.S. Vol. 59, 1933, p. 261; p. 401.

Kraus, E. .... Climate made by Man.
Q.J.R.Met.S. Vol. 71, 1945, p. 397.

Manley, G. .... Topographical Features and the Climate of Britain.
Geog. Journ. Vol. 103, 1944, p. 241.

Manley, G. .... The Effective Rate of Altitudinal Change in Temperate Atlantic Climates.
G.R. Vol. 35, 1945, p. 408.

Manley, G. .... Variations in the length of the frost-free season.
Q.J.R.Met.S. Vol. 72, 1946, p. 180.

Pick, W. H. .... Fogs during winter with unsaturated air at various towns, rural and seaside stations in the British Isles.
Q.J.R.Met.S. Vol. 55, 1929, p. 305.

Pick, W. H. .... A note on the relationship between fog and relative humidity.
Q.J.R.Met.S. Vol. 57, 1931, p. 288.

Pye, N. .... The Formation of Land Fogs and the Atmospheric Pollution of Towns.
Geography, Vol. 29, 1944, p. 71.

Schmidt, W. .... Observations on local climatology in Austrian Mountains.
Q.J.R.Met.S. Vol. 60, 1934, p. 345.

Spence, M. T. .... Temperature Changes over Short Distances as shown by records in the Edinburgh District.
Q.J.R.Met.S. Vol. 62, 1936, p. 25.

Tinn, A. B. .... Local Temperature Variations in the Nottingham District.
Q.J.R.Met.S. Vol. 64, 1938, p. 391.

The Nation's Water Supply

W. G. V. BALCHIN

" All the rivers run into the sea; yet the sea is not full: unto the place from whence the rivers come thither they return again " (Ecclesiastes 1. 7).

ALL WATER MOVES IN A HYDROLOGICAL CYCLE. Precipitation in the form of rain, or melted hail or snow, is absorbed by the soil of the earth and retained as ground water, or forms streams on the surface whence it is collected into lakes and oceans. Evaporation from lakes and oceans is supplemented by the moisture transpired by plants, and by the process of condensation rain is again formed and the cycle completed. The movement of water across the surface of the ground in response to gravity is usually spoken of as run-off; the movement into the ground is referred to as either infiltration or percolation, and off the ground as evaporation.

The cyclic movement of the water is thus continuous, but so far as man is concerned the supply and availability of water at any point in the cycle is by no means certain. There are many variations and great inconvenience arises by an absence or over-abundance of water. The conservation of water therefore becomes of importance whenever extremes are normally experienced, or when the demand for water by a growing community begins to exceed the minimum supply available. There is mounting evidence that we are rapidly approaching a time when the latter situation will arise in Great Britain. In a traditionally wet climate this statement frequently occasions surprise: few realize the enormous quantities of water needed to maintain our industrial existence and standard of living. There is an increasing need to regard water as a prime natural resource basic to our existence, and to work for its conservation and proper use.

If the cycle is studied it will be seen that any control or manipulation which man can exert must take place very largely in the stages of run-off and percolation. We are still a long way from any effective control of either precipitation or evaporation. Nature's temporary storage of water in lakes can be imitated by the construction of artificial overground reservoirs and these can function as flood control units as well as water storage units but they are dependent on precipitation for their contents. Man can also utilize nature's sub-surface reservoirs of ground water and is beginning to learn how to offset periods of deficiency by recharging them in times of plenty.

THE NEED FOR WATER

An organized society needs water for a wide variety of uses and in a broad survey we may divide these into about six major categories.

➤ Professor W. G. V. Balchin, who is Head of the Department of Geography at University College, Swansea. delivered his lecture on 1st January, 1957, to the Annual Conference of the Association.

The uses sometimes overlap, sometimes supplement and sometimes interfere with each other; but in all cases water is vital to the society.

Water for domestic purposes. This need for water will probably spring to the minds of most people in the first instance, for water is basic to health, personal well-being and personal cleanliness; and the more highly civilized the community the greater its dependence on, and its consumption of water. Cooking, drinking, cleanliness, sanitation, fire control, watering of gardens, etc. involve a daily consumption of some 40–50 gallons per head in Great Britain.

Satisfactory household water must not only be adequate in amount, it must be clear, free from harmful bacteria, odourless and 'soft' (free from excess calcium and magnesium salts), and it must also have "life" and not be "flat".

Water for the transportation of waste. Flowing water is vital to an organized community as a means of disposing of much of its waste matter, both by transport and by proper oxidation and dilution of the material. It is not perhaps as fully realized as it should be that most manufacturing and processing industries, especially those dealing with food, animal products, chemicals and minerals, along with sewered communities, must have water outlets for waste. This immediately raises the problem of pollution of the water downstream from the point of entry of the offending effluent. Increasing industrialization and a growing population inevitably aggravate the problem but it is not insoluble. Pollution can be prevented or controlled at a price and if the community insists. The steadier the flow in the stream, however, the easier is the task of maintaining purity: herein lies the importance of flood control and water conservation.

Water for industrial purposes. To some extent this category overlaps with the preceding category as water is commonly used in the manufacture and processing of ores, textiles, chemicals, pulps, foods, beverages, etc. Some industries however are exceptionally heavy users of water and this factor may determine their location. The biggest user of water is the electrical supply industry which needs upwards of 15,000 million gallons a day. Expressed in another way a coal-burning power station needs 600 tons of water for every ton of coal consumed. Atomic power stations will probably need even more. The iron and steel industry is another heavy consumer—it takes 18,000 gallons to make a one-ton iron ingot and another 65,000 gallons to turn the iron into steel, i.e. about one hundred tons of water are needed for each ton of steel produced. All told the industry needs upwards of 350 million gallons a day. But this is eclipsed by the chemical industry which now takes 820 million gallons a day and will probably need 1,200 million gallons a day by 1966.

A large oil refinery needs 60,000 gallons of pure water every hour and in the same period 3 or 4 million gallons of second-grade water for cooling purposes. Paper production similarly involves the use of exceptional water supplies—a ton of paper needs 100 tons of water in its manufacture, and the industry at present consumes about 200 million gallons daily. Plastics require up to 30 tons of water for each ton produced.

Some activities involve a water consumption much greater than is commonly realized. The Flying Scotsman uses 10,000 gallons in a single journey: locomotives in Edinburgh draw a million gallons daily from the mains. The production of a car needs 200,000 gallons of water. These examples which could be multiplied many times serve to emphasize the importance of water in industry in which field there has been such a dramatic rise in consumption in the last few decades. This rise is likely to continue with the introduction of the principle of automation and the continuous flow techniques of the chemical engineer. The only relief lies in the fact that much of this water can be re-used and re-cycling is becoming increasingly common, also the water need not always be potable or pure. But industry in Great Britain has in the past depended to a large extent on local authorities for its water supply, and the latter are fundamentally concerned with potable water for domestic purposes. The larger industrial concerns of the future may find it necessary to be responsible for their own water arrangements and will doubtless increasingly turn to second-grade supplies, especially where cooling processes are involved.

Water for agriculture. Food cannot be produced without water and here again much more is needed than is commonly realized. Counting the water necessary to produce the crops consumed as well as the amount taken directly by the animal it will be a surprise to many to learn that one pound of beef has needed 30 tons of water for its production. Vegetables are 80–90 per cent water; milk is 87 per cent water; a bullock needs 10 gallons a day. The whole farm economy is clearly dependent on the availability of adequate supplies of water. It is only during the present century that piped water has begun to reach farming communities in Great Britain and a great deal still remains to be done in rural areas. As the network expands so consumption increases and at the same time new ideas increase the actual and potential demand.

The greatest increase in the more immediate future is likely to arise from the spread of summer irrigation in Great Britain. This is another paradoxical situation in our traditionally wet climate. The knowledge gained by irrigation experts in semi-arid and arid regions of the world is now, however, being applied to humid areas with pronounced success. Basically one tries to supply deficiencies of water to ensure maximum crop production and, in our variable and unreliable climate, irrigation can be usefully applied at some time of the growing season almost every year. Potatoes, root crops and grass benefit most from controlled irrigation. Careful water management will increase a potato yield by two tons an acre, whilst irrigated grass pastures enable the maximum head of stock to be carried. Sprinkling systems are already appearing in southeast England and will become increasingly familiar in future. But the prospective demand on the water supply is phenomenal: if the agricultural land, excluding the cereals, were fully irrigated in a dry year some two million million gallons (i.e. about three times the total amount now being supplied by all combined water undertakings) would be needed.

Water for power. Power from flowing water has had an interesting development. The first mills were located on streams and falling water provided the motive power. Later the development of the steam engine caused a shift on to the coalfields. Next came the development of electric power which could be produced either by hydro-electric methods or by coal via high-pressure steam plants. In either case water in large quantities again became necessary and this is one of the most important features in both locating and determining the output of an electric power station.

Effective hydro-electric power stations in Great Britain are limited to parts of Scotland and Wales; but thermal electric power stations are found throughout the land and are usually located where coal can be easily delivered to the site, and where adequate supplies of water are available for steam-raising and cooling purposes. Atomic power stations similarly need large quantities of water. The location of all these projects becomes increasingly difficult as available supplies of water diminish. The greater re-use of water and the use of sea water will become more important.

Water for transportation and recreation. The use of rivers and canals for transportation is not now so important as in the past. Nevertheless in terms of tonnage carried, large quantities of goods are moved in Great Britain during any one year by water transport, a use for water which must not be overlooked in any conservation plans. Similarly it is difficult to imagine any completely satisfactory mental and spiritual outdoor recreation without water in the picture. Whatever the pursuit, whether to look at, swim in, sail on, fish in, or for the opportunities of skating, skiing and tobogganing, water is necessary in quantity. Conservation for recreational uses must also be considered.

From this brief examination of the possible major uses of water, it is clear that the uses overlap, supplement and sometimes interfere with each other. Transportation of waste precludes recreational use. Power production may impede navigation. A reservoir on the other hand may create recreational facilities, but in all cases the conservation of the available supplies of water is desirable for the continuance of the use by the maintenance of a steady flow.

THE DEVELOPMENT OF THE WATER SUPPLY ORGANIZATION IN
GREAT BRITAIN

The earliest inhabitants of these islands were for long dependent on natural water supplies from springs, rivers and lakes—the availability

156

of water was often the key factor in the determination of settlement sites—the Anglo-Saxon nucleated villages placed along spring lines in southeast England are notable examples. As a settlement grew in size it became desirable to organize the supply of water. Hull has a water charter dating back to 1447; Plymouth's first water Act dates from 1585 and was in fact a civil venture promoted by Sir Francis Drake. London's New River project dates from 1613.

The movement, however, was slow to spread and it was not until the sudden expansion of towns with the industrial revolution that the problem of water supply became acute. This was partly because the needs of increasing population outgrew local supplies, and partly because the fear of cholera led to the sanitary idea becoming dominant in local government. The Royal Commission of 1844 recommended that local authorities should have definite responsibilities for water supplies as well as drainage. The provision of a town's water was now taken up afresh although it was not until the Public Health Acts of 1872–78 that the duty was laid upon sanitary authorities to secure the provision of wholesome and sufficient water for the needs of their areas. Water supply thus ranks as the oldest of our public utilities and this largely explains some of the present day difficulties. The existing system largely grew up when the administrative unit was the parish or town and long before the concept of conservation or any ideas of wider integration had evolved.

The latter years of the nineteenth century saw Parliament increasingly occupied with water bills for new undertakings. Some of the applications were from local authorities, some from private persons who had formed limited companies. Before long the number of individual companies had passed the four-figure mark and the greater part of the urban community had access to reasonable supplies of water. For many years local sources, which as we have seen originally determined the siting of local communities, sufficed for local needs. But the towns grew to cities and the improved availability of water led to increased consumption. Turning on a tap was not the same as drawing water from a distant well or spring. The larger urban units hence outgrew their local supplies and began to look elsewhere for water. Between 1879 and 1904, Manchester, Liverpool and Birmingham developed sources in the Lake District and Wales, some 106, 68 and 74 miles away respectively from the cities.

The piecemeal growth of the system continued and there was a considerable amount of competition between the companies in obtaining and supplying water. This led to a great deal of rivalry and a certain amount of wastage took place with the rather absurd situation of two companies occasionally laying pipes along the same routes. It was not until after the drought of 1921 that the first glimmerings of the need for a wider approach became noticeable. In 1924 the Ministry of Health encouraged the formation of Regional Advisory Water

Committees for certain areas. In 1927 the Water Pollution Research Board was set up as a result of the increasing pollution in many rivers which were being used as a source of water for the public supplies.

A new phase occurred in the 1930's. The period 1932–34 was marked by a series of dry winters and summers and an almost unprecedented drought occurred in 1934. A spate of Water Acts followed! The Rural Water Supplies Act 1934 was passed to stimulate the provision of water supplies to those rural localities which had hitherto been neglected. As a result districts where inhabitants are not within reasonable distance of a piped water supply have been reduced considerably. The Supply of Water in Bulk Act 1934 provided for the bulk supplies between water undertakings and marks a first step of balancing surpluses with deficiencies and a more co-operative approach to the problem of water supply.

The drought also threw into relief a lack of information about our water resources. The Meteorological Office had adequate statistics of rainfall and the Geological Survey had collected details of underground resources. But little or nothing was known statistically of the surface waters in the British Isles. To offset this deficiency the Inland Water Survey was set up in 1935 to collect and correlate available records of surface waters. The old Advisory Committee on Water in the Ministry of Health was reconstituted in 1937 as the Central Advisory Water Committee, and this marks the first step towards the concept of conservation, since the Committee was concerned with water generally rather than with water supplies. In a series of reports the Committee dealt with underground water (1938), the planning of water resources and supplies (1938), Parliamentary and local aspects of water supply (1939), and the policy of River Boards (1943).

The effect of the drought of the early 1930's can therefore now be regarded as significant and beneficial in the development of the water supply organization. It led to a new attitude towards the problem and provoked an encouraging start towards conservation. Progress at the same rate has not alas been maintained since 1940. The outbreak of the war very quickly caused the suspension of the Inland Water Survey and many water schemes were postponed or abandoned.

New hopes were raised by an admirable Government White Paper in 1944 which formed the basis for the Water Act of 1945. The latter imposed upon the Minister of Health the duty, since transferred to the Minister of Housing and Local Government, "to promote the conservation and proper use of water resources and the provision of water supplies in England and Wales, and to secure the effective execution by water undertakers under his control and direction, of a national policy relating to water."

The necessary administrative organization to achieve this has, however, failed to emerge, and a disturbing number of setbacks have occurred in the post-war period. The Minister did not set up the

158

Regional Advisory Committees which the Water Act empowered him to appoint. The reconstituted Inland Water Survey began again after the war but was suspended as an economy measure in 1952. The Central Advisory Water Committee also lapsed in 1952, whilst the River Boards Act of 1948 set up boards responsible to the Minister of Agriculture. Many water supply schemes were thwarted by the lack of capital. Manchester's Haweswater reservoir was completed by 1941 but could not be used to alleviate the drought of 1949 as pipe lines had not then been laid. As recently as the 1st of May, 1956, the Minister of Housing and Local Government announced the postponement of 156 rural water schemes to the value of £5,800,000.

It is true that there has been progress in the amalgamation of some of the smaller companies but there still remain nearly 1,100 separate water undertakings in England and Wales responsible for providing public supplies. More than 900 are local authority organizations, just over 100 are water companies, 57 are water boards. Scotland has nearly 200 water undertakings. In addition to the public supply authorities there are innumerable private water developers—the City of London has over a hundred who draw considerable supplies from their own "wells."

THE RISING DEMAND FOR WATER

A review of the statistics of water supplied in recent years in most undertakings throughout the country reveals a steadily increasing consumption per day and also a rising consumption per head per day. It is now realized that if this continues without adequate preparations to meet the increase the country will face a grave water crisis in the near future.

With some 1,300 different undertakings in Great Britain it is difficult to present a completely accurate picture of the situation, but the trend can be clearly seen from a sample of 26 geographically representative undertakings (Table I). The population served by these undertakings is about 20 million or some 40 per cent of the total, and approximately half of the country's statistically recorded water consumption is covered by the table.

The table gives the consumption in million gallons per day (m.g.d.) and also the consumption in gallons per head per day (g.p.h.d.) for 1938, 1948, and 1955. With very few exceptions the upward trend is everywhere evident. In England and Wales the total quantity of water supplied by these undertakings rose from 651 m.g.d. in 1938 to 778 m.g.d. in 1948 and 856 m.g.d. in 1955—a fairly steady increase of about 12 m.g.d. per year. If the Metropolitan Water Board is excluded, as the position here appears to be temporarily static perhaps as a result of population dispersal, we see that the rise in the remaining 21 undertakings has been from 341 m.g.d. in 1938 to 444 m.g.d. in 1948 and on to 534 m.g.d. in 1955. The 1948 figure is 30 per cent, and the 1955 figure 56 per cent higher than in 1938, a rate of increase which implies that before 1970 many water undertakings will be faced with a demand for twice the amount of water consumed in 1938. The four sample undertakings from Scotland reveal the same upward trend from 121 m.g.d. in 1938, to 133 m.g.d. in 1948, rising to 148 m.g.d. in 1955: but the rate of increase is less than that of England and Wales.

We see the same upward trend in the consumption in gallons per head per day. In England and Wales the range varied in 1938 from 20·6 to 43·8 g.p.h.d. with an average of 32·3 g.p.h.d.: in 1948 it had become 27·3 to 68·0 g.p.h.d. with an average of 40·0 g.p.h.d.: and by 1955 the range was 29·0 to 94·0 g.p.h.d. with an average of 44·7 g.p.h.d.

Table I
RECENT TRENDS IN WATER CONSUMPTION

	Consumption in Million Gallons per Day			Consumption in Gallons per Head per Day		
	1938	1948	1955	1938	1948	1955
England and Wales						
Manchester Corporation	50·4	62·5	74·2	41·0	52·8	58·0
Liverpool Corporation	39·9	45·7	52·1	37·2	45·5	48·0
Birmingham Corporation	36·0	44·0	52·6	31·8	37·3	42·0
South Staffs. Water Co.	25·0	33·9	38·6	24·3	29·2	36·0
Newcastle Gateshead Water Co.	24·9	28·6	33·9	37·2	42·7	47·4
Leeds Corporation	17·0	20·9	22·7	34·4	42·1	41·0
South Essex Water Co.	17·3	24·6	32·6	28·6	40·4	44·0
Bristol Waterworks Co.	15·9	18·9	25·5	34·7	40·4	47·0
Colne Valley Water Co.	14·3	20·4	23·2	34·1	37·0	40·0
Nottingham Corporation	13·6	18·5	21·5	29·0	38·3	41·0
Portsmouth Water Co.	11·3	14·0	18·4	37·9	47·0	46·0
Staff. Potteries Water Board	12·1	14·1	17·4	34·0	38·0	42·6
Sheffield Corporation	10·7	24·2	34·6	36·1	45·5	49·0
Southampton Corporation	9·5	13·5	14·8	31·9	43·7	47·6
Cardiff Corporation	8·9	11·7	14·3	33·5	43·4	47·0
Durham County Water Board	8·9	13·3	13·2	23·8	30·4	32·0
Sutton & District Water Co.	7·6	9·2	8·6	23·0	31·5	29·0
Wolverhampton Corporation	6·4	8·8	10·9	30·2	35·9	42·1
Southend Water Co.	5·0	6·7	8·1	20·6	27·3	31·5
Newport Corporation	4·3	8·3	11·4	42·0	68·0	94·0
Barnsley Corporation	2·0	2·6	5·0	24·2	31·7	29·0
Totals	341·0	444·4	533·6	—	—	—
Metropolitan Water Board	310·1	333·9	322·2	43·8	51·8	49·5
Totals: England and Wales	651·1	778·3	855·8	—	—	—
Scotland						
Glasgow	74·4	81·7	90·2	59·3	69·5	74·0
Edinburgh	27·9	30·6	34·3	53·8	55·4	58·6
Dundee	10·8	12·0	12·9	52·9	59·0	63·0
Aberdeen	8·4	9·2	10·2	46·5	47·7	53·0
Totals: Scotland	121·5	133·5	147·6	—	—	—
Combined Totals: England, Wales, Scotland	772·6	911·8	1003·4	—	—	—

In Scotland again there is the same tendency evident: in 1938 the range was 46·5 to 59·3 g.p.h.d. with an average of 53·1 g.p.h.d.: in 1948 this had become 47·7 to 69·5 g.p.h.d. with an average of 57·9 g.p.h.d.: and in 1955 this had further risen from 53·0 to 74·0 g.p.h.d. with an average of 62·1 g.p.h.d.

The g.p.h.d. figures reflect the rising standard of living throughout the country and in this connection it is well to bear in mind the experience of the United States in water consumption. Here, with a very much higher standard of living, averages of over 100 g.p.h.d. are common. To these figures we must add the unrecorded and in some cases much heavier consumption of industry, and recollect that in both industry and agriculture the same upward trend in consumption exists. It is clear that if our own standard of living is to continue to rise then the water industry must be prepared to meet formidable prospective demands in the immediate future.

WATER IN THE FUTURE

It has been demonstrated that the total amount of water now being consumed has been rising steadily during the past two decades. The rise is partly a result of the increased population and its rising standard of living, although it is probably in the industrial field that the most notable direct increases in consumption have occurred. We have noted that the consumption here is likely to go on rising and to this need we must add the prospect of extensive demands from agriculture.

The natural resources of the country in terms of rainfall are however adequate, and at first sight appear far more than adequate for any demands that are likely to be made. Estimates of averages of 2,000 gallons per head per day of the population have been given, and the amount available after evaporation is thought to be some fifteen times the total present consumption in the country as a whole. But the greater part returns very rapidly to the sea via direct run-off and the rivers. The construction of more roads and roofs in the urban areas and the activities of the land drainage engineer in rural areas accelerate this process and hurry the rainfall back to its source: the slightest interruption in the hydrological cycle is now rapidly reflected by diminished streams and diminished water supplies.

The total water supply in Great Britain may be adequate but it is of little use unless it is available in the right place at the right time. Nature has a habit of distributing the rainfall unevenly both in time and place, and if the local demand for water outgrows the local minimum supply the only way to escape from the dilemma presented by nature is to conserve supplies in reservoirs locally or at a distance in areas with surplus water. It is becoming apparent that the situation which the larger urban units faced at the end of the last century may shortly be reached by the country as a whole. With the present organization of the water industry we now have the prospect of a

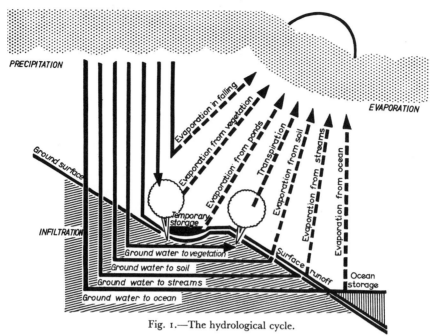

Fig. 1.—The hydrological cycle.

multiplicity of undertakings all seeking additional water outside their present areas and inevitably clashing with other interests. Conflicting cases are already rising. The Thames Conservancy Board for example is objecting to the activities of the Eastern Gas Board in the Dunstable area and to the work of the Banbury Corporation at Grimsbury. Liverpool is finding increasing opposition in attempting to secure additional water from North Wales. The North Devon Water Board is in difficulties with the Dartmoor National Park Committee.

A geographer looking at the water supply problem in relation to the country as a whole is inevitably struck by the lack of any central co-ordinating body for water. Water is our number one public utility: we cannot exist without it. We already have responsible bodies and long-term national plans for coal, gas, electricity, transport and afforestation and yet we have no such authority or plan for water upon which everything else depends!

It is true that good work is being done at present by the reconstituted Central Advisory Water Committee and Surface Water Survey responsible to the Minister of Housing and Local Government: by the River Boards responsible to the Minister of Agriculture: by the Water Pollution Research Board, the Hydraulics Research Board and the Geological Survey responsible to the Department of Scientific and Industrial Research: and by the Meteorological Office responsible to the Air Ministry.

But we need to know more about water deficiencies, moisture balance, liability to floods and droughts, whether afforestation is or is not detrimental to water supply, the effect of extensive irrigation, how to recharge underground sources artificially and on what basis compensation water should be organized. There are numerous problems within the water supply industry itself that need further study: such as methods of waste avoidance, recycling of water, use of sea water, the metering of supplies, the repurification of used water, problems of pollution and sewage disposal, the possibility of artificially induced precipitation and the control of evaporation.

There thus appears to be an urgent need for a Hydrological Research Board to study these and other related problems and to provide the basic information needed for the formulation of a national policy for water. Such a Board would have as its first duty the systematic collection of hydrological data, such that it became a storehouse of information on matters hydrological in much the same way as the Geological Survey functions for geology and the Meteorological Office for meteorology. It would then rapidly become a suitable national clearing house for all internal inter-departmental contacts, and external international contacts on hydrological matters. On the basis of the collected information it could begin to assess the country's water resources both over- and underground and future water needs; work out potential gathering grounds and reservoir sites; study regional water grid schemes; and investigate the possibility of flood control and hydro-electric power development as an integral part of a policy of water conservation. Much if not all of this data needs to be expressed cartographically for a correct appraisal of the situation. the geographer notices immediately the almost complete lack of any official maps dealing with the various parts of the hydrological cycle. A Hydrological Research Board would also hold a watching brief upon the position of water in the national economy and guidance would be given in the determination of priorities of possible developments in relation to the financial, technical and other resources available at any time.

Rising consumption in water, increasing pollution, falling water tables, diminishing resources and increased competition for the available land all suggest that the problem is urgent. We are prepared to plan ahead for the future in the case of coal, electricity, transport and forestry; why not for water?

REFERENCES

R. C. S. Walters, *The Nation's Water Supply*, London, 1936.
A National Water Policy, H.M.S.O. Cmd. 6515, London, 1944.
Interim Report of the Committee on Causes of Increase in the Consumption of Water, Ministry of Health, London, 1949.
Sir Cyril Fox, *Water*, London, 1951.
Editorial, "River Floods in Great Britain", *Nature*, vol. 172, p. 263, 15th August, 1953.
Editorial, "Flood Control and Water Conservation", *Nature*, vol. 172, p. 823, 7th November, 1953.
Shirley W. Allen, *Conserving Natural Resources*, New York, 1955.
Editorial, "The Water Problem in Great Britain", *Nature*, vol. 176, p. 1133, 17th December, 1955.
Annual Volumes of the *Water Engineer's Handbook*, The Colliery Guardian Co. Ltd., London.
W. G. V. Balchin, "Water and the National Economy", *River Boards Association Year Book* for 1956.

A WATER USE SURVEY

W. G. V. BALCHIN

I HAVE BEEN INVITED this afternoon to initiate a discussion upon the water problem in Great Britain by stating the case for a water use survey. The presentation of this case will, I hope, conveniently introduce the wider aspects of the situation that we face with regard to water—paradoxically the only raw material with which the country is really well endowed. But although it is self-replenishing, water cannot be regarded as inexhaustible. As local demand begins to outstrip local supplies the community increasingly comes to realize its dependence upon water and on the need for its careful conservation. The water problem in Great Britain is a subject which is particularly amenable to a geographical approach: for it calls for an appreciation of geological structures, morphological features and climatic conditions, which must then be taken into consideration with the distribution of population, land use, and industrial and agricultural techniques. In short, a study of man in relationship to his environment with particular reference to one chosen commodity.

An organized community needs water for a wide variety of purposes. Water is required for transportation and for power, for domestic purposes and the disposal of waste products, for agricultural and industrial activities, and for recreation.[1] The uses overlap, sometimes supplementing and sometimes conflicting with each other. Transportation of waste may preclude recreational use. Power production may impede navigation. A reservoir, on the other hand, may create recreational facilities. In all cases, however, the conservation of the available supplies and the maintenance of a steady flow of water is desirable for the continuance of the use. A broad division may be made in these categories between, on the one hand, those uses such as transportation, power production and recreational facilities where little water is actually consumed and where the community takes advantage of opportunities provided by Nature—here rivers, streams and lakes are harnessed and utilized, and man goes to the water; and on the other hand, in the remaining categories of domestic, industrial and agricultural usage, in which water is abstracted from its natural environment and conveyed to some other point before being employed. And in its use most, if not all, is often consumed.

The increasing population of Great Britain and its rising standard of living have produced problems in both of these major groups. For although the country as a whole has a relative abundance of precipitation, the majority of the population actually lives where the rainfall is lowest and the surface water least. In relationship to land area Britain undoubtedly has some of the highest water consumption figures for the whole world. The consequence of this state of affairs has been an increasing pollution of many lowland rivers and a rising consumption of water abstracted from both overground and underground sources. The situation has now been reached where many areas in south-east Britain must needs look elsewhere than their immediate locality for water supplies in normal years, quite apart from the special difficulties created by drought conditions.

It is in the problem of water abstraction that most public concern has been expressed. The explanation is not far to seek. There has been a steady and, more recently, a dramatic increase in water consumption over the last century. The domestic user of 1830 consumed less than four gallons per person per day. In 1958 averages of 50–60 gallons are common. Ninety-five per cent. of our greatly increased population now has water on tap, and it is clear that the more highly civilized the community becomes the greater is its dependence upon water for drinking, cooking, cleaning, sanitation, fire control, the watering of gardens and the like. The latest available figures for Great Britain indicate that in 1956 a total daily supply of some 2386 million gallons of water was needed from the public water undertakings, of which approximately 65 per cent. is thought to have been for domestic purposes. Large as this figure is it is dwarfed by the amount of water abstracted outside the public supply system for industrial purposes. The new continuous flow techniques, automation and huge plant lay-outs have resulted in dramatic increases in water consumption in the post-war years. The biggest user of water is the electrical supply industry which needs upwards of 15,000 million gallons a day for cooling and steam raising purposes: the chemical industry now takes some 820 m.g.d.: the steel industry needs 350 m.g.d. and paper manufacture some 200 m.g.d. The importance of water is perhaps more fully appreciated if these figures are expressed in a slightly different way. Thus a coal-burning power station needs 600 tons of water for every ton of coal consumed, about 100 tons of water are necessary for each ton of steel produced, another 100 tons are needed for each ton of paper made, whilst some plastics require 30 tons of water for each ton manufactured.[2] These figures are necessarily rough estimates since no records are maintained nor returns made: but it does seem that there is a total water usage of something like 20,000 m.g.d. Availability of water will increasingly control the location of industry in the future and this is abundantly clear from the siting of the nuclear power stations. An atomic power station of 500 MW needs 840 million gallons of water a day (some 3,600,000 tons) for cooling purposes. No river in the country could supply such a volume in dry weather, and if cooling towers were resorted to they would need to be even larger and more costly than for conventional stations. Hence we find Bradwell, Berkeley, Hinkley Point and Hunterston all located in estuaries or on the coast. The projected station in North Wales at Trawsfynydd will depend on the lake there, the water of which will be theoretically pumped through the power house once every nine days, and also have its temperature permanently raised by some 10 degrees Fahrenheit.

On top of this increasing industrial demand there are now signs of a trend towards the adoption of summer irrigation in the drier south-eastern parts of England. The knowledge gained by irrigation experts in semi-arid and arid regions is now being applied to humid areas with pronounced success. If deficiencies of water can be supplied maximum crop production follows. Careful water management will increase a potato yield by two tons an acre, whilst irrigated grass pastures enable a maximum head of stock to be carried. Rotary sprinkling devices are becoming familiar in south-east England for hay crops, root crops and sugar beet. With short-term and long-term weather forecasts and electrical pumps capable of delivering 300 gallons per minute the farmer of the future can, if water is available, really farm scientifically. But the prospective demand on the water supply is enormous: a single farmer might need a quarter of a million gallons a day (enough for a small town), and total amounts of between 5 and 10,000 m.g.d. might be needed in south-east England in a really dry year. All of which would be required in that part of the country where the resources are at present fully employed.

It is difficult to draw precise conclusions because of the lack of accurate statistics. Only the public water supply undertakings publish figures of actual consumption. Although this gives us but part of the picture the study of these figures is illuminating.[3] With over 1000 statistical returns available for analysis it is difficult to present a complete picture of the situation, but an indication is clearly given by the sample of twenty-six representative undertakings in Table I. These authorities

TABLE I

Recent trends in water consumption in gallons

	Consumption in million gallons per day			Consumption in gallons per head per day		
	1938	1948	1956	1938	1948	1956
England and Wales						
Manchester Corporation ..	50·4	62·5	90·0	41·0	52·8	60·3
Liverpool Corporation	39·9	45·7	54·6	37·2	45·5	50·0
Birmingham Corporation ..	36·0	44·0	59·6	31·8	37·3	45·0
South Staffs. Water Co... ..	25·0	33·9	40·4	24·3	29·2	42·0
Newcastle Gateshead Water Co.	24·9	28·6	35·1	37·2	42·7	48·2
Leeds Corporation	17·0	20·9	22·3	34·4	42·1	39·0
South Essex Water Co... ..	17·3	24·6	33·3	28·6	40·4	44·0
Bristol Waterworks Co... ..	15·9	18·9	27·0	34·7	40·4	48·0
Colne Valley Water Co... ..	14·3	20·4	24·2	34·1	37·0	41·0
Nottingham Corporation ..	13·6	18·5	22·2	29·0	38·3	41·0
Portsmouth Water Co.	11·3	14·0	19·4	37·9	47·0	49·0
Staffs. Potteries Water Board ..	12·1	14·1	17·6	34·0	38·0	42·7
Sheffield Corporation	10·7	24·2	35·6	36·1	45·5	50·0
Southampton Corporation ..	9·5	13·5	16·0	31·9	43·7	50·5
Cardiff Corporation	8·9	11·7	14·0	33·5	43·4	46·0
Durham County Water Board ..	8·9	13·3	11·8	23·8	30·4	28·5
Sutton and District Water Co...	7·6	9·2	9·2	23·0	31·5	30·3
Wolverhampton Corporation ..	6·4	8·8	11·3	30·2	35·9	43·5
Southend Water Co.	5·0	6·7	8·8	20·6	27·3	32·8
Newport Corporation	4·3	8·3	12·1	42·0	68·0	100·0
Barnsley Corporation	2·0	2·6	5·0	24·2	31·7	29·0
Totals	341·0	444·4	569·5	—	—	—
Metropolitan Water Board ..	310·1	333·9	335·5	43·8	51·8	51·7
Totals: England and Wales	651·1	778·3	905·0	—	—	—
Scotland						
Glasgow	74·4	81·7	91·7	59·3	69·5	75·0
Edinburgh	27·9	30·6	34·5	53·8	55·4	58·7
Dundee	10·8	12·0	11·9	52·9	59·0	58·0
Aberdeen	8·4	9·2	10·4	46·5	47·7	54·0
Totals: Scotland	121·5	133·5	148·5	—	—	—
Combined totals: England, Wales, Scotland	772·6	911·8	1053·5	—	—	—

were selected by a Committee of the Ministry of Health in 1949 which was then investigating trends in water consumption. This Committee was responsible for the now oft quoted forecast that "water undertakings would be faced by 1970 with a demand for twice the amount consumed in 1938." [4] The 1956 figures which have been put alongside the 1938 and 1948 figures for comparison indicate that for these undertakings the forecast is if anything an underestimate: many undertakings will be called upon to supply twice the 1938 amount well before 1970 and some have already done so. There has, however, been some criticism of the presentation of the situation by means of these twenty-six representative undertakings, although they were originally selected by the Ministry of Health, serve some 20 million people (*i.e.* about 40 per cent. of the total population), and also embrace about half of the statistically recorded water consumption. The boundaries of some undertakings have, it is true, altered slightly and there have been population changes: it has also been argued that the increase is largely an urban-industrial phenomena and not a rural-agricultural trend. The present Minister of Housing and Local Government has further maintained that the situation is not so serious as might be imagined as these larger undertakings have schemes in hand to increase supplies by amounts ranging from 40–90 per cent. However, the same picture of a steadily increasing consumption per day and a rising consumption per head per day emerges if we take the country as a whole and make a summation of all the annual returns available, excluding as far as is possible those bulk supplies which are known to appear more than once in the statistics. The result of this analysis is given in Table II. The consumption is shown to be increasing steadily year by year, and by 1956 was 50 per

WATER SUPPLY UNDERTAKINGS

TABLE II

Average daily consumption in gallons

			England and Wales	% increase over 1938	Scotland	% increase over 1938
1938	..	..	1,360,905,000	—	246,223,000	—
1946	..	..	1,654,924,000	22	280,725,000	14
1948	..	..	1,761,210,000	29	288,230,000	17
1950	..	..	1,771,265,000	30	301,285,000	22
1952	..	..	1,864,896,000	37	318,319,000	29
1954	..	..	1,942,942,000	43	321,881,000	31
1956	..	..	2,040,092,000	50	346,924,000	41

cent. above the 1938 figure for England and Wales and 41 per cent. above 1938 for Scotland. These figures, taken into consideration with Table I, suggest that we are dealing with a nation-wide phenomena rather than with an urban-industrial trend. So far, then, there seems no reason for doubting the validity of the 1949 Committee's forecast.

Against these figures we should set for comparison the total storage capacity, since this gives us a measure of the country's immediate reserve capacity and ability to withstand emergency droughts and increased demands. Total storage capacities can also be worked out from the annual returns of the water undertakings and these are shown in Table III. Whilst the storage capacity has grown considerably since 1938 the increase has not been at the same rate as the growth in consumption. This means that for the country as a whole emergency stocks do not now give the same measure of insurance against both drought and higher demands as they did in 1938. When considered in detail, of course we find that in some localities storage is temporarily well ahead of consumption; but correspondingly in others storage has now seriously deteriorated in relation to consumption. It has been shown in another analysis that less than 35 per cent. of the population has a water supply of more than three months' duration in man-made storage, another 22 per cent. has between three months and a week in man-made storage; whilst the remainder, more than 40 per cent., has less than five days' water supply in man-made storage.[5]

TABLE III

Total storage capacity in gallons

	England and Wales	% increase over 1938	Scotland	% increase over 1938
1938	164,300,342,000	—	56,082,891,000	—
1946	197,523,776,000	20	63,205,566,000	13
1948	202,655,645,000	23	64,280,334,000	15
1950	208,664,652,000	27	64,280,334,000	15
1952	226,159,081,000	38	65,278,224,000	16
1954	239,458,961,000	46	65,424,904,000	17
1956	240,498,711,000	46	73,306,890,000	31

These figures are the nearest approach to accuracy that is possible with existing published information, since only the public water supply undertakings make their data readily available. At present a comprehensive examination of "Information about water resources" and "The growing demand for water" is being made by sub-committees of the Central Advisory Water Committee. These two inquiries were begun in 1955, and it is hoped that when the reports are available they will provide much material at present unobtainable. Despite the lack of precise statistical information, however, the general picture which emerges is clear enough. Most parts of the country are going to need steadily increasing amounts of water and some parts much more than others. The implication of this is that additional storage will be necessary, and the investment of much new capital will be needed if water is always to be available in adequate amounts wherever it is required. This is a view which is often stated in the water industry and will be found echoed in the recent P.E.P. report on "Policy for water." [6] Compared with other public utilities the water industry has had a relatively small capital investment rate since the war. Only £17 million was invested in 1948–9; an amount which, keeping pace with inflation, had risen to £39½ million in 1955–6. From the national point of view, however, we must be thankful that we can obtain most of our water at so little cost. It is not only the most necessary and most abundant natural raw material that we possess, it is also the cheapest. But because it is the cheapest we are perhaps wasting far too much of it.

Therefore, before embarking upon any large scale capital expenditure designed to meet the rising consumption, would it not be prudent first to find out just how much we are wasting? It is felt in many quarters that a "water use" survey should be made in order to ascertain how far a more economical use can be achieved of the existing resources and distributive organization. Although vast figures have been quoted for the industrial use of water it must not be overlooked that there is a very distinct difference between water which is consumed in the process of manufacture (as in breweries, paper mills, chemical factories, etc.) and water which is employed for cooling and transportation purposes (as in electricity stations, sugar beet factories, coal washeries, etc.). In the latter category the water can be re-used or re-cycled many times. A notable example of efficiency in the use of water in this respect is provided by the Fontana iron and steel works in California. These works were located for strategic reasons in a dry, almost waterless, region some 50 miles from the coast. Instead of the usual consumption figures of 65,000 gallons of water needed per ton of finished steel Fontana has reduced its water consumption to 1,400 gallons per ton by re-cycling the limited amount available. Every gallon of water is circulated between forty and fifty times before final evaporation or replacement. In the same way many thermal electricity stations resort to re-cycling through cooling towers—but only in the absence of adequate supplies of cooling water. Greater re-use of water should also be possible if industrial abstraction and return is arranged in descending order of purity required. An industry needing pure consumption water should come before one requiring cooling water, and this should precede cleaning water and finally transportation water. At present a factory discharging partially polluted water into the upper reaches of a river can destroy the natural water supply of all other potential users at all points downstream from the effluent. Ideally, such a factory should be last in the sequence. As many factories are already sited, however, the only alternative is to insist on more stringent anti-pollution measures. The chemical engineer nowadays seems to be able to work miracles in this respect—the vast Sparrows Point iron and steel works in Chesapeake Bay runs on a daily intake of 100 million gallons of treated water taken from Baltimore's sewage plant! And pollution prevention can sometimes be profitable. A steel company in the Ohio valley expended 516,000 dollars on a treatment plant and ended up the first year with a profit of 581,000 dollars on the sale of reclaimed materials![7]

Industry does not always require potable water although the public supply system is often employed. On the other hand, even the best quality tap water is sometimes inadequate—it would be ruinous to some modern boilers, although drinkable. The use of water for cooling is also very variable. Low quality water can only be used once and large quantities are needed. But good quality water can be recirculated many times before being discarded. We are therefore concerned not only with the *quantity* of water but also its *quality*, and at present no information is available in Great Britain to indicate just how much water of different kinds is used in different places by the major industrial consumers. The agricultural use of water for summer irrigation is also worthy of detailed attention. The use of this water is often extravagant and misapplied—evaporation losses should be reduced by operating sprinklers during the cool of the evening or at night rather than in the heat of the day. The water supply industry itself suffers enormous losses of water as a result of underground leaks, many of which go undetected for years. Evaporation losses from open reservoirs is another unknown factor which might well receive attention.

It seems, therefore, that the information gained from any enquiry into water resources, such as is now being carried out by the sub-committee of the Central

Advisory Water Committee, can only be fully effective if up-to-date data are also available on water use. We need to know the detailed quantities, qualities and the use made of water supplied by statutory undertakings for the various domestic, industrial and agricultural purposes, along with the amounts self-extracted by industry and agriculture from private sources. Statistical evidence is further needed on the amount and extent of pollution and the possibilities of purification so that water re-use within the drainage basin can be improved. The part that compensation water should play in the hydrological cycle also needs evaluation, and the integration of flood control schemes into water supply schemes should not be overlooked. Investigation is also needed into the technological possibilities of using marine and estuarine water for a wider range of industrial activities, and of its economic conversion into potable supplies. Quantitative studies are not as yet available of the competing claims of statutory water supply, industrial abstraction, effluent and sewage disposal, agriculture, fisheries and transport upon the total water resources of any one drainage basin.

Seen in the broad context the picture that emerges with the few statistics now available indicates an increasing demand and consumption throughout Great Britain, more especially in lowland Britain, and particularly in the great urban-industrial complexes. But we do not know at present the answer to the question "How is all this water used?" The area where the consumption is greatest is also the area where the population is densest, the rainfall least, and where the local water resources are already fully employed. Highland Britain, on the other hand, has a low population, the highest rainfall and a relative overabundance of water of which only a small proportion has yet been tapped. Estimates have been made of the reliable yields of water, and over 90 per cent. still remains undeveloped in Wales, over 80 per cent. in the Pennines and the Lake District, and 95 per cent. in Scotland.[8] Lowland Britain must increasingly turn to highland Britain for its water unless we learn to use existing supplies more economically. A quantitative approach to the question of existing water use would immediately reveal the magnitude of the likely savings that could be effected by a more intelligent and integrated use of our water resources. A survey of this kind is surely indicated before the community embarks upon any long-term programme of heavy capital expenditure. If more water could be taken from our lowland rivers there might be considerable saving in the construction of upland reservoirs and the aqueducts needed to convey the water to the areas of consumption. Unfortunately we do not yet possess a suitable central and independent hydrological research agency capable of producing the basic scientific data upon which all major policy decisions should be made.[9]

REFERENCES

[1] Balchin, W. G. V., "The nation's water supply," *Geography*, July 1957, p. 149.

[2] "Is water short?" *The Economist*, 26 January 1957.

[3] 'Water engineer's handbooks,' Annual publication, The Colliery Guardian Company, Ltd., London.

[4] Interim report of the Committee on Causes of Increase in the Consumption of Water, Ministry of Health, London, 1949.

[5] Balchin, W. G. V., "Britain's water supply problem," *Wat. & Wat. Engng.*, July 1957.

[6] "Policy for water," *Political and economic planning*, 24, 418 (1958).

[7] White, C. Langdon, "Water, a neglected factor in the geographical literature of iron and steel," *Geogr. Rev.*, October 1957.

[8] Gregory, S., "The contribution of the uplands to the public water supplies of England and Wales"; *Trans. Inst. Brit. Geogr.* (1958).

[9] Balchin, W. G. V., "Hydrological research," *Wat. & Wat. Engng.*, April 1957.

DISCUSSION

Afternoon Meeting, 24 March 1958

The CHAIRMAN (Professor Dudley Stamp): Professor Balchin, as most of you know, is Professor of Geography at the University College of Swansea, and he has interested himself in some of the present-day problems of water supply in this country. I do not think it is any secret that the question of water supply has of recent years assumed a quite remarkable importance. There are many of our new industries which require very large quantities of water, and in physical planning water supplies are proving themselves a limiting factor. So, despite the fact that many of us have long thought that we get too much water coming downwards, there are still difficulties of distribution and supply. At the same time there are many different viewpoints in connection with the character and distribution of our water supplies, and I hope that Professor Balchin's paper this afternoon will provide an introduction to a general discussion of the problems involved.

Professor Balchin then read his paper

The CHAIRMAN: Thank you, Professor Balchin, for giving us a good lead, and for surveying such a broad field in such a short time. I propose now to ask a few people who are present this afternoon to give us their particular points of view before I throw the matter open for general discussion. First, many will have read recent contributions by one who has been portraying cartographically, for the use particularly of geographers and town-planners, some of the features of water distribution—Mr. Gregory is here and I will ask him to come to the microphone and make his contribution. Mr. Gregory is on the staff of the department of geography, University of Liverpool.

Mr. S. GREGORY: Mr. Chairman, Ladies and Gentlemen, may I begin by wholeheartedly echoing Professor Balchin's plea for more factual information on industrial water use. Data are required not only for each industry in general, but also for individual plants, especially concerning: (i) quantities of water supplied by public undertakings; (ii) quantities abstracted privately from various sources; (iii) the purposes for which water is used within the plant and the quantities employed per operation; (iv) internal re-use of water within the plant, and the impact of this on water consumption per unit of production; (v) external re-use of water by several plants within a river valley, especially in relation to problems of river pollution; (vi) minimum, normal and maximum rates of water use and abstraction related to a minimum availability of supply.

Before such a survey is carried out on a national scale, however, it is essential that a series of exploratory pilot studies be made, both of specific industries and of selected areas. These should ensure that the information ultimately provided in a national survey would be of the most useful character, rather than that which is easiest to obtain. Several such limited projects are at present being pursued through the department of geography at Liverpool. Thanks to the cooperation of the respective undertakings, I am trying to produce detailed maps and accounts of the industrial use of water supplied by Liverpool Corporation and by the Burgh of Paisley (Renfrewshire) —two areas of markedly contrasted industrial activity, and of differing potentialities for the private abstraction of water. Furthermore, one of our research students, J. R. Gibson, has recently completed a study of the paper industry in Lancashire and Cheshire. From this he has obtained considerable detailed information, previously not available, on sources and rates of water abstraction, water use and re-use, and on effluent disposal and its influence on neighbouring industries. Such studies stress the essential falsity of any broad generalization about an industry as a whole, for the differences in water use, both quantitative and qualitative, between one branch of an industry and another, or between different plants concerned with the same industrial process, are often as great as the difference between contrasted industries.

The main theme on which I wish to comment, touched on briefly by Professor

171

Balchin towards the end of his remarks, concerns the problem of competition for water resources, especially of the uplands, between different users and different public supply undertakings. From a consideration of the major conurbations it will be seen that the undertakings concerned with supplying these large populations in fact often also supply, in both detail and bulk, many areas outside the conurbations. Some of the water comes from within the conurbations themselves, especially in the case of west Yorkshire, but most is obtained from outside; and in all cases except Greater London this water is drawn essentially from the uplands. A series of conurbation-upland relationships have developed, with very little overlap between them. Thus Merseyside draws water from north and north-central Wales, and Rossendale; south-east Lancashire from the Lake District, the south Pennines, and again from Rossendale; the west Midlands from central Wales; west Yorkshire from the central Pennines; Tyneside from the northern Pennines; and central Clydeside from the hills to the north and the south-west.

This is only a partial picture of the demands made on upland water, however, for there are many other densely populated areas, not of conurbation status, which also draw on it.[1] North Wales, for example, provides water not only for Merseyside but also for much of Cheshire and Shropshire, as well as parts of Lancashire, apart from satisfying the demands of the holiday resorts of the North Wales coast and of the towns and rural areas inland. Looking at England and Wales as a whole, it becomes apparent that of the more densely populated areas, with over 400 people per square mile, all except those in south-eastern England rely entirely or mainly upon upland water. There is thus considerable competition between the numerous industrial areas within northern England, the Midlands and South Wales for those water resources which are most readily available, most easily exploited and most economically developed. Southern Lancashire provides an excellent illustration not only of this competition between public undertakings for Rossendale water, with the need for larger supplies to be brought from far afield for Liverpool and Manchester, but also of the conflicting claims and requirements of a wide range of large water-using industries. These include cotton textiles, paper, brewing, leather tanning, heavy chemicals, soap, iron and steel, and engineering, and many of these firms obtain their own water from wells, boreholes or the rivers. The resulting water difficulties are such that expansion is frequently impeded or completely prevented, whilst the size of stream-flow often imposes a further limitation upon industrial expansion because of its inadequacy for coping with excessive quantities of industrial effluent.

With demand for water continuing to increase in the future, at a rate which may well be greater than it was in the past, this competition for water resources will also steadily increase. This will make even more apparent than it is at present the need for a carefully planned allocation of national and regional water resources. To do this satisfactorily requires detailed quantitative data of present demand, from which to assess probable future requirements. This information can be, and in large measure already is, provided by the public water undertakings. It is from the industrial user, especially the private abstractor of water, that detailed information is at present not available. A water use survey, such as Professor Balchin suggested tonight, which requires industrial users to return specified quantitative data regularly, is a necessary prerequisite for a logical allocation and exploitation of the nation's water resources.

Professor DUDLEY STAMP: For some time past, the Oxford University Press has been preparing a comprehensive atlas of the United Kingdom, under the general direction of our good friend Mr. Bickmore. In the course of preparing new maps for that atlas, much information has been collected relative to water. I know Mr. Bickmore is here, but I understand Miss Chadwick has really been doing this particular part of the work and I am going to ask her to come up and speak, and show some slides.

Miss CHADWICK: The Clarendon Press has been preparing two maps to show the

[1] Gregory, S. "The contribution of the uplands to the public water supplies of England and Wales," *Trans. Inst. Brit. Geogr.* (1958).

172

pattern of water consumption and the sources of the water used in the United Kingdom. These are for a comprehensive 'Atlas of Britain' which aims to give a picture of the physical features of the land and its economic development. The scale of the maps is 1:2M. Both maps show, by means of circles of graded sizes, the quantity of water supplied by each of some 1100 supplying authorities. One map shows, by colour, which authorities derive their supplies from bores, wells and mines. The background will be a map showing the aquifers at the surface and underground. The map will show the areas, known as "defined areas," where licenses are required to put down new bores, a measure designed to avoid indiscriminate use of underground water where the water table is known to be falling; included are large areas to the north of the London Basin and also in the Midlands. This map will also show where underground water is saline. On an inset map the contours of the water table around London will be shown, illustrating the core of depletion formed there as a result of the high rate of abstraction.

The second map, of surface water supplies, shows which authorities derive their supplies from rivers, upland catchment and springs, or major reservoirs. As a background this map will show water balance—rainfall minus evaporation, indicating the surface water resources; it will also show the areas where ample water supplies are available, in the west and north, and those where the demand is greatest, in the south-east and Midlands.

Professor DUDLEY STAMP: This afternoon we are honoured by the presence of Mr. W. Allard, Vice-President of the International Association of Hydrology. I could tell you a lot of things about Mr. Allard, a member of my own college, but I associate him particularly with a struggle carried on for decades to persuade successive governments to do something about an inland water survey, something of the type being discussed this afternoon. For some years I served with Mr. Allard on an Inland Water Survey Advisory Committee, under the chairmanship of a distinguished ex-Director General of the Ordnance Survey; we got more and more positive in our statements regarding the necessity for a survey, and so we were quietly disbanded. Mr. Allard, we shall listen with great interest to what you have to say on this subject.

Mr. W. ALLARD remarked that the discussion should be linked with what the Society had heard said on 11 March 1935,[1] when Dr. Brysson Cunningham, an engineer, had dealt with the need for a systematic national inland water survey in this country, in contrast with what had then already been achieved in this respect by other nations. The other speakers had included Vice-Admiral Sir Percy Douglas, Chairman of a British Association committee formed in 1932 to study the same matter, and Sir Henry Lyons, chairman of the first committee established by the Government to observe and report on the progress of the survey, which was begun in 1935. Still earlier there had been an investigation, under the auspices of the Society, of the hydrology of the rivers Severn, Exe, Culm, Creedy and Medway by A. Strahan, N. F. MacKenzie, H. R. Mill and J. S. Owens, whose final report was published in 1916.

Whilst engineers had much to do with the utilization of water resources he thought that there was no one outside the geographer's profession who had done as much in recent years as Professor Balchin to awaken public interest in our water problems, by bringing together in a striking manner some of the information about them. The interest thus aroused had been evinced in the press and on several occasions in Parliament, notably in a debate initiated by the Earl of Albemarle in the Upper House in 1957. Another geographer who had for many years past given water adequate recognition in his teaching and writings was Professor Stamp himself. It could not, however, be an easy matter for anyone such as Professor Balchin to collect the facts for his studies of the subject. There was at times undue reticence on the part of those in Whitehall about revealing to the public what planning was being done, or progress made with a task until it was completed. To quote an example, the Government's Water Survey Committee which sat from 1935 to 1939 and from 1950 to 1951 had, before it was converted into a sub-committee of the Central Advisory Water

[1] *Geogr. J.*, **85** (1935), pp. 531–52.

Committee, submitted six annual reports to the Minister concerned, of which four were printed and published. They were more than mere progress reports; they contained, for instance, a long-term bibliography, notes about instrumentation, and indications of what was going to be done in the future to measure resources. The Stationery Office had just told him that not a single one of the reports, even that published for 1950, was now on sale. What of that kind had been provided subsequently? Nothing whatever. What had been heard from the Central Advisory Water Committee by the public since 1951? Equally, nothing.

It was true that hydrometric results from existing gauging stations were collected by the Air Ministry and the Ministry of Housing and Local Government and published under the titles 'British rainfall' and 'The surface water year book,' but there was as yet no comparable information published about ground water. In any case such data by themselves were not enough. We ought to be given at the least a definite outline of the operational plans for the future, so that we could form our own ideas as to their sufficiency in both nature and amount and, if we so wished, communicate our views through any appropriate channel to the Advisory Committee. [1]

Professor Balchin had given thought as to how the needs of the several classes of users of our water resources could be reconciled with one another and the resources thus be used with a maximum of benefit. The scheme of Liverpool Corporation to obtain water from the River Dee in North Wales under powers obtained from Parliament in 1957 was an admirable instance of how reconciliation of claims and resultant conservation of water resources could be effected regionally rather than at a higher level. Before Liverpool appeared on the scene half a dozen other water supply undertakings and the British Transport Commission had already established their right each to abstract a fixed amount of water from the river, and had then, in company with the Dee and Clwyd River Board, made Bala Lake more effective as a reservoir that would moderate the flow of the river when there was an undue flood or shortage of water. The operation of the reservoir was a duty of the River Board which would consult the other partners as necessary. Liverpool wished to construct another reservoir on a tributary, the River Tryweryn, and had agreed to join the consultative body and allow the River Board to direct the operation of the Tryweryn reservoir as well as of Bala Lake. Besides those mentioned there were other substantial interests dependent on the volume of flow and behaviour of the Dee, such as salmon fishing, industry, electrical power generation, agriculture and navigation. These would rely upon the River Board to represent their needs when consultation occurred and to get a balance established between them and those of the authorized abstractors. The story of these arrangements had not yet been published but soon would be. [2]

Mr. Allard suggested accordingly that in England and Wales devolution to the River Boards, about thirty in number, of the task of securing an optimum use of surface water resources might be a sounder course to adopt than imposing it upon a single central body.

Professor DUDLEY STAMP: I think that the Fellows present would like to know something of the work of the Water Research Association, whose Director, Dr. Allen, is here.

Dr. R. G. ALLEN: Professor Stamp, Ladies and Gentlemen, the work of the Water Research Association embraces the research interests of domestic and industrial water supply. Three of its research projects touch upon issues raised by Professor Balchin. We are investigating the problem of the detection of leaks from mains used for the distribution of potable water, and are at present exploring the technique of deter-

[1] Two months after the discussion reported above at least a little of the information sought by the speaker was provided in the report of the Ministry of Housing and Local Government for 1957, which gave special attention to the subject of water problems and policy since 1945. —Editor.

[2] Reference should be made to an article by G. A. Wright, in the issue for July 1958 of the *J. Inst. Wat. Engrs.*

mining their presence by locating the noise they make. Electronics helps us to magnify these sounds, but frequently they are masked by extraneous noises from nearby transport and industrial activity. Though the problem is difficult its solution will be rewarding to water undertakings. Most of them would expect a 10 per cent. improvement in supply available if their distribution system was watertight; a few of them would expect much more. Mains laid fifty and one hundred years ago cannot be expected to survive indefinitely earth movements and the vibrations of our industrial age, not to mention the ravages of wars and of corrosive soils. The research facilities of the Association are helping to ensure also that leak detection shall not be as necessary in the future as it is at present. Our work on the application of plastic materials to water distribution is expected to lead eventually to water mains made from non-corrodible materials—materials which are non-polar and therefore show none of the electrolytic chemical attack which makes metal fail.

It is clear that future demands for potable water will involve the exploitation of sources of increasing impurity. The Water Research Association has a major research project designed to assist in the purification of such sources. Treatment by the use of chemical coagulants will benefit from the investigations of the fundamentals of these problems which are under way in our laboratories. I question the validity of predictions of future demands on the basis of an examination of the past. The domestic consumer is not looking for more cold water. He may be tempted to use more hot by labour saving dishwashers and washing machines and to take more baths, but as long as fuel costs continue to rise, economies in water heating are certain to curb such demand. Industry, too, will find that further supplies will be more difficult and therefore more costly to obtain. It will then be seen to be worth while to re-use process water even though treatment plant must be installed. The survey of water resources and demand is, in my view, an insuperable task. Differentiation must be made between water consumed, water used once, used water recovered, sewage recovered, water used again and again. Measurements must be taken where none have been taken before, with instruments which may not yet have been designed. Legislation will be needed to make possible the collection of these data, for present powers are not adequate. The economics of the supply of water represent the regulating influence of future trends, and as such lessen the need for a water survey of the kind proposed. A survey would show weaknesses in the pattern of distribution of our resources, but predictions for the future would still be uncertain and interpretations still subject to influences of an economic origin.

Professor DUDLEY STAMP: Dr. Allen's interesting contribution reminds me what happens when a piped water supply is laid on to a dairy farm; the consumption per cow, including water for drinking, washing, cleaning the stalls and apparatus, jumps immediately from something like 2 or 3 gallons a day to perhaps 30 gallons a day. A limitation of demand is difficult to envisage.

Now, on the engineering side, is Mr. Rowntree here? Mr. Rowntree is consulting engineer to the firm of Messrs. Rofe and Rafferty.

Mr. N. A. F. ROWNTREE made the point that water was still extremely cheap, and had not greatly risen in price—yet. But as new works were needed there would be a great increase in cost. The average price of 1000 gallons was 2s 6d; in some places it was as low as 1s. Where new water supplies had to be brought in the cost might easily be 4s per 1000 gallons, and for some reason people hated paying more than a few pence for water. Industrialists said there was no need to be economical in the use of water because it was so cheap. Wasteful use now was due to water's cheapness.

Dealing with the difficulty of a water use survey, Mr. Rowntree said it would be necessary to be clear what was "water use." He instanced a hypothetical raindrop which fell in the hills, passed into a storage reservoir and went into the town's water supply. There it was not lost. It was almost certain to turn up in the sewage works from where it would go into a river. In many rivers, the raindrop went through one or two factories on the way. Ultimately it reached the estuary, where it met the sea water. But it had still a considerable value for power stations. Battersea Power Station was using tidal water which was of little other value except to convey sewage out to sea, and ships out to sea. A survey would be of little value unless very accurate.

Since 1949 there had been a great deal of amalgamation in the water undertakings listed, and most of the increase in consumption was due to this. Underground storage was as effective, if not more effective, than overground storage. The River Dee and Bala Lake project was a step forward in organizing the whole regime of a river. But storage of itself did not represent a true picture of water resources. It was much more difficult to convey a ton of iron ore than a ton of water; therefore, it was more economic to site works in the iron-ore field and if necessary convey water quite long distances. On the other hand, with cotton the reverse applied. A survey of water use should take that into account. It should also take into account the quality, and the constancy of quality. It was not enough to say to an industry: "You have taken all the water you can from that source; therefore you must go somewhere else:" the quality might not be suitable for the process.

The increase in consumption had not occurred only since 1938. It had been going on for 150 years, and Mr. Rowntree thought he was right in saying that over the recent years the trend over the country as a whole was not much greater than before the war. The trouble arose in particular areas where the rise in consumption was much greater than they had previously been accustomed to. One district supplying 6 million gallons was now suddenly faced with supplying perhaps another 20 million gallons a day. A time and money factor determined very often whether there was a water shortage or not.

Professor DUDLEY STAMP: In case it should be thought the study of water in general is neglected, our neighbours just down the road here, Imperial College, have a department of hydrology. It is obviously a very wise department of hydrology, because they have at the present time a visiting Fellow from Leland Stanford University in California, and I am going to ask Professor Linsley if he would care to say a few words from the American point of view.

Professor R. K. LINSLEY: I am certainly not here to tell you how to manage your water supplies, but I did listen to Professor Balchin's talk with much interest, because I come from a State which has very serious water problems. It is only too true that the public, as a whole, takes water supply as a matter of course and does not worry very much about it. This is a testimonial to our water engineers who have, for the last hundred years or more, met the demand for water as it has developed. It is a distinct service, therefore, to point out to the public that water problems do exist and must be met squarely. Figures for water storage, however, need careful interpretation. Cities may rely on groundwater supply and require no storage in surface reservoirs. Many cities obtain water from large perennial streams and require nothing more than temporary storage of purified water. In both cases the supply system may be perfectly adequate although the amount of storage is small.

Professor Balchin quoted water use figures in millions of gallons per day and these always seem very large. A unit which we find useful in the United States is the "acre-foot," or the quantity of water required to cover an acre one foot deep. An acre-foot is thus about 271,000 imperial gallons and a million gallons per day is a little less than four acre-feet per day. A total irrigation use of 10 million gallons per day is thus about 40 acre-feet per day, which could be supplied by the annual run-off from 40 acres of land receiving 30 inches of rainfall annually. In these terms, it seems that your water problem is not one of total quantity but only that of providing an economic supply at the right place.

I found it a little difficult to see precisely what Professor Balchin meant by a water use survey. In California our annual water yield is about 75,000,000 acre-feet, and we have estimated that our ultimate water needs will be about 70,000,000 acre-feet. We are, therefore, very much concerned with estimates of ultimate water need. Fortunately, our ultimate need is largely for irrigation and this can be estimated reasonably

Wright Rain, Ltd., Ringwood, Hampshire

Sprinkler irrigation of strip grazing

Steel Co. of Wales

The 80-inch continuous strip mill at the Abbey Works of the Steel Company of Wales. An example of industrial use of water, being used here to cool strip issuing from the finishing stands onto the run-out table

Aerofilms Ltd., London

Thermal electrical power station, Birmingham. Limited supply of water necessitates construction of cooling towers

Aerofilms Ltd., London

Thermal electrical power station, Battersea, London. Supplies of water available from Thames, so no cooling towers are needed; heated water also serves adjacent flats before rejoining Thames. Example of integrated water use

well. The difficulties of making ultimate use estimates for industry have already been mentioned. Water use per unit of product is meaningless without considering the technological efficiency of an industry and the possible improvements of the future. Economics play an important part in water use. Professor Balchin mentioned the Fontana steel plant in California which has a water use of about two per cent. of a typical English steel plant. There is a very good reason for this. There is very little water available at the Fontana site and the plant could not exist without drastic water economies. I think that it would be quite uneconomical for a British steel plant to go to the expense that Fontana did to conserve water. Thus, as cost of water and availability of water limit supplies, use of water is curtailed and economics become a controlling factor in determining water use.

It is difficult also to predict domestic water use. The average *per capita* consumption in the United States is 150 gallons per day, while in England it is about 50 gallons per day. I do not know all the reasons for this difference. In part, some of the extra water is used for watering lawns and gardens, for there are large areas in the United States where lawns can be maintained only with irrigation. Some of the extra water goes down the sewers from automatic washing machines, dishwashers, garbage disposals and similar gadgets. It has been suggested that the water use in England will not increase, but can you be sure that you, too, will not have more water-consuming household equipment in the future? This is something which the women of England may decide and which man cannot now forecast.

One may well ask the value of a water use survey in view of the fact that the resulting unit-use values may change rapidly. Projections of total regional water requirements as a basis for planning future expansion of water supply facilities would be much more useful. Equally important is the collection of adequate information of precipitation, stream-flow, and the other hydrologic factors so that the engineer planning water supply facilities can have factual bases for estimating the water available from alternative sources.

Another important aspect of the water-supply problem is the subject of pollution control. Pollution of streams increases the cost of water by requiring more expensive purification plants. In some cases chemical pollution may make a stream totally unfit for other uses. Professor Balchin mentioned a steel plant on the Ohio River which recovered by-products from its waste water which more than paid for the cost of the treatment plant in one year. Combining the recovery of waste products with the reduction in treatment cost at downstream communities should offer a powerful economic lever to accelerate pollution control measures by industry and often by municipalities.

A final point in dealing with water problems was made by Mr. Allard in describing the situation at Liverpool. We must accept the conditions which now exist in the various catchments as a *status quo* from which further planning must proceed. Thus each river basin becomes a problem of its own which is unique in many ways—hydrologically, economically and socially. Each catchment must therefore be treated as a separate entity. There is grave danger in generalizing the data for all of England and assuming that these figures apply to a specific catchment.

Professor DUDLEY STAMP: I am sure we all thank Professor Linsley very much indeed for that illuminating contribution from his own experience. As Mr. Bleasdale of the Meteorological Office is here, may we have the point of view of the Met. Office?

Mr. A. BLEASDALE indicated that he was prepared to contribute to the discussion since the Chairman had called upon him to do so, though he had felt some hesitation about this. He had had doubts because on the particular subject which Professor Balchin had dealt with, the Meteorological Office, strictly speaking, had no point of view. The topic was outside the scope of their official work. It was relevant to mention, however, that in recent months there had been some discussion within the Office, on the possible extension of their work in the hydrological field. For a long time past they had of course been interested in rainfall, and had taken over the work begun in the last century by G. J. Symons and continued, until 1919, by H. R. Mill. They had also been interested in evaporation, as a primarily meteorological phenomenon, and to that extent they had long been interested in hydrology, or at any rate in hydro-meteorology. But there had been discussions as to whether this interest should be taken further, arising partly from developments in the international field which had led to a proposal that the World Meteorological Organization "should assume responsi-bilities in hydrology similar to its present responsibilities in meteorology" (Sir Graham Sutton, "World Meteorological Organization: Ninth Session of the Executive Com-mittee," *Meteorological Magazine*, **86**, 1026 (1957), p. 353). Such discussions were, of course, concerned with the purely scientific side of hydrology, and it was probably correct to say that the kind of work proposed by Professor Balchin covered a parallel, but not to any great extent overlapping, field. He had dealt with practical matters of water supply and water use which involved economics, and even political issues, with which the purely scientific side was not directly concerned.

Mr. Bleasdale said that among the topics raised during the discussion he had been most interested in the suggestion made by Mr. Allard, if he had understood him cor-rectly, that it was perhaps a little unwise to look forward to an all-embracing central hydrological organization, without also considering what we already have, at least for England and Wales, as a very good beginning for a regional organization covering the whole country, namely the River Board organization. Again thinking of scientific activities, rather than any other functions which Mr. Allard may have had in mind, Mr. Bleasdale said that he would like to see the River Boards becoming increasingly the recognized and accepted authorities within their areas for all hydrological matters. Any central organization could be in large measure a coordinating body to encourage uniform standards in the work which River Boards would be capable of doing, if they were able to develop as the accepted regional authorities. In his official work he was trying to develop methods which he hoped would eventually be helpful in this direc-tion, starting by basing all work to do with rainfall and associated data on a rational hydrological system of station grouping, based entirely on River Board areas and natural drainage areas.

Professor DUDLEY STAMP: I have referred to the interest of the Imperial College in water problems. Mr. Wolf, reader in hydrology at Imperial College, may like to say something?

Mr. P. O. WOLF: Mr. Chairman, Ladies and Gentlemen, all the technical points which had occurred to me when listening to Professor Balchin's address have been taken up and very well dealt with by the previous contributors to the discussion. If I may refer to one or two non-technical recommendations made by the Professor, I can be brief. Professor Balchin has given us the impression, both in his previous publica-tions and in his talk tonight, that he feels a great effort has to be made to persuade the national authorities to undertake more hydrometric measurement, to coordinate the work of analysis of the data so collected, and of course, as we have heard tonight, to study the relation between what water resources are available and what is needed. I would support what Mr. Allard and Mr. Bleasdale have said in regard to the national organization of this work. Speaking as an academic person (and I think the same applies to Professor Balchin), for us to dictate or forcefully to suggest the form the national organization should take would, I think, be a mistake. I need say no more about this, for the case has been well stated, but I would like to comment more posi-tively on the campaign for more hydrometric and hydrological work and for a water use survey. Let us assume that the water use survey is largely carried out by geo-graphers (although the engineers in the Ministry of Housing and Local Government will no doubt be very active in this field, and in fact have been working in this field for years), and that this is your main interest: Professor Balchin, for one, has published many persuasive articles whose general effectiveness is admirable. Many of us wish we could write so well, but some of these articles in their broad sweep have perhaps lacked precision. Because I heard them discussed rather disparagingly, I asked Professor Balchin to come and discuss this problem, and I would renew my appeal to geographers in general: if you are taking a great interest in water resources, if you feel that a national campaign is in fact indicated, as I believe it is, then it would strengthen the case very greatly if references to particular technical matters could be checked and re-checked. For example, one should avoid making the sort of error that crept into a well-meaning leading article in *The Times* ten days ago, referring to an organization for which I have a very high regard, the British Hydro-Mechanics Research Association (which is mainly concerned with research on hydraulic machines) as doing excellent work in the hydrological field: a slip, I know, but enough to condemn that article completely. I would ask for much closer cooperation between geographers and scientific specialists, whether they are ground-water or surface-water hydrologists or, for that matter, industrial specialists in the use of water. The last category has a particularly important part to play in the work for which Professor Balchin has been so insistently calling. The difficulty of comparing and interpreting figures for industrial water consumption and re-use is very great; but as one of the best contributions made tonight by a Fellow of the Society succeeded in showing, a sound basis of comparison is fundamental in these water use studies. Until the figures are checked in detail for their true meaning, Professor Balchin's tables will meet with some scepticism.

Professor DUDLEY STAMP: No reference has yet been made this afternoon to the fact that we have a central organization officially charged with the study of our water resources. I refer, of course, to the Geological Survey of Great Britain, which has a Water Division; I wonder if I could persuade Dr. Buchan, the head of the Division, to say a few words?

Dr. S. BUCHAN said there was certainly scope for conserving our water resources, but the need for it was not always obvious. Over the greater part of the country and throughout most years supplies were adequate. Shortages were local and temporary. The overall water resources of the nation were adequate for all our needs and for considerable expansion in use, and water could be made available to the areas with shortages when they needed it—at a price. Industry, the largest user of water, might decide that it could not afford to pay the higher price for extra water and might limit its call for new supplies by economizing in use or by re-using existing supplies. On a larger scale, some river waters were already being used several times over: this could be extended with proper treatment. He was sure that the nation could and would use water more wisely when required, but conservation would be determined to a large extent by economics.

Referring to the statement that storage had not kept pace with increase in use of water between 1938 and 1956, Dr. Buchan asked if Professor Balchin had considered the possibility that water authorities might have over-insured by providing too much storage for 1938 and that the present storage capacity might be a more realistic insurance. Alternatively, funds might not be available to pay the higher premium for a comparable insurance. Dr. Buchan also asked if Professor Balchin had taken into consideration potential underground storage. In the central part of the London Basin, in and around London, demand had exceeded natural replenishment at the average rate of about 3 million gallons a day for 100 years and created a storage capacity of some 100,000 million gallons. Here and in other parts of the country the spare capacity could be used to store winter water for summer use or water in wet years for use in droughts.

Dr. F. GREENSHIELDS (Metropolitan Water Board): What I am about to say is slightly aside from the appeal made by Professor Balchin for a water use survey, but some of the things he said do have a bearing on matters in which I am especially interested. When one studies the history of reservoir development in lowland Britain, that is to say in the area south and east of the Jurassic escarpment, the impression arises that drinking-water shortage was often due not to a deficiency in the amount of liquid available, but only that it was unfit for use. In other words, it was largely a question of stagnation in the reservoirs, and this in turn was to a large extent a biological and hydrographic problem. In many cases it appears that more and more land was taken over for reservoir sites largely because we were not using the existing sites to the best advantage. Reservoirs have tended to be too shallow; possibly through ignorance of the fundamental physics involved in thermal-density stratification. The underlying difficulty was often due to anaerobic processes associated with this state in summer, and it tended to make designers think that reservoirs should, in the area we are considering, be not appreciably deeper than 10 metres. Now, recent work with which I have been associated has shown that reservoirs, from the biological standpoint, should be either appreciably shallower than 10 metres, or substantially deeper. These studies have revealed that summer thermal-density stratification is not the bogey it was regarded as even a few years ago. I think it can be safely said today that in certain parts of Britain the present depth of reservoirs could with advantage be doubled, trebled and in some cases even quadrupled. This might be a nationally important consideration in view of the growing need to conserve both land and water.

The studies to which I refer have been local to this area, but they have attempted to assign values to the several parameters involved. It would be a good thing economically for the development of water storage reservoirs if some survey could be made, even internationally, of the basic physics of lakes and reservoirs, possibly even across northern Europe, Britain, and extending to the lakes of the northern United States. In that way we might hope to attain to useful generalizations. I do not think it would ever be possible to make mathematically rigorous generalizations, but something better than we have done so far seems to be called for, and seems possible. The problem I have been studying has been principally that of the behaviour of reservoirs built up from ground level and storing water from polluted rivers, but impounded waters in lowland Britain would behave in very much the same way, and could be more usefully studied than they have been.

Mr. E. GOLD (Royal Meteorological Society): In the first place I should like to congratulate Professor Balchin on the way he illuminated the statistics by some beautiful illustrations. One was an illustration of the Birmingham works and cooling towers at Hams Hall; sixty years ago Birmingham had its water works with a great chimney not far away from Hams Hall, then Lord Norton's home. He got a very substantial sum from the Birmingham corporation because the chimney spoiled the country landscape; the spoiling by that chimney was nothing to the spoiling by the emission from these cooling towers, which I saw recently from the high ground 4 miles away. Use of water is only one part of a much greater problem, the hydrology of this country; the plan of one part ought to fit into a plan for the whole. I am quite an unrepentant advocate of a hydrometeorological service which planned the hydrology and meteorology in combination for this country. After all, you cannot separate hydrology and meteorology; the same evaporation which brings us the water also affects the water supply, and all the rest of hydrology; and the water all comes from the atmosphere and goes back to it. Really, water use is only one very small part of the problem; the Nile flood makes Egypt, but our floods don't make England, they unmake it. A proper service would control them; it is a long term project, but we ought not to be planning now for what happens tomorrow, we ought to be planning for what happens 10, 20, 30, 40, 50 years ahead. Irrigation has been mentioned; we are not always going to get our food supplies so easily as we get them at the present time. We have got to produce more of our own unless we reduce our population. And the production of more food in this country depends more on irrigation than anything else; more on the supply of water, and the proper use of it. I am not going to keep you any longer, but do think about things in a larger sense—have vision!

Professor DUDLEY STAMP: If there are no other comments after that wonderful wind-up, I will just ask Professor Balchin if he has any remarks in reply.

Professor BALCHIN: May I first thank you, Mr. Chairman, and all the other speakers who have contributed this afternoon. I feel, myself, that one of the functions of the geographer with his holistic view is to bring the specialists together to look at and discuss a problem such as we have attempted this afternoon in the case of "water." I feel sure that the full and frank exchange of data will have been most helpful to us all. I did not expect my opening statement to escape unscathed and I am quite happy to accept some of the criticisms. Both Dr. Allen and Mr. Rowntree have commented upon the magnitude of the work that might be involved in a water use survey. I do not doubt that a country-wide survey in minute detail would entail much effort. But initially might it not be possible to carry out pilot surveys through selected River Boards in catchment basins where the problem is more acute? Here I do agree with Mr. Allard and Mr. Bleasdale that more use ought to be made of our River Board organization—because, after all, the river basin is in the first instance the hydrological unit.

Mr. Wolf commented on the dangers of generalization, and of these I am very conscious. But very often the available statistics are far from perfect. Despite the difficulties, however, the main trends can be readily distinguished. Mr. Wolf also mentioned the erroneous *Times* leader of a few days ago. I do not think that this emanated from any geographer. Dr. Buchan raised the question of insurance against drought. This, of course, is a thorny problem. How far should the community invest money to cope with a situation that comes perhaps once in every five, ten or fifteen years? Whether the 1938 storage was adequate or not I cannot say, but I was trying to make the point this afternoon that storage capacity had fallen behind the rise in consumption and that, therefore, the situation must have deteriorated. Time has not permitted the detailed examination of the possibilities of natural underground storage, but this has not been overlooked in other contributions. It is an aspect of the problem that we may well need to pay a great deal more attention to in the future.

Professor DUDLEY STAMP: It only remains for me to express the thanks of the audience here this afternoon, and of the Council of the Society, both to Professor Balchin for initiating an interesting and wide-ranging discussion, and to all those who have taken part.

CORNWALL

I

The Face of the Landscape

OﾠﾠNE of the first impressions that comes inevitably to the sensitive traveller in Cornwall is the awareness of a landscape that has a unity and a quality of its very own. Although of England it is quite un-English. The fields and farms,

PLATE 1

A characteristic view of the bare plateau-like interior of Cornwall near Trevique Farm.

hamlets and hedges, mines and monuments, all speak of past centuries, of times when Cornwall, surrounded on three sides by the sea and divided on the fourth by the River Tamar, was isolated from the rest of England. Protected by its geographical position from the more violent results of the successive invasions which have swept through the English Plain, Cornwall has preserved many of the very early elements which through the centuries have contributed to the making of the landscape. Here one finds historical geography written in the field rather than in the library: a living reality which makes a journey through Cornwall of lasting value and interest to the informed traveller.

PLATE 2

The Looe estuary: a typical drowned valley showing the towns of East and West Looe joined by a bridge.

The physical landscape upon which this story is written has its own unique qualities. A broad view of the peninsula reveals a series of wind-swept rolling plateau surfaces cut in granites and slates, rising in step-like sequence from the coast to the interior (Plate 1). Frequently ill-drained, exposed, and covered with cotton grass at lower levels and Molinia and Calluna heaths at higher levels, one cannot avoid the use of adjectives such as bleak and dull to describe much of the scene: but there are two unfailing compensations. The flatter surfaces are interrupted by deep picturesque valleys, often steep sided, sheltered and well wooded, and in their lower parts drowned by the sea to form attractive estuaries (Plate 2). And where these upland surfaces reach the sea we find the glory of Cornwall, for on the coast tremendous cliffs rise sheer several hundred feet from the Atlantic swell. These magnificent volcanic and granitic cliffs, interspersed with sandy bays eroded in the less resistant slates and shales, form that beautiful and rugged fringe of Cornwall which appeals so much to the holiday-maker.

But can we persuade him to leave his beloved cliffs and beaches and travel inland for a while? For in a day he may walk not only through fields and lanes, through farms and hamlets, through tiny fishing ports and torn-up mining areas, but also through four thousand years of time during which man has visibly moulded the landscape. Here he may see the hand of the megalithic builder, walk through fields reclaimed by Celtic farmers, or linger on a farm recorded in Domesday Book and already old even then. He may make his way over the moors by Cornish wayside crosses, eat his lunch in an unspoiled Anglo-Saxon village, pause for tea in a minute medieval fishing port, and dine in a twentieth-century tourist town. All these features constitute the man-made landscape, which is superimposed in a complex and almost complete cover upon the physical foundation of rock and earth.

The traveller will find much to puzzle him, but it is a landscape well worth deciphering. Understanding will come most easily if he regards the landscape as a document, a palimpsest in which the writings of different ages partially obscure one another. With patience he will be able to decipher each writing, unravel their individual meanings, and trace the continuity between them. This will take him far, but it will not give quite the whole explanation; for unlike the palimpsest, the cultural landscape has been influenced by the parchment upon which it is inscribed. The facts of geography have guided, and at times controlled, the making of the human landscape. Hence, in interpreting the man-made aspects, the intelligent traveller must employ a dual code of reference—the physical stage or *scena* and then the actions of the men who have lived and acted upon it for the past four thousand years.

The traveller will see a landscape abundantly scattered with hamlets. This is the Celtic under-writing. Small settlements of only two or three farmhouses and labourers' cottages, carrying Celtic names, are common at cross-roads. In some will be found the parish church, but often this stands alone, with only the rectory or vicarage near by (Plate 3). Between the hamlets stretches open farmland of mixed pasture and arable, in which the fields are characteristically small irregular-shaped enclosures bounded by massive granite- or slate-walled hedges. Set down in this chequerboard pattern of fields, at remarkably regular intervals, are isolated

186

farmsteads, joined to each other by narrow and often tunnel-like lanes where trees and bushes grow on the top of massive hedgebanks (Plate 4). These narrow lanes, when seen on the map, have no systematic plan. They wander from farm to farm and have clearly evolved piecemeal over the centuries in response to local needs. Even the modern motor-roads occasionally assume the same pattern, for they in turn have evolved out of sections of earlier trackways.

PLATE 3

Morwenstow: the isolated church built beside the holy well of St. Morwenna. The adjacent vicarage, built by Robert Stephen Hawker, was his home for more than forty years (1834-75).

In the fields and hedgerows, and along some of the roads, one finds in certain areas scores of prehistoric and historic monuments: here a megalithic tomb, there a Bronze Age barrow or stone circle, elsewhere an Iron Age camp or even a complete prehistoric village site, and stone wayside crosses by the dozen. There are few English counties with so rich a store of antiquities and so continuous a story to tell in such a visible form.

The pattern of tiny fields and dispersed settlements is more marked in Cornwall

PLATE 4

A sunken lane near St. Ives, of medieval origin or earlier. Notice the granite boulders in the hedgebanks.

than in any other English county. Occasionally, however, large nucleated villages of the Anglo-Saxon type are found, more particularly in the east and north-east; and where the surrounding fields are long and narrow, strip-like in appearance, we may be fairly certain that here we have a pattern of Anglo-Saxon origin. In other parts of the county much of the story of Cornwall unfolds itself to the observant traveller through the castles, churches, wayside chapels, mansions, farmhouses, fish cellars, and bridges which dot the landscape. Norman architecture in church and castle, medieval bridges, Elizabethan manor houses, nineteenth-century chapels, all in native stone, speak more eloquently than words of human activities long ago.

Cornwall also has two unique landscapes in the mining and quarrying areas of the south-west. The skeletal remains of ancient tin and copper mining, and the white china-clay waste heaps, produce a scene quite unlike the normal industrial landscape of smoking tips and belching chimneys. The Cornish tin and copper mining industry is now nearly dead and gone, but it has made its mark on the county: acres of derelict land, of gorse and briar, of silent engine-houses and crumbling chimney-stacks, now bear witness to the work of the eighteenth- and nineteenth-century miners. The china-clay industry on the other hand continues to flourish, and the growing pyramids of white scintillating silica-waste give an air of volcanic unreality to such areas as Hensbarrow Down near St. Austell.

Cornwall is very largely a product of its own environment. Its own stone has been used in its farmhouses, cottages, churches and public buildings from time immemorial, and though this gives a greyness and a certain sadness to many of the inland settlements the buildings are in harmony with their surroundings. The architectural styles reflect the climate: slate-hung walls and cemented low-pitched roofs protect the granite and slate houses from strong winds and heavy rains, whilst solid squat church towers stand foursquare against Atlantic storms. Here in Cornwall we can see with a clarity perhaps greater than in any other county of England how the man-made landscape has evolved out of the natural landscape.

II

The Natural Landscape

UNLIKE most English counties Cornwall can still show fragments of the natural landscape which must have confronted early man. From these, and with the aid of our knowledge of geology and climate, we may reconstruct to some

PLATE 5

Natural landscape on Bodmin Moor: a view on the De Lank river with Carkees Tor in the background.

degree the type of country successive generations have faced and fashioned to their needs. Dominating the interior of the peninsula are great stretches of moorland, situated on and around the granitic domes which date from Carboniferous times. The largest of these domes—Dartmoor—lies in Devon, but Cornwall

190

PLATE 6

The Cheesewring near Liskeard: a granite tor.

embraces the four remaining masses—Bodmin Moor, St. Austell Moor, the Carn Menellis area west of Falmouth, and the Land's End or Penwith peninsula. The higher parts of these granite bosses rise to over a thousand feet above sea-level and form extensive unreclaimed moors. Strewn with weathered granitic blocks and covered by heath of Calluna and Erica associations, marked with occasional ill-drained peat-bogs, they afford a glimpse of the natural landscape from which early man wrested his first fields (Plate 5). The granite is usually well jointed, and

PLATE 7

Natural landscape on Crousa Downs in St. Keverne, showing residual blocks of weathered gabbro.

so gives rise to the picturesque *tors* on which craggy piles of weathered rock surmount the higher parts. Below these are boulder-strewn slopes known as *clitters*. Rough Tor and the Cheesewring on Bodmin Moor are fine examples. Bleak and exposed, with poor soils full of undecomposed fragments of rocks, it is not surprising that much of the high granite landscape has never been tamed by man (Plates 6 and 7).

Surrounding these granitic moorlands we find another type of landscape, related to the Devonian and Carboniferous slates and mudstones into which the

192

granite was intruded long ago. In the immediate vicinity of the intrusions many rocks were altered and bodies of ore were formed in cavities and fissures, thus giving rise to the silver, copper, lead, tin, zinc and other mineral deposits which have been so important in the history of Cornwall. The folding and faulting of the rocks at this time are now, however, of limited significance in a landscape which is largely

PLATE 8

Lamorna Cove in the Penwith peninsula, showing the completely man-made field pattern on the plateau surface.

a product of the sea-invasions of Tertiary time. The re-emergence of Cornwall from these inundations appears to have been discontinuous, with the result that a series of planes of marine erosion have been cut into the pre-existing sub-aerial topography at successively lower levels. These flatter surfaces now remain as narrow shelves planed around the island-like masses associated with the granite

193

domes. As the land emerged from the sea the rivers were lengthened and rejuvenated, and where old valleys were not followed sharp V-shaped incisions were cut into the levels which had previously been the old sea floors.

The "fierce and furious wyndes" that "sharply assayle the naked hills" (Norden) are not so damaging in the sheltered valleys, which must have been well wooded in prehistoric times, presenting many difficulties to early man. The lower plateau surfaces, however, were probably more open and less difficult to colonize even if more exposed. Almost the whole of this area has been settled today and the landscape is almost entirely man-made (Plate 8). It is only occasionally that we are reminded of the original natural scene when we come across an odd patch of moorland on the pre-Cambrian Lizard peninsula, a thick unmanaged woodland on a steep valley-side, or areas of cotton grass in boggy patches on the flatter surfaces.

But if man has altered the landscape it must not be forgotten that Nature too has continued her work. There was a further fall of sea-level during and after the Ice Age and an extensive deepening of the lower reaches of the major rivers resulted. When the sea returned to its old level in Neolithic times these parts were submerged and the ria-like indentations of the Camel, Helford, Fal, Fowey, Looe and other valleys were formed. These, while helping to create valuable ports and harbours, have in the past formed major obstacles on the through-roads. Moreover, silting downstream from the ria heads has occurred, with the result that the estuaries are now much less extensive than when they were first formed. Tregoney, for instance, was a port in the Middle Ages, and barges were once able to reach Lostwithiel on the tide. Leland records of Lostwithiel bridge: ".... in Tyme of memorie of Men lyving was of Arches very depe to the sight but the sand is now cum to within 4 or 5 fote of the very Hedde of them."

Cornwall still retains much of its natural wildness and charm along its magnificent coast. Towering cliffs present a massive front to the storm-waves which come rolling in from the Atlantic: but the appearance of stability is more apparent than real, for a detailed inspection soon shows that marine erosion has in places bitten deeply into the land. The less resistant shales and slates crumble more readily than the granite, greenstone and gneiss, and the alternation of bay and headland which is such an essential feature of the Cornish coast is often directly related to different rock formations (Plate 9). Such changes have occurred, however, in geological rather than historic time, and the only noticeable alteration in the natural coastal landscape within human experience has been the accumulation of great masses of sand on the west coast, which have been piled into dunes or towans by the prevailing south-westerly winds. These dunes reach heights of up to 200 feet and cover many square miles in localities such as Daymer Bay in the Camel estuary, and along the coast near Perranporth and Gwithian. Proof of the relatively recent migration of the sand is afforded by the destruction and disappearance from time to time of oratories, chapels, and farmlands dating from the

194

medieval period. St. Piran's oratory at Perranporth, the medieval chapel of St. Constantine, and the Norman church at St. Enodoc have all been over-whelmed. In the early sixteenth century, Leland found St. Ives "sore oppressed or over coverid with sandes . . ." and Norden records that the St. Minver area was ". . . much annoyed with the sea sand. . . ."

Granite and gneiss, schists and slates, moulded into picturesque and rugged

PLATE 9

The north coast near Newquay, looking across to the headland called The Kelseys and showing the characteristic alternation of bay and headland arising from different rock formations.

country, with rapidly alternating steep and flat slopes, such is the physical stage upon which Cornishmen have been at work during the last four or five thousand years, gradually reclaiming and altering, building and rebuilding endlessly. Even in Cornwall, relatively little is left of the natural landscape, though more than in most parts of England. A hundred and fifty or so human generations have laboured to make a new landscape, and are still labouring on the airfields and the arterial roads.

Epilogue

THE Cornwall of the twentieth century is a synthesis of the labours of more than a hundred generations of men working ant-like through the ages upon the natural landscape. Our exploration of this man-made landscape has been both historical and geographical, but we have not been concerned with the rebuilding of past geographies, nor with a strictly historical analysis of individual elements in the changing scene. We have, however, in our efforts to interpret the present landscape, properly drawn attention to the activities of earlier generations of which traces yet remain. And how rich Cornwall is in those remains!

But no landscape is static and even as we study what it has become it is in process of becoming something different. We are the spectators of a transient scene. The process is never ending whether man is there or not: but the presence of man will often accelerate the rate of change, for although at times he appears to achieve a balance which may persist for several generations, ultimately some new factor favouring alteration appears and once again a new transformation takes place.

Cornwall is much more than the piskies at Polperro, the bathing at Bude, or the surf riding at St. Ives. It is a county with a landscape which for its interest, continuity, and fascination is unique in England. Looking back, the intelligent traveller will not only remember the delights of swimming in quiet little bays and the pleasures of Cornish cream eaten in the open air. He will also call to mind, and dwell upon, the various landscape patterns: the bleak moors of the granite bosses and the sun-drenched rocky coves of an indented coastline; the small, irregular fields of Celtic origin, and the long narrow fields of Anglo-Saxon creation; the dispersed settlement dating from a prehistoric time, and the nucleated groups of more recent origin; the intricate pattern of deep narrow lanes handed down from medieval days and the grandeur of the vistas from the nineteenth-century railway; the grey sadness of the abandoned tin-mining areas and the sparkling activity of the china-clay districts. Prehistoric monuments, remote and majestic Norman castles, beautiful Elizabethan manor houses and sturdy medieval churches, fascinating fishing ports with their silver-washed flat-pitched roofs, old granite farmsteads on the moorland edge—all these and much more contribute to the picture and excite one to explore further. And if the traveller is anything like the writer the pursuit of this delightful and inexhaustible task will take him again and again into the field in search of the secret history of Cornwall.

SWANSEA AND ITS REGION

INTRODUCTION

IT WAS Wynford Vaughan Thomas, a native of Swansea, who said that his home town had as many layers as an onion and that each could reduce one to tears. The story of Swansea has indeed been that of a town with a tenfold personality. An ancient borough, a seaside resort, a market centre, a pioneer in the manipulation of coal, copper, lead, iron, steel, tinplate and oil, a great ocean port of some antiquity, and a town too with a Devonian and a Caledonian layer.

It has also been said that Swansea looks in two directions, for here is an urban centre in Wales where the Church is as important as the Chapel, which seems Welsh to the English and yet English to the Welsh. A situation symbolised, perhaps intentionally, by the entrance doors of the City's Guildhall. These doors commemorate St. David on the left-hand side and St. George on the right-hand side.

The Norsemen, the pirate traders of the early eleventh century, scouring the Bristol Channel, were the first to realise the possibilities of the natural harbour at the mouth of the River Tawe. One of these, by name Sveinn or Sweyn, settled in an 'ey' or island of the river and Sweyn's Ey, later to become Swansea, was duly founded.

The first intensive settlement however appears to date from the end of the eleventh century after the arrival of the Normans. They rapidly confirmed that here was a site of great strategic and commercial opportunity and before long had built a castle and settled around it. In the twelfth century sometime between 1153 and 1184 the burgesses were granted their first charter. Meanwhile Anglo-Norman settlement of the Gower peninsula and the Vale of Glamorgan had continued apace. After the turbulent troubles of the twelfth and thirteenth centuries the region settled down into a long period of relative stability with Swansea acting as the trading port and market centre. The rural charm of the area is aptly expressed in a poem written about nearby Hafod in the early part of the eighteenth century

> "Thy verdant fields, which wide extended lie,
> For ever please, for ever charm the eye;
> Thy stately oaks to heaven aspiring rise,
> And with their utmost tops salute the skies;
> While lowlier shrubs amidst thy lawns are seen,
> All clad in liveries of the loveliest green;
> Here Swansea virgins every morn repair
> To range the fields and breathe in purer air."

By the end of the eighteenth century, however, Swansea suddenly emerged as a town with a future. Its previous static population of around 2,000 had reached 6,000 by 1801. It was to go on increasing throughout the nineteenth and twentieth centuries. By 1831 it had risen to 10,000 and by 1851 to 31,000. Coal exports were increasing from the port and potteries had been founded, whilst copper and lead smelting had begun to spread up the Tawe valley following the construction of the Swansea canal in 1798.

Paradoxically, at the same time Swansea was becoming a watering place. Invalids took the waters at St. Helens, now famous for its rugby and cricket. On the sea front one could bathe from machines for 6d a time, with a guide for 3d and an umbrella for 9d. The very first commercial passenger railway in the world was constructed along the sea-front from Swansea to Mumbles.

Not only was Swansea an emergent industrial and seaside town; it was also the cultural and intellectual centre of Wales. It possessed a famous Royal Institution for the Arts and Sciences, a notable theatre and assembly rooms, and it published the first weekly and first daily paper to appear in Wales. Its citizens were far sighted enough to zone the town for industry, residence and commerce. This is why today we find no major industrial development in Swansea west of the line of the High Street. All this was achieved whilst Cardiff remained virtually unknown.

Industry was confined to the broad valley of the Tawe and extended north to Morriston where, by the end of the nineteenth century, there arose a great metallurgical centre based on lead, copper, Siemens steel and chemicals. George Borrow in his 'Wild Wales' gives us a picture of this area just a hundred years ago – 'As I proceeded, I sometimes passed pleasant groves and hedgerows, sometimes huge works, in this valley there was a singular mixture of nature and art, of the voices of birds and the clanking of chains, of the mists of heaven and the smoke of furnaces . . .'

By the end of the century the 'smoke of furnaces' combined with continued development had, alas, laid the foundations for what was to become one of the most concentrated areas of industrial dereliction, desolation and decay in Britain. The Lower Swansea Valley eventually became the subject of a special investigation in the nineteen-sixties and is now happily going through a phase of rehabilitation.

Nineteenth-century Swansea burst the bounds of the old town walls with residential development taking place westwards along the foreshore and industry spreading north along the valley. Twentieth century Swansea has continued the process over the surrounding hills. Few town dwellers can boast the wonderful views that even council houses possess in Swansea. But the difficult terrain has its problems. Outside the town centre streets shoot up the hills at alarming angles and the visitor 'will find schools carved out of the rock face like the temples of Abu Simbel'.

The almost medieval quaintness of the old town centre was destroyed by air raids in the early days of World War II. As a key western port Swansea suffered many grievous air raids but the disasters of the war have since resulted in a modern planned town centre.

Today Swansea is surrounded by the modern descendants of its past metallurgical greatness. To the east lies the massive integrated iron and steel works of the British Steel

Corporation. To the north and west lie the modern and associated tinplate works of Velindre and Trostre which have replaced several hundred earlier hand mills. From this complex comes most of Britain's sheet steel and all of her tinplate. Aluminium smelting still maintains an important role in the economy but copper smelting has passed. A more recent but by now well established activity is oil refining at Llandarcy from which has grown a flourishing petro-chemical industry at Baglan Bay.

Civil and mechanical engineering, electrical machinery, motor car components, fuel oil systems, heating and ventilating systems, packaging and other industrial activities are also present, whilst diversification of manufacturing has been encouraged by the creation of a trading estate at Fforestfach where a variety of goods, ranging from toys to clothes, are made.

Despite the difficulties that many of Britain's ports find themselves in at the present time Swansea has managed to retain much of its trade. Anthracite, oil, steel and tinplate movements are still important and there is a considerable trade in general merchandise.

These basic and historic activities have naturally led to the consolidation of Swansea as a market and distributive centre for south and west Wales, and to the emergence of the town as an administrative, cultural and academic centre serving a population of well over half a million people. All this, then, is the Swansea of today, where countryside and town, industry and agriculture, the arts and the sciences, Welsh and English, have all met, inter-mingled, lived together and been all the livelier for the experience. Swansea has all the elements of a city, but remains small enough to have a strong community spirit. It is an incredibly friendly town of open hearts, open doors, open spaces and open minds.

At its maximum Swansea's urban sphere of influence extends westwards into Pembroke-shire and northwards to Aberystwyth and Brecon, whilst in the east it competes vigorously in the Vale of Glamorgan with the urban sphere of influence of Cardiff. Within a distance of twenty to thirty miles from the city centre, moreover, the influence of Swansea usually reigns supreme and it is this area which constitutes the Swansea Region.

The following chapters of this survey reveal again and again that there are four clear sub-divisions of the region – Swansea itself, the Gower peninsula to the west, the western part of the Vale of Glamorgan to the east and the plateau of the South Wales Coalfield to the north.

The Plateau of the South Wales Coalfield

The largest of the sub-regions is the plateau area of the South Wales Coalfield lying to the north of Swansea. Physiographically the coalfield plateau is a southern extension of the High Plateau of Central Wales and like the latter carries many traces of high level erosion surfaces. Geologically the region is dominated by the rocks of the Carboniferous system with the Pennant Sandstone series occupying the greater part of the plateau. Below this series are the Lower Coal Measures, Millstone Grit and Carboniferous Limestone, structur-ally arranged in a great syncline of Hercynian age such that conspicuous scarps mark the edge of the basin. The surface of the coalfield plateau is trenched by numerous deep river valleys, the denudation chronology of which continues to provoke considerable discussion amongst geomorphologists. The general framework of upland and deep valley incisions was doubt-less complete by the end of the Tertiary era but thereafter we have to add the landscape modifications of the Pleistocene glaciation and finally historic Man.

Before the Industrial Revolution the coalfield area was a human as well as a physical continuation of the moorland area of Central Wales. The native Welsh community lived in small scattered hill farms and obtained a living from the raising of cattle, sheep and horses, supplemented by small arable fields. In the seventeenth century, however, coal was increasingly exploited and in the late eighteenth century came the large scale development of the iron industry in the north-east of the coalfield. Coal working, iron making, copper smelting, lead and zinc smelting, tinplate manufacture and steel production have since successively dominated the human activities in this region. All this has left a legacy of hills of shale and rubbish, and the crystallisation of the settlement into long and tightly packed urban areas confined to the deeply incised valleys.

The prosperity of the early nineteenth century produced a great influx of population. Glamorgan alone increased from 80,000 in 1801 to 240,000 in 1851. This has resulted in some very mixed communities and cultures with a good deal of anglicization. Whilst the surnames of the present day inhabitants reveal the past migrations all too clearly their descendants have easily and naturally identified themselves with matters Welsh.

For the plateau area coal has dominated the industrial story. Peak production came in 1913 when 56 million tons were raised in South Wales. From that time onwards, however, there has been a progressive decline and the output is now less than 12 million tons a year of which the Swansea region contributes about a third. Coal of course is a non-replaceable commodity and a decline sooner or later is inevitable. Only the anthracite region north-west of Swansea has maintained its figures, here an annual output of 2 million tons supplies most of Britain's total anthracite needs.

Today however the plateau area of the coalfield has achieved a new level of prosperity as a result of the rationalisation and modernisation of the old basic industries and the introduc-tion of a diversity of new industries through Government action. Industrial estates such as that at Hirwaun together with various other projects have brought many new factories and new jobs to the region.

The Gower Peninsula

Westward of Swansea there stretches for nearly twenty miles the Gower peninsula, Britain's first area of outstanding natural beauty to be so designated. It remains relatively unspoilt with magnificent limestone cliffs, smooth sandy beaches and expansive dune and salt marsh areas throughout its coast. Inland, heath and common, a pastoral landscape with early villages, ruined castles and ancient churches, form a fascinating landscape threaded by a maze of roads and tracks inviting exploration and discovery.

Structurally the peninsula is an anticline to the south of the coalfield syncline. The body of the peninsula is made up of Carboniferous rocks. Immediately south-west of the Pennant scarp there is an outcrop of the Lower Coal Measure series which is succeeded by a narrow outcrop of the Millstone Grit shales, but thereafter the Carboniferous Limestone dominates apart from minor synclinal areas such as Oxwich Bay and Port Eynon where Millstone Grit reappears.

Morphologically the whole area is dominated by platforms of marine abrasion into which the present day valleys have been incised. Above the remarkably even skylines of the 200 ft. (61 m) coastal erosion surface rise monadnocks of Old Red Sandstone to heights of 600 ft. (183 m). These in turn appear to be remnants of a yet earlier erosion surface. Depressions, disappearing streams, underground drainage, dry valleys and other karstic characteristics are associated with the limestone areas. Glacial deposition and a marked series of raised beaches additionally provide a happy hunting ground for the geomorphologist.

The cultural landscape in Gower still owes much to the Norman conquest for the minor Marcher Lordship of which Swansea was the centre was divided into an Englishry (Gower Anglicana) and a Welshry (Gower Wallicana). To the south and west of the dividing line nucleated rural settlements were founded and English was spoken. To the north and east of the dividing line single farms and hamlets were the dominant element in the settlement pattern and Welsh was spoken. It seems fairly clear that the Normans took the land with the better soils and climate for their own use. The cultural boundary thus has close affinities with the geological boundary.

Gower has succeeded in retaining its individuality despite the passage of time and despite also the heavy industrialisation of the area to the east and to the north. In some ways this has only served to further accentuate culturally the geological divisions which were recognised by the Normans.

Today Gower remains essentially an agricultural region with a dominant interest in dairy and mixed farming, and increasing amounts of market gardening. As a result of the mobility afforded by car, bus and coach transport the peninsula is now subject to considerable tourist and recreational pressure from the urban populations of Swansea and South Wales. Public opinion and a vigorous Gower Society have so far been instrumental in preventing a rash of caravan sites appearing and the area is now well protected by various planning powers, Nature Conservancy agreements, and National Trust and Glamorgan County Naturalists' Trust acquisitions.

The Western Vale of Glamorgan

Eastward of Swansea lies a further distinctive area usually referred to as the Vale of Glamorgan. It must be emphasised that this area is in no sense a physical vale and that the term is loosely applied to the region lying between the River Taff and Swansea Bay south of the Coalfield Border ridges. The urban spheres of influence of Cardiff and Swansea compete for and meet in the Vale of Glamorgan.

Geologically the Vale is dominated by outcrops of limestones and shales of the Lower Lias and Carboniferous periods, with anticlinal structures bringing Old Red Sandstone to the surface in places. Morphologically the Vale is dominated by erosion surfaces at a variety of levels, notably, as in Gower, at 200 ft. (61 m). Into these surfaces the Ely, Taff and Ogmore systems have eroded a complex of valleys which give considerable variety to the physical landscape. The region is terminated to the north by a south-facing scarp of the hard Pennant Sandstone.

In the larger context it can be readily seen that the Vale of Glamorgan is a westward continuation of the border lowlands of England. There has always been a tendency for the cultures of the Lowland Zone of Britain to spread along this fringe or be carried across the narrow Bristol Channel. It is not surprising therefore that, as in Gower, we find a division of the Vale between the northern border areas where a scattered settlement pattern derived from the Celtic background still survives, which contrasts with the middle and south of the Vale where a nucleated settlement pattern derived from the Norman conquest exists. Today both the division and the pattern is blurred but the underwriting on the landscape palimpsest is clearly visible to those who look closely. Once again the distribution of spoken Welsh has been affected by the Norman occupation.

The Vale of Glamorgan has long been considered one of the most fertile and productive agricultural areas in Wales. Traditionally there have been three sources of income for the farmers – corn, beef and milk. Most large farms are mixed with a basic dairy component. Small farms, however, are dominantly reliant on the monthly cheque from the Milk Marketing Board. As a result pasture fields stand out everywhere, broken only on the steeper slopes of some of the valleys by a scrub vegetation which is now tending to pass into afforestation. Nearer the urban areas some market gardening is also found.

Unlike Gower, however, extractive and manufacturing industry also figures in the present day landscape of the Vale of Glamorgan. Both the Carboniferous and Lias limestones are extensively quarried for roadstones, fluxing purposes, agricultural uses and cement manufacture. Coal is also mined in a narrow strip along the northern border.

Industrial activities now dominate the cultural landscape in the western part of the Vale. The wartime Ordnance factory at Bridgend has become a trading estate whilst the Margam coastal strip has been taken over by the great complex of the British Steel Corporation and the Baglan Bay Petro-chemical industry.

*   *   *

It has been said that wherever Welshmen gather together, be it in a camp for prisoners of war or in the depths of hell, there are three things that they will form immediately – a rugby team, a choir and an eisteddfod committee! This is indeed true of Swansea and its Region and no sketch of the area would be complete without a mention of this facet of its life. Rugby teams abound and details of the great defeat of New Zealand in 1905 have become part of the local folklore. Great too is the interest in eisteddfods, choral societies, amateur dramatics, etc. Although the golden age of indigenous cultural activity has doubtless passed in this time of TV, numerous choral and amateur dramatic groups still flourish throughout the region.

UNIVERSITY EXPANSION IN GREAT BRITAIN

The past decade has been marked by the expansion and consolidation of existing universities, coupled with a very conservative attitude towards proposals for new foundations. There is now every indication that a new set of regional university colleges is needed to meet the demand

by Professor W. G. V. BALCHIN

THE dramatic transformation in the universities of Great Britain since the end of the Second World War largely arises from the Barlow Report of 1946 and its implementation by means of Government aid through the University Grants Committee. The Barlow Committee recommended that the output of scientists should be doubled in ten years from the untapped reserves of talent in the country. It also urged that the five university colleges of Nottingham, Southampton, Exeter, Hull and Leicester should be enabled to make a substantial contribution towards filling the gap and that at least one further university should be founded. 'There is nothing sacrosanct about the present number of universities in the Kingdom,' the Committee stated. Much that the Barlow Committee urged has been achieved. Student numbers have doubled from 50,000 to almost 100,000, the five named colleges have all attained university status and the new University College of North Staffordshire was founded in 1949.

All this could not have been achieved without substantial local and Government aid to both universities and students. The University Grants Committee was constituted by the Treasury in 1919 to allocate limited funds to existing university institutions. In 1946 its terms of reference were enlarged and the recurrent Treasury grants rose from a pre-war total of £2 million a year to £16 million in 1947, and to some £28 million in 1956. Substantial non-recurrent grants also became available. The keynote of the decade has, however, been one of expansion and consolidation of existing universities and colleges coupled with a very conservative attitude towards proposals for new foundations.

The progress made in the decade is undoubtedly unique in the history of the universities, but it is clear that they are still in the midst of a continuing dynamic situation owing to the emergence of a completely new set of factors. The full impact of these has yet to be felt. In the first place, a rise in the post-war birthrate will produce in the 1960s a larger group of potential university entrants (the 'bulge' of which so much has been written). Secondly, the Butler Education Act of 1944, together with the rising standard of living, will in future permit the great majority of these potential students to reach the university portals. Thirdly, the universities are being called upon to contribute still more to the scientific and technological needs of the nation.

The Association of University Teachers, taking into account the increase in the birthrate and the changing social trends, estimates a rise to a maximum potential of

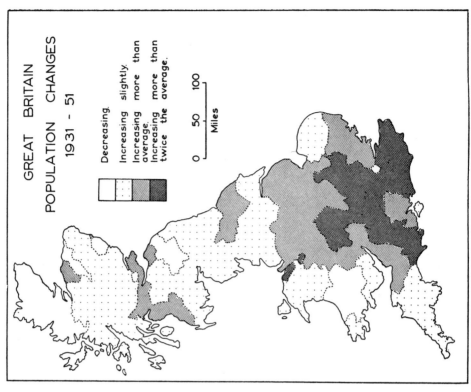

GREAT BRITAIN
POPULATION CHANGES
1931 - 51

Decreasing.

Increasing slightly.

Increasing more than
average.

Increasing more than
twice the average.

0   50   100

Miles

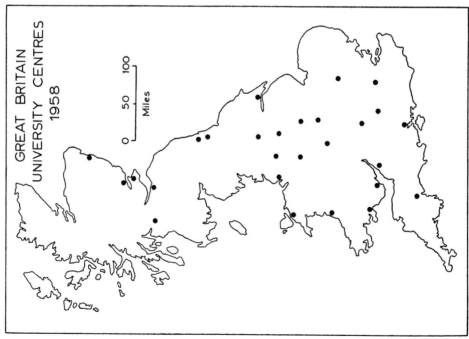

GREAT BRITAIN
UNIVERSITY CENTRES
1958

0   50   100

Miles

176,000 students by 1966, subsequently falling to stabilise at 145,000 places a few years later. The University Grants Committee report for 1952–57 envisages a continued expansion of existing institutions to an estimated overall figure of 136,000 students before the end of the 1960s. The U.G.C., however, does not state precisely where these students are to be accommodated.

The doubling of the student numbers in a decade and their continued growth is now producing formidable problems of accommodation, administration and teaching in some universities, and begins to threaten accepted university standards. Doubts as to the wisdom of a continued expansion of existing universities are increasingly being heard in senior common rooms, and have recently been publicly aired by the retiring Vice-Chancellor of Oxford and by a number of speakers at the Home Universities Conference.

It is known that many of the larger universities such as Oxford, Cambridge, London, Edinburgh and Glasgow have reached or are nearing the limit of their absorptive capacities, while many of the smaller universities such as Hull and Leicester can make but a limited contribution even by doubling their numbers. No systematic survey of the maximum capacity under optimum conditions of our existing universities yet appears to exist: much depends on academic structure, and this is as variable as the universities are numerous. There is a widely held belief that the optimum size for a university lies between 3,000 and 4,500 students; this is often vigorously contested in favour of smaller units of from 2,000 to 2,500 places.

The Association of University Teachers, using the two guides that no university should be asked to more than double its existing number in ten years, nor exceed 4,500 or its present number whichever is the greater, calculates that existing universities could rise to a total of 122,000 places. This is 14,000 places short of the maximum envisaged by the U.G.C.; 23,000 places short of the stabilised maximum potential envisaged by the A.U.T.; and 54,000 places short of the overall maximum potential of 1966. Whichever way the problem is approached the need for additional university facilities seems clear.

If student numbers had doubled in a decade at the beginning of the century, new foundations would have emerged naturally. The disappearance of the local benefactor through taxation has, however, increased the dependence of the universities on the Government acting through the U.G.C., and this has had the effect of slowing down the evolving distribution pattern of university education. The new pressures which are arising clearly indicate that a more liberal attitude must be adopted towards schemes for new foundations – despite the argument that it is more economic to go on expanding existing institutions. But where should the new foundations be located and how will they arise? At the end of the First World War Great Britain had four old-established universities in Scotland (St. Andrews, Glasgow, Aberdeen and Edinburgh), a federal university in Wales (with colleges at Aberystwyth, Cardiff and Bangor), and in England ten universities (Oxford, Cambridge, London, Durham, and the civic group of Manchester, Birmingham, Liverpool, Leeds, Sheffield and Bristol), together with four university colleges (at Nottingham, Exeter, Reading and Southampton).

In England each of the seven largest towns had its own university. Of the next seven largest, only two had university colleges and five (Hull, Bradford, Portsmouth, Stoke-on-Trent and Leicester) had no university facilities. While the first group had populations mainly upwards of half a million, the second group had populations of the order of a quarter of a million. It is not without significance that more recent developments have largely occurred in this second group of towns. University colleges were founded at Leicester in 1918, Hull in 1927 and at Keele near Stoke-on-Trent in 1949. Only in Bradford (in close proximity to Leeds) and in Portsmouth (in close proximity to

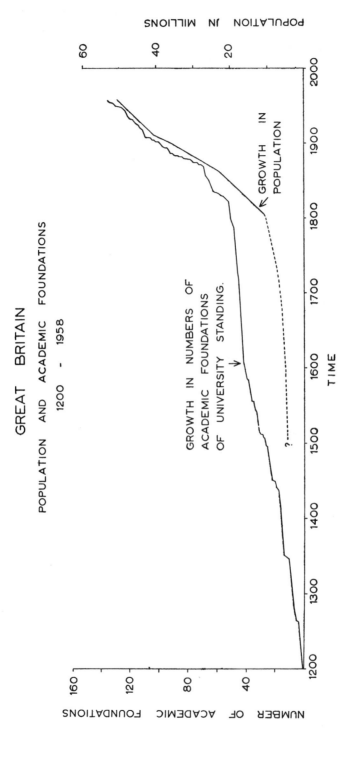

GREAT BRITAIN

POPULATION AND ACADEMIC FOUNDATIONS

1200 - 1958

GROWTH IN NUMBERS OF
ACADEMIC FOUNDATIONS
OF UNIVERSITY STANDING.

GROWTH IN
POPULATION

POPULATION IN MILLIONS

TIME

NUMBER OF ACADEMIC FOUNDATIONS

Southampton) have university colleges failed to emerge. In Wales also there was a further response to population in the foundation of a fourth college at Swansea in 1920.

A detailed investigation into the historical evolution and geographical distribution of existing university institutions in Great Britain clearly shows that they are a product of population and have arisen in response to *national, civic* and *regional* needs. National universities tend to appear first, and these are followed by civic universities related to large urban populations. But as the standard of living rises, so the size of population needed to support the university diminishes. Finally, smaller regional groups of population may with further improvements also produce university institutions.

There is also a marked space separation factor between universities and this is generally not less than sixty miles, except for the Midlands, where distances of thirty-five to forty miles occur. No conurbation as yet supports more than one university. University colleges, however, may arise in close proximity to each other, but they tend to coalesce into a unitary university. A federated university made up of widely separated colleges survives as such only when held together by a national concept. Otherwise it eventually dissolves into separate universities.

So far as the future pattern of distribution is concerned, if the correlation with population densities were to be strictly adhered to an increase in university facilities in existing conurbations would be implied. But continued expansion of these centres would produce very large universities and would only aggravate the 'civic elephantiasis' deprecated in the Barlow Industrial Report of 1940 (and to which the U.G.C. has perhaps unintentionally already contributed in considerable measure). Doubtless additional specialist colleges can be envisaged in the London area, or on Tees-side, within the framework of the federal universities of London and Durham. But to cater for the greater part of the future demand it would be more logical to encourage the distribution pattern to continue to spread into those areas with substantial populations, but which have at present no readily accessible university facilities.

The national and civic forces which have produced the greater part of the present pattern are now largely satisfied. Only one further city – Coventry – has in recent years grown to the quarter-million level of population and now aspires to its own university college. Its ambitions are clearly in accord with the general evolving pattern. Apart from Coventry it seems that the regional force is likely to be more important in the future. Now that 'distant' students in nearly all universities are in excess of 'local' students this statement may seem a little anomalous. However, despite the mobility given to students as a result of the new post-war principles of awards by the State and local authorities, there has been a great increase in the regional nature of universities. This situation arises from the McNair Education Report of 1944, the Goodenough Medical Report of 1944, the Percy Technological Report of 1945, the Barlow Scientific Report of 1946, the National Health Act of 1948 and Medical Act of 1950. Extramural activities have also been strengthened, and this has all tended to emphasise still further the regional responsibilities and functions of the universities.

If we now plot the distribution of existing university centres we note that, although variable, the radius of significant influence in those areas where the pattern is already dense is of the order of twenty miles. Applying this to the rest of the distribution pattern we have a rough yardstick of the extent to which the country has readily available university facilities. Substantial areas, notably south and east England, south-west England and the Welsh borderland, are revealed as being remote from existing facilities. If these areas are now studied in relationship to the distribution of population, we rapidly discover those regions remote from existing facilities but with substantial populations. We also observe that a number of these areas already have regional centres which merit consideration as potential sites for university education.

Regional centres in alphabetical order	Approximate population of centre	Approximate population of centre and hinterland
Brighton	158,000	450,000
Canterbury	30,000	350,000
Carlisle	68,000	90,000
Gloucester/Cheltenham	135,000	200,000
Hereford	32,000	100,000
Ipswich	108,000	250,000
Lancaster	50,000	500,000
Lincoln	70,000	125,000
Norwich	121,000	250,000
Plymouth	217,000	300,000
Shrewsbury	47,000	90,000
Truro	14,000	150,000
Weymouth	38,000	150,000
York	106,000	110,000

All these localities are well removed from existing university facilities, all have good accessibility to their region, most have substantial population hinterlands comparable with many established university centres, some have good accommodation possibilities and some have good cultural backgrounds.

It is significant that Brighton will in fact achieve the next new university college, that Norwich with the support of Ipswich now has an active sponsoring committee at work, that discussions are in progress at Hereford and that earlier efforts to found a college have been made in the Gloucester/Cheltenham area. The significance of numbers is also illustrated in the case of East Kent, where although the centre is Canterbury the population is largely distributed on the coastal periphery. An active movement in support of a new foundation already exists in the Thanet towns of Broadstairs, Margate and Ramsgate, where the total population is of the order of 100,000. The Thanet towns have the added advantage that they could, like Brighton, offer immediate student accommodation.

One other population factor of significance must be mentioned. Whereas the nineteenth century saw the growth of the great urban areas in the Midlands and northern England, the twentieth century has seen the growth and expansion of population in southern and eastern England. Some five million people have been added to this part of Great Britain since 1931, both as a result of natural increase and migration from elsewhere. With the present distribution pattern of university facilities reflecting the late nineteenth and early twentieth century distribution of population, it would not be surprising to see the emergence of new foundations in southern and eastern England, since this area only has seven of the twenty-seven university centres in Great Britain.

Since 1921 each decade has produced an average of about seven new academic foundations of university standing. These have clearly appeared as a response to the needs of a steadily increasing population and its growing standard of living. It would be reasonable to assume that this trend will continue into the future. What will emerge in the 1960s and 1970s?

It might be thought that the U.G.C. should be active in founding new institutions, but it is doubtful if the Committee's terms of reference permit such action: moreover, since a university is a fully self-governing community of teachers and students working together it is difficult to see just how the U.G.C. could effect the operation. Once such a body comes into being, however, financial aid can be provided by the U.G.C. if it approves. Until the Second World War all of our universities and colleges had been founded by private enterprise. Names such as Boots (Nottingham), Ferens (Hull), Firth (Sheffield), Hartley (Southampton), Fielding Johnson (Leicester), Mason (Birmingham), Owens (Manchester), Palmer (Reading) and Wills (Bristol), to name but a few, will long be remembered for the part they played in making university facilities available. But how are future foundations to be achieved now that taxation has removed private fortunes?

Clearly the initiative will have to be taken by public bodies, large industrial concerns, local authorities and the central Government, working through the U.G.C., from the outset. Both the new University College of North Staffordshire and the future University College of Sussex afford examples of this kind of action. But if our traditional methods are to be followed, local and regional initiative must come first. Given this the financial path ahead has to some extent already been mapped out. But the Treasury and the U.G.C. must be persuaded of the desirability of permitting new foundations to continue to emerge. There now seems every indication that a new set of regional university colleges is desirable in order to satisfy the future demand for places, to maintain the standards of existing institutions and to permit continued experimentation. It would be against historic precedent to 'freeze' the existing pattern, but the concentration of university benefaction in the hands of the Treasury, acting through the U.G.C. clearly carries this danger.

COMPARATIVE STUDENT/POPULATION NUMBERS FOR 1954/55

(U.N. Statistical Yearbooks)

Country	Students	Population	Ratio Student/ Population
U.S.A.	2,283,718	162,409,000	1 : 71
Italy	208,742	24,127,000	1 : 116
U.S.S.R.	1,228,000	200,200,000	1 : 163
Canada	71,600	15,601,000	1 : 218
France	150,096	43,000,000	1 : 286
Australia	29,445	8,987,000	1 : 305
Switzerland	15,622	4,923,000	1 : 315
Sweden	20,801	7,214,000	1 : 347
W. Germany	133,195	52,690,000	1 : 396
U.K.	83,758	51,217,000	1 : 611

Note that the *U.N. Yearbook* states 'inter country comparisons are subject to caution owing to variations in systems as well as differing criteria adopted in gathering and presenting the data'.

THE PLANNING AND EQUIPPING OF A UNIVERSITY DEPARTMENT OF GEOGRAPHY

Some basic principles

Notes prepared by Professor W. G. V. Balchin for a study group held during the Institute of British Geographers Annual Conference at Swansea in January 1963.

(a) *Initial Conditions*

There are four possible initial conditions and whichever arises will clearly greatly affect subsequent decisions. Geography will be *either* on its own *or* associated with other subjects within one building, and there will be *either* an architectural 'straight-jacket' within which one has to work, *or* those responsible for the planning will have a completely free hand which the architect subsequently interprets.

(b) *Accessibility*

The grouping of several subjects within one building raises questions of accessibility, circulation, the establishment of the identity of each department and the extent to which there are inter-departmental facilities.

Inter-departmental facilities should clearly be central to the whole building and readily accessible. Departmental identity can be preserved in either vertical or horizontal units. Vertical (tower) units, however, produce circulation problems when numbers are large, since movement might become dependent on lift capacity. Horizontal units solve some movement problems with large numbers, but accessibility can be decreased.

Either within a department or where several departments are concerned accessibility may be achieved in any one plane by one of three methods. Corridors can either be linear, T shaped or + shaped. The + shape gives the highest accessibility ratio. These shapes can of course be repeated in more than one plane.

With several departments in one building the most economical arrangement appears to be central inter-departmental services with T shaped departmental offshoots. A variety of patterns are possible:

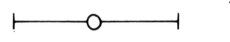 

If space permits, two, three or four departments could all be accommodated on one level. Beyond four departments, or if they become very large, or if space is initially limited, then a vertical growth will be necessary. Small departments might then occupy one floor each of a T pattern whilst large departments could occupy several T shapes on one floor or several floors of one T shape.

(c) *Academic Structure*

In planning a Geography Department attention must be paid to the academic structure of the university in question since important differences in accommodation needs may arise therefrom. Thus we can draw a distinction between the Honours only type of department with a steady 40–40–40 flow of students over the three years of a degree course and the General Purpose type of department catering for both Honours and Pass degree along with subsidiary students. In the latter case where three subjects are being studied in the first year a first year entry of say 120 might be followed by a 30–30 Honours group and a 30–30 Pass group. Laboratory and lecture room space have to be planned in relation to the needs and timetable problems of the different academic structures.

(d) *Size of the Department*

The size of the building for a Department of Geography will clearly reflect the size of the department in terms of staff, students, postgraduate students and the relative weight envisaged as between teaching and research in the life of the department. In the majority of cases the resultant size of the department stems from the number of the first year entry of undergraduate students. This should be recognised as one of the most important factors since on it depends second and third year numbers, staff numbers and likely postgraduate numbers.

Ideally each student will have his own working space but this may not be possible for multi-subject courses nor for economy reasons. An Honours department can however achieve more with combined lecture/laboratories, whilst the General Purpose department can do the same and achieve still greater economy by the duplication of laboratory periods. One lecture/laboratory per year of study facilitates arrangements. More staff will be needed to cope with higher numbers and this implies more staff rooms where large first year intakes are concerned.

In addition to a lecture/laboratory for each year one large lecture theatre should be accessible to the Department for general lectures, general assembly, society and other meetings involving the whole department. An Honours department with a first year entry of 40 would need a general lecture theatre of 150–170 capacity to cater for a combined staff/postgraduate/student assembly: whilst a General Purpose department with a first year entry of 120 might need a lecture theatre with a capacity of 275–300 to cater for a general assembly. This is an important point which has been overlooked in the planning of some departments.

In planning laboratory space there should also be enough places in the department to seat the largest year at any one time for practical examinations.

(e) *General Requirements*

In addition to the lecture/laboratories and the large assembly lecture theatre we may list a number of requirements that need consideration in the planning of a Geography Department. Where these are included they should be positioned in the final plan in relation to their use and accessibility. Requirements to consider include the following:

(i) Staff rooms – these can either be grouped together or placed adjacent to related laboratories or lecture rooms.
(ii) Book Library – much will depend here on whether any university policy regarding university or departmental libraries is in operation. Ideally the geographer will want his own library and this should be centrally positioned.
(iii) Map Library – this may or may not be combined with the book library. A central position is desirable and facilities for atlas and rolled map storage will be needed.
(iv) Seminar room(s) – these will be needed if staff rooms are too small for tutorial groups. From a timetabling and general amenity point of view it is better to aim at large staff rooms.

(v) Administrative facilities – the department will need a general office with adequate space for typists. It should have counter facilities and be strategically placed. It cannot be both near the entrance and central in all cases, but care should be given to its siting. Adequate typing space is also needed – this facility has increased steadily over the last decade and some U.S. universities seem to be moving towards one typist per member of staff. This may not be so far fetched when one remembers that engineering, physics and chemistry in the U.K. often average one technician per member of staff.

(vi) Technical facilities – the department will need to consider photographic, drafting, metal and wood working facilities. This will produce special room requirements in the shape of dark rooms, drawing rooms, instrument rooms etc. Geography departments have hitherto been poorly equipped with these facilities in comparison with other subjects.

(vii) Postgraduate accommodation – ideally individual rooms are desirable but failing this a 'research room'.

(viii) General purpose room to act as a conference room, staff/student common room, with tea/coffee facilities.

(ix) General concourse area for receptions, display and exhibition purposes.

(x) An effort should be made to include some unallocated space to meet future unforeseen contingencies.

(f) *Specialist Requirements*

Any specialist requirements are likely to be related to specialist research interests. The question must be asked whether any particular types of accommodation should be provided. Specialist requirements of this kind are more likely to arise on the 'physical' side of the subject rather than the 'human', thus:

(i) Geomorphology can give rise to the need for a 'wet' laboratory to accommodate earth sculpture tanks, stream flumes, wave troughs and the like. A 'wet' laboratory needs underfloor drainage and overhead water and electrical points.

(ii) Pedology can give rise to specialist laboratory requirements in special bench tops, fume cupboards, constant temperature rooms, isolated floors for rock crushers, isolated solvent stores, etc.

(iii) Photogrammetry may need special reinforced or isolated floors to eliminate vibration on plotting machines.

(iv) Cartography can call for extensive space requirements.

(v) Climatology may need special storage requirements and instrument repair facilities.

All these fundamentals added together make up the essential ingredients for the initial layout. This layout should be thought of in relation to the life and movement within the department. Congestion should be avoided and accessibility made easy.

(g) *General Services*

This is a major problem which affects all rooms within a department. It will be necessary to decide where to position *water, gas, electricity, telephones, clocks, tracing frames, vacuum* and *compressed air* services. Here the future needs (unknown) of the department should be borne in mind as well as the present (known) needs.

Since for efficiency a department will need to run on accurate time keeping, a master controlled clock can be regarded as a general requirement in all rooms.

Undergraduate laboratories will generally need water, gas, electricity, tracing frames.

Postgraduate laboratories will need water, gas, electricity, tracing frames, three phase electricity, vacuum and compressed air.

Staff rooms will need water, gas, electricity, tracing frames, telephones – which can all be combined in a service bench.

Technicians rooms will vary but in general will doubtless resemble staff rooms so far as service needs are concerned.

Lecture rooms will need power operated blackout curtains, dimming devices, projection facilities, blackboard, white board, graph board and pin up board.

All services should be planned for ease of access for maintenance purposes. Considerable economy can be achieved in pipework by carefully thought out positioning.

Consideration will also have to be given to:

Display facilities — a geography department will require adequate display facilities and walls should be treated so that map and photographic displays can be mounted. This means methods of both hanging and pinning should be available. Cork or celotex wall panelling is desirable and some areas need treatment from floor to ceiling.
Adequate illumination from the ceiling will also be desirable.

Lighting — a decision will have to be made as to whether lighting is to be general or fluorescent, pendant or ceiling concealed, direct or indirect. Each room will need careful thought as to the best kind of lighting.

Heating — the form of heating will need decision. As geographers are interested in obtaining the maximum wall space, radiators and panels are to be avoided. Overhead Frenger type ceiling heating is the most satisfactory.

Flooring — a great variety of flooring is now possible – cork, lino, stone, tiles, P.V.C., rubber, wood blocks, composition etc. Laboratories, lecture rooms may have special needs; otherwise ease of cleaning should be a determining factor plus resistance to stiletto heels.

Windows — A satisfactory balance must be struck between wall space and window space. The geographer does not want too much window space. Lack of wall space, problems of solar build-up, position of laboratories, a need for sun blinds otherwises arise.

Toilet and Cloakroom facilities — this really falls to the architect but care should be taken to see that he is fully acquainted with the maximum number of folk likely to be using the building at any one time. Inadequate cloakroom facilities are often found.

Waste Disposal — another point often overlooked by architects. Any large office building generates a great deal of disposal. An incinerator or a dustbin store may be needed.

Lifts — A goods lift is desirable in any building with more than one floor and a passenger lift after two floors.

213

(h) *Storage Problems*

A special note is desirable regarding storage problems since these arise in all rooms throughout a department. A well run and organised department depends on tidyness and tidyness is only possible with adequate storage space.

Some rooms will need to be set aside as simple store rooms e.g. for

> cleaning materials
> survey apparatus
> meteorological apparatus
> paper store
> pedological store (soil profiles)
> dust bin store
> garage for field vehicles.

In all these rooms and also in the working rooms special storage units will need to be thought out in relation to the function of the room, thus:
– departmental office, needs paper and stencil storage, filing cabinets.
– map library, needs shallow drawers of appropriate size, depth and size to be worked out.
– laboratories, need storage for student possessions, map set storage, instrument storage.
– postgraduate laboratories, will need individual specialist storage requirements.
– staff rooms, need book, map, cupboard, desk and filing storage facilities.

These requirements will produce the need for the construction of special units since one cannot buy furniture and laboratory equipment for a Geography Department 'off the peg', as one can with say physics or chemistry. Accompanying the construction of this equipment will be laboratory benches and lecture room seats. There is a variety of choice here and it will be necessary to decide whether laboratory bench facilities be fixed or mobile, at standing or sitting level.

In the planning of any room three dimensional modelling will give a better answer (although more laborious) than two dimensional.

(i) *Some General Points*
(i) Adopt the module principle of building to allow for possible future alteration and reconstruction.
(ii) Check that the building and the department include adequate facilities for the reception of visitors and goods. Crates, parcels etc. should preferably have a trades-man's entrance and there should be an unpacking store.
(iii) Doors can sometimes produce problems – which way do they move – inwards, outwards or both, which side are they hung?
(iv) The architect at some stage will include fire precaution devices, fuse boxes and the like which are liable to have an effect on room space. He should be asked to include these as early as possible.
(v) Planning should take into account ease of cleaning in both methods and materials. Cleaning is an expensive maintenance item and the cheapest construction or equipment is not always the least expensive in the long run.

214

(vi) Adequate car parking space should be available for the users of the whole building.

(vii) It is worthwhile remembering that not all builders and tradesmen accurately measure from agreed plans. A considerable amount of 'estimation' takes place and serious problems can arise in the positioning of fixtures, gas, water and electric points. These can be put right easily in the early stages and it is advisable to check through the building say once a week as it is going up.

(This would also bring to light any other more serious mistake).

Graphicacy

W. G. V. Balchin

ABSTRACT. Graphicacy is described as the educated counterpart of the visual-spatial aspect of human intelligence and communication; it is seen as fundamental in education along with literacy, numeracy, and articulacy. Early investigations of the visual-spatial aspect of human intelligence are described. Since maps, diagrams, photography, and other spatial documents are the tools of graphicacy as well as the basis of geography it is argued that the skill of graphicacy is best imparted at school, college, and university level through geography. An attempt is made to define the content of graphicacy as an intellectual discipline.

J. P. GUILFORD has claimed that there can be as many as 120 different aspects of intelligence,[1] but whatever the number the range may be grouped into four basic types which also encompass the four basic modes of communication among human beings. The first type to evolve seems to have been spatial ability. Animals possess enough spatial ability for route finding and for exploring the environment in search of food. This is the beginning of highly civilized skills such as map reading and spatial planning. The second type to evolve emerged with the higher animals, who can communicate with each other by means of social noises. Here we see the beginnings of civilized oral language and all other forms of social intelligence. Thirdly, after the evolution of man, there came written communication and with it permanent records and the handing on of information which allowed civilization to escalate. Finally there has evolved the human faculty for dealing with numerical symbols which has grown up into the field of mathematics with all its practical applications (Fig. 1).

In a brain as highly evolved as that of a human being the potential for all four types of ability is inborn, but none of them can come to full fruition without education. We cannot, for example, master written language without being taught by definite procedures, and a special word exists for the educated product of these procedures, literacy. The connotation of literacy and its associated adjectives, literate and illiterate, had proved to be so potent that in 1959 the Crowther Commission recognized the need for a similarly potent term to stress the importance of educated numerical ability.[2] The word coined to fill the gap, "numeracy," is now in general use in Britain and seems to have had a considerable effect. Almost unnoticed, the term "articulacy" has crept in from the pre-existing adjective, articulate, to express ability in social intercourse. However, the educated counterpart of visual-spatial ability remained unnamed until recently.

In the choice of a word to denote the educated counterpart of visual-spatial ability one must first ask the question, What exactly does this form of communication involve? It is fundamentally the communication of spatial information that cannot be conveyed adequately by verbal or numerical means, for example, the plan of a town, the pattern of a drainage network, or the picture of a distant place, in other words the whole field of cartography, computer-graphics, photography, the graphic arts, and much of geography itself. All of these words contain the root "graph" which seems a logical stem for "graphicacy," which was completed by analogy with literacy, numeracy, and articulacy.

It was the recognition of the need for a word to cover this form of communication by Miss A. M. Coleman of King's College, London, and myself in 1965 that led us to

Professor Balchin is Head of the Department of Geography, University College of Swansea, Singleton Park, Swansea SA 2, U.K.

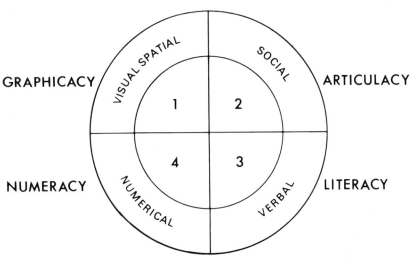

Fig. 1. The four basic types of intelligence or modes of communication and their educated counterparts.

send an article to *The Times Educational Supplement* proposing the word "graphicacy" to describe the educated counterpart of the visual-spatial aspect of human intelligence and communication.[3] A strong plea was made that educationists should recognize the existence of this essential ingredient in communication and that provision should be made for it in the normal educational curriculum.

The article and the proposed term seem to have crystallized, almost by accident, ideas and thoughts that were in the air at this period. We were not at the time aware of the existence of a number of research papers and books which subsequently came to light. Whereas most articles and papers rarely produce more than several enquiries and reactions, the *Times Educational* article was followed by what almost amounted to fan mail from a wide spectrum of the educational world. Enquiries came from publishers for books on the subject, and requests to reprint the article were received from places as far away as Canada, the United States, South Africa, Australia, and New Zealand.

Since 1965 there has been a steady flow of material on the concept ranging from research papers to chapters in books, and from presidential addresses to conferences on the theme.[4] Papers have been re-

printed additionally in Denmark, Switzerland, as well as in Great Britain. Aided by the increasing use of the term, graphics, the concept of graphicacy, standing alongside literacy, numeracy, and articulacy, now seems to have become well established in much of the English-speaking world.

If we accept the premise that the well-educated person will be articulate, literate, numerate, and graphicate we have an immediate indication of what the school foundation subjects should be. Articulacy and literacy will be clearly derived from the study of English, or whatever the native language, and numeracy from the study of mathematics. In most English-speaking countries, however, it is only in the study of geography that the possibility exists at the school level of a wide and rigorous training in graphicacy. Geography, which will of course embrace much cartography, thus emerges as a foundation subject along with English and mathematics. It is perhaps significant that several British public examining boards already record that the three largest subjects at the Ordinary level of examination are English, mathematics, and geography, but there are still too many schools where geography is an alternative to other subjects and where pupils are denied the opportunity to develop their latent graphicate skills.

217

As might be expected we find that teachers of geography in both Europe and North America have already published relevant material based on investigations in various aspects of the field of graphicacy. As early as 1932 G. F. Howe studied in North America the child's ability to use cardinal directions and found that clear ideas of directions in space could be acquired by the age of eight years.[5] In Britain P. G. Moss in 1931 and O. Garnett in 1934 promoted the idea of working from large scales of familiar ground to small scales of unfamiliar ground.[6] The Geographical Association of Great Britain in 1941 and E. David in 1944 investigated the teaching of contours and came to the conclusion that children could cope with contours at a younger age than is commonly supposed.[7] The doyen of British geography teachers, James Fairgrieve, anticipated the substance of this article in the 1946 edition of his book by calling for a definite, thought-out, graded course in map reading instead of it being regarded as a means of filling up odd moments in the timetable.[8]

In 1956 Piaget demonstrated that the ability to understand plan, even in a simple way, emerges gradually and is not accurate until nine or ten years of age in the average child.[9] He presented his pupils with a three-dimensional model showing trees, houses, and roads and asked them to make a plan on a piece of paper half the size, thus compelling a scale reduction. At six or seven years the average child could make a rough grouping of the houses, at seven or eight years he could coordinate their positions, and at nine or ten he could scale distances accurately.

This work was followed in 1959 by a notable report from the International Geographical Union (I.G.U.) on an investigation into the ability of over 1,000 pupils to understand map concepts of scale, distance, grid reference, conventional signs, and settlement problems.[10] The principal findings included the fact that understanding conventional signs was well within the grasp of eight-year-olds, but direction presented more difficulty. The appreciation

of contour lines was also found to be less difficult than had been supposed. By nine or ten years grid references were easily understood. At ten years location was fully understood. The relation of relief to settlement, however, proved harder to grasp and a full appreciation here did not come until much later. Much of this report agrees broadly with the findings of Piaget. A similar confirmatory investigation followed in 1964 by D. Blair, which also showed increased understanding up to the age of 14 years, but this was then followed by a slight recession before understanding continued to improve again.[11]

In the mid-sixties J. Lowe in Great Britain investigated the growth of map drawing abilities in primary school children.[12] A sample population of 1,242 pupils were required to draw their route from home to school to see what they could achieve without specific instruction. The children carried out this task four times, at yearly intervals, beginning at the age of seven years. The map drawings were rated in four grades—0, 1, 2, and 3—in ascending value for each of three cartographic qualities: position, scale, and plan. Position meant the relative distance between features, and plan meant the drawing of the features as seen from above. Lowe found that most children reached his grade 1. He also found that more seven-year-olds reached this grade for position than for scale, and more for scale than for plan, suggesting that position was the easiest concept and plan the most difficult. At each successive age more children reached the grade 1 in each aspect and the order of difficulty remained the same. The results were thus broadly in agreement with Piaget's work. Lowe, however, was able to isolate a spatially gifted group who reached his grade 3 in all three aspects. He found that these children started at seven years of age understanding plan better than position or scale.

While the general trend of these investigations had revealed abilities to appreciate concepts of graphicacy at an earlier age than had been anticipated, a mild corrective was administered in 1967 by H. A. Sandford's enquiry into children's ability to understand school atlases.[13] The results here were not as favorable as with large scale maps.

In the United States J. O. Towler and L. D. Nelson in 1968 and J. O. Towler in 1970 investigated the understanding of reference systems and scales and found a sequence similar to Piaget and the I.G.U. report but with development levels two years later than in Europe.[14] In Britain in 1970 Miss P. H. Pemberton describes the use of maps with young children and reports that they seem to have an ability with maps at an earlier age than supposed by many.[15]

In 1971 J. M. Blaut and D. Stea published a notable research work on uninstructed map reading.[16] They chose preliterate six-year-old school starters and eliminated the problem of conventional signs by using vertical air photographs of the school area at very large scales of 1 : 2,000 and 1 : 3,000. The children were given no information but were simply asked what they could recognize. Only two out of 107 Massachusetts children failed to realize that they were looking down on a landscape. The rest managed to rotate their viewpoint through 90 degrees and to recognize an average of 6.4 types of feature with very few incorrect identifications. Puerto Rican children were found to score similarly and no cultural difference was detected. Blaut and Stea later investigated younger children and found several three-year-olds and even one precocious two-year-old able to recognize at least one feature on the given air photograph.

Thus while Piaget and Lowe indicate a groping towards the concept of plan in mapmaking by the age of nine or ten, or in the most spatially gifted children by the age of seven, Blaut and Stea claim a grasp of plan in map reading at six or even earlier. The analogy with literacy should be clear: Just as children progress more rapidly in reading than in writing so they may progress more rapidly in map reading than in mapmaking. It would appear that the classic beginning of the geography syllabus, "make a map of the classroom," should be rescheduled for a later stage and replaced by some incoming aspect of graphicacy.

The most recent investigation (1975) is that by Mrs. K. E. Charlton who has studied pupil understanding of map symbolism, scale, direction, and location in the age range eight to 13 years in Britain.[17] She confirms that comprehension of the concepts improves with age. Definite stages can be detected in understanding the concepts of scale and location, but these are less obvious for map symbolism and direction where much depends on instruction. Once again pupils' understanding emerged at earlier ages than might have been expected.

One gains the impression that in both Britain and North America, where emphasis is placed on literate and numerate work in the middle and upper age ranges, the early natural graphicate ability is not allowed to develop, to the detriment of many pupils. This may provide the explanation of something that is certainly puzzling to university teachers in Britain where it is often found that students with quite poor examination results before university do extremely well in engineering, architecture, and planning at university. The converse is often true for geography, in which it is almost notoriously difficult to obtain a first class degree. It seems that the individual who excels in literacy, numeracy, and graphicacy (all needed in good measure by the first class geographer) is indeed rare. If we are testing for only one or two of these abilities the statistical chance of "good" results are that much greater.

Graphicacy then has an important message for primary schools. Visual-spatial ability is liberally present in young children. Most of them spontaneously draw pictures and "maps," before they learn to read. Why then do we wait until the age of seven or eight before we begin to develop this ability? All the evidence suggests that many graphicate topics could be introduced earlier in the educational sequence

219

and so help most individuals to progress further along that sequence than at present. It seems that the start of school life is not too early to begin bridging this gap between what the brain can do for itself and what has to be explicitly taught and explicitly learned. What is there in the growing spatial intelligence that can be matched with skills that will be required later, and how can it best be educated at a younger age? Obviously it would have to be divided into small topics that lie within the short attention span of the young school child, and each topic would have to appeal through its inherent fascination and in no way depend on the fascination of broader integrating relationships, which can only come later when sufficient foundations have been laid.

Going on through the primary into the secondary stage we must make sure that opportunities are provided for both the incoming and outgoing aspects of graphicacy. The incoming, or reading, aspect of graphic communication has been given a great impetus in recent years by the visual aids movement, but the outgoing, or writing, aspect remains fragmentary. There is tremendous opportunity for achievement here open to anyone who can formulate and develop the overall field. An interesting start in this field has been made by J. P. Cole and N. J. Beynon in their *New Ways in Geography*.[18]

From the secondary to the tertiary stage and on to university it will be clear that graphicate skills become increasingly important in a wide range of disciplines such as engineering, photogrammetry, survey, planning, architecture, mathematics, and biology, as well as in geography and cartography. In all these subjects visual-spatial communication, both incoming and outgoing, are fundamental. Increasingly also graphicacy figures in public life with symbolization, films, television, and pictorial communication.

It is significant that in France in the last decade there has been considerable discussion hinged around the concept of the "four languages" in communication skills and of the need to teach all pupils the

four skills which we have distinguished. A recent curriculum innovation in France aims at making all seventh grade pupils graphicate by the introduction of technical drawing. Such a step is not necessary in Britain with the base which already exists in geography. There is need however to define the content of graphicacy so that a logical syllabus of instruction can be drawn up. In this way coverage might be achieved and one could proceed from the simple to the more complex throughout the pupil's career.

From discussions held so far it would seem that in a condensed form the content of graphicacy might embrace in increasing order of complexity the following concepts and skills:

appreciation of direction and distance
appreciation of size, shape, and area
linear and angular measurement
space relations and map forms
grid references and use of coordinates
appreciation of scale
conventional signs
graphics
color distinctions, pattern recognition
mathematical graphs and their interpretation
map interpretation
cartographic diagrams and their interpretation
map projection and art projection
perspective in field sketching and photography
mapmaking
mental maps
networks and distributions
ground and air photo interpretation
photogrammetry
color, radar, and infrared photography
computer graphics
remote sensing devices

It will be clear from this sketch list that much of the field of graphicacy falls within the field of cartography which at school and university level is largely the responsibility of the geographer. To date the graphicate skill has been acquired by the average pupil fortuitously rather than by careful planning. We are now, however,

220

beginning to recognize the pressing need for systematic teaching in graphicacy as a result of the findings of perception geography—many people have mental maps of distance, time, space, and economic and social conditions along with mental images of places which differ substantially from reality. Graphicacy aims at an accurate interpretation of the real world and is concerned with Euclidean precision measurement, representation, and interpretation. It should be an integral part of the education of each individual to enable him fully to appreciate and understand his environment.

REFERENCES

1. Guilford, J. P., "Three Faces of Intellect," *American Psychologist*, Vol. 14, 1959, p. 459.

2. Crowther Commission, Ministry of Education Central Advisory Council for Education, *"15–18"—A Report*, two vols., 1959–60.

3. Balchin, W. G. V. and Alice M. Coleman, "Graphicacy should be the Fourth Ace in the Pack," *Times Educational Supplement*, Nov. 5, 1965.

4. Balchin, W. G. V., (Ed.), *Geography, An Outline for the Intending Student*, Routledge and Kegan Paul, London, 1970; Balchin, W. G. V., "Graphicacy," *Geography*, Vol. 57, Part 3, July 1972, p. 185.

5. Howe, G. F., "Teaching Directions in Space," *Journal of Geography*, 1932, Vol. 31, p. 207.

6. Moss, P. G., "The Teaching of Geography in Secondary Schools with special reference to Maps and Mapwork," unpublished M.Phil. thesis, University of Liverpool 1931; Garnett, O., *Fundamentals in School Geography*, George G. Harrap & Co. Ltd., 1934.

7. Geographical Association, "An Investigation into Children's Ability to interpret Contour Lines," *Geography*, Vol. 26, 1941, p. 131.

8. Fairgrieve, J., *Geography in School*, University of London Press, London, 1946.

9. Piaget, J. and B. Inhelder, *The Child's Conception of Space*, Routledge and Kegan Paul, London, 1956.

10. International Geographical Union Commission on the Teaching of Geography, *An investigation into the optimum age at which different types of map questions may best be set to pupils in the teaching of Geography*, manuscript, 1959.

11. Blair, D., "A practical study of the ability of some secondary school children to handle the representation of spatial relationships," unpublished Dip.Ed. thesis, University of Liverpool, 1964.

12. Lowe, J., "Notes on two enquiries into the understanding of maps at the primary school stage," unpublished M.S. thesis, undated.

13. Sandford, H. A., "A study of the concepts involved in the reading and interpretation of atlases by secondary school children," unpublished Ph.D. thesis, University of London, 1971.

14. Towler, J. O. and L. D. Nelson, "The Elementary School Child's Concept of Scale," *Journal of Geography*, Vol. 67, 1968, p. 24; Towler, J. O., "The Elementary School Child's Concept of Reference Systems," *Journal of Geography*, Vol. 69, 1970, p. 89.

15. Pemberton, P. H., (Ed.), *Geography in Primary Schools*, The Geographical Association, Sheffield, 1970.

16. Blaut, J. M. and D. Stea, "Studies in Geographic Learning," *Annals*, Association of American Geographers, Vol. 61, 1971, p. 387.

17. Charlton, K. E., "A Study of Pupil Understanding of Map Symbolism, Scale, Direction and Location," unpublished M.Phil. thesis, University of Leeds, 1975.

18. Cole, J. P. and N. J. Beynon, *New Ways in Geography*, Blackwell, Oxford, 1969.

NATURAL AND MAN-MADE DISASTERS
STRATEGIES FOR SURVIVAL

W. G. V. BALCHIN

Presidential Address delivered in Leicester to Section E (Geography) of The British Association for The Advancement of Science at 10.00 a.m. Wednesday 6th September 1972.

When the Council of the British Association invited me in October 1970 to be President of Section E for 1972 I little thought that one of the major aspects of the topic which I chose at that time for a presidential address would figure so largely in the international headlines during 1972. Regrettably newspapers thrive on disasters and prophecies of doom and I would not be surprised if circulations have increased considerably during the present year. This morning, then, I would like to take an objective look at both natural and man-made disasters and outline some ideas of various strategies for survival.

We must first bear in mind that disasters can affect us at two levels, as individuals and as organised societies. It is often assumed that with man's recent dramatic advance in technology his conquest of nature is almost complete. It is certainly true that in order to survive as individuals we are less vulnerable than primitive man who struggled daily with his environment. Modern organised society has largely resolved the problem of food, clothing and shelter for the individual, but both the individual and the society are still subject from time to time to natural forces which can lead to disaster situations.

For the civilised individual the Man against Nature situation is now largely confined to recreational and sporting activities. Boating, swimming, skiing, mountaineering, climbing and other outdoor pursuits exact a regular toll of lives which in this country exceeds a thousand annually. Most of these disaster situations occur as isolated incidents and are classified as accidents but many are avoidable since most are related to a lack of knowledge which if available would have enabled those involved to survive. There are strong grounds, therefore, for arguing that all engaged in such activities should be made fully aware of the potential dangers which they face and also of the survival techniques if they do become involved in a disaster situation. The geographer is clearly well placed to impart much of this knowledge.

An organised society may from time to time be overwhelmed by the forces of Nature, for Nature in her more violent moods can release far more energy than anything deployed by man. All natural energy disasters are related to the rapid movement of either air or water or land and the inter-connection between these elements when the movement takes place. Within the atmosphere we label such events as hurricanes, tornadoes, typhoons, tropical cyclones, whirlwinds, gales and thunderstorms. These phenomena are essential elements in the circulation of the atmosphere and will remain so. Unfortunately many are a continual cause of damage to both life and the environment. The casualty rate may vary from a single individual struck down by lightning to figures approaching half a million when a tropical cyclone hits a vulnerable area such

222

as North Vietnam in 1881 or East Pakistan (Bangladesh) in 1970. In some parts of the world such phenomena occur with monotonous regularity. The southern parts of the U.S.A for instance have to endure an average of over 150 hurricanes of varying intensity every year. The worst to date was the 1925 tornado which resulted in 689 deaths. To reduce casualties in these circumstances Man can only rely in potential disaster areas on forecasting techniques combined with protective shelters so that avoiding action can be taken as and when necessary.

Meteorological extremes can also produce extensive river flooding, coastal flooding and ocean storm damage. Of these river flooding is by far the most common and should in fact be regarded as a natural process rather than an infrequent disaster force. We now have enough knowledge of flood plain geomorphology to comprehend the role of flooding in both the hydrologic and geomorphic cycles. A combination of forecasting and avoiding action is again our best defence but failing this casualty figures may range from a single person in an isolated farmhouse to more than a million in a major river basin. The Yangtse and Yellow Rivers in China have particularly bad records in this respect and it is thought that throughout the long history of China casualty rates of over a million have been exceeded on a number of occasions, the last being in 1931 when over 180 million people were affected by widespread flooding in the Yangtse and Yellow River basins.

Coastal flooding is another hazard, fortunately much less frequent, which may occur as a result of meteorological extremes coinciding with high tides. The high casualty rate approaching half a million in the East Pakistan (Bangladesh) disaster of 1970 was in part related to coastal flooding. Nearer to us in space but not in time is the North Sea disaster of 1953 with a death toll of over 300 in Britain and 1,800 in the Netherlands. Even these figures are thought to have been exceeded by the great English Channel storm of 1703 when some 8,000 lives were lost. The major North Sea disaster of all time seems to have been the inundation of 1421 when the Zuider Zee was formed. It is estimated that 72 villages were destroyed and over 100,000 lives lost in this disaster.

The mass movements of the land also produces disaster situations. These movements are usually referred to as earthquakes, avalanches, landslides, lava flows and volcanic eruptions. Earthquakes are potentially the most disastrous with a record casualty figure of 830,000 in the Shansi Province of China in 1556. The frequency and distribution of earthquakes are more widespread than is commonly realised. It has been estimated that there are at least 16,000 potentially damaging earthquakes occurring each year. Fortunately the majority take place beneath the sea or far from inhabited regions but between 1949 and 1969 at least 521 earthquakes were recorded which are known to have caused damage. Two-thirds of the potentially damaging earthquakes take place in the Circum-Pacific Belt, but most earthquakes that actually cause damage occur in the more densely populated Himalayan–Middle Eastern–Mediterranean belt. There have been some 80,000 earthquake deaths in the last 20 years and without adequate building precautions in the earthquake zones it is axiomatic that future population increases in these zones will result in higher casualty rates.

Associated with earthquakes and earth tremors are the mass movements of landslides and avalanches. These arise where material is in a state of instability and is set in motion as a result of the quake or tremor. Their effects will often be lost in the general devastation caused by an earthquake but sometimes they dominate as in the Kansu Province, China, landslide of 1920 which claimed some 200,000 casualties. A more recent incident was the Mount Huascaran, Peru, landslide of 1970 with an estimated 5,000 casualties.

Volcanic activity is fortunately much more restricted than earthquake activity in its distribution over the Earth. With few exceptions volcanoes and lava flows can be pinpointed and normally good warning of impending activity is available. The most dangerous situation is the apparently extinct or long dormant volcano with a vent blocked by acidic lava which suddenly erupts producing the much feared *nuées ardentes*. These high temperature clouds of hot gases and suspended material may travel at speeds of over a hundred miles per hour down the sides of the volcano overwhelming everything in their wake. The most famous instance is, of course, the *nuée ardente* from Mont Pelée which destroyed St. Pierre in Martinique in 1902 with some 40,000 casualties. Ash flows, lava flows, hot mud flows and the discharge of glacial melt-water by volcanic action all contribute to the hazards of living in a volcanic region but fortunately the casualty rate is at a much lower level than that of earthquakes. From 1949 to 1969 of 740 known eruptions only 23 produced disaster situations although these involved some 10,000 casualties. The worst ever recorded activity in recent times seems to have been the eruption of Etna in 1669 and the consequent destruction of Catania with the loss of 100,000 lives. In prehistoric time the eruption of Santorini appears to have changed the whole course of civilisation in the Eastern Mediterranean. The Minoan language and culture, and the power of Crete, which was dominant until about 1400 BC gave way after the eruption to the Achaen civilisation of the Greek mainland. Similarly the eruption of Merapi in AD 1006 is believed to have destroyed the Hindu–Javanese state of Mataram.

Both earthquakes and volcanic action can produce major oceanic waves or tsunami which can travel great distances and these may increase in height dramatically when they reach relatively shallow waters. These waves may often cause much greater devastation than the originating force. The tsunami which followed upon the 1883 Krakatoa volcanic eruption reached heights of over 100 feet and was responsible for over 35,000 casualties, whilst the tsunami produced by the Andaman Islands earthquake of 1876 is thought to have been responsible for over 200,000 casualties in the Bay of Bengal. Coastal landslides can also produce major waves – recently 90 million tons of rock dropped 3,000 feet into Lituya Bay Alaska and the resultant wave removed 4 square miles of forest from the opposite shore.

Other natural disaster situations may arise from exceptional amounts of snow leading to avalanches, from excessive amounts of hail or fog, or from exceptional drought leading to forest fires or dust-bowl conditions. Another potential natural disaster situation lies in the fall of meteorites. Apart from avalanches which claim an average of over 100 victims a year none of these events fortunately produce high casualties. The snow avalanche casualty figure of 5,000 victims at Huaras in Peru in 1941 and the hail casualty figure of 246 deaths in Uttar Pradesh, India, in 1888 seem to be quite exceptional. The killers are without doubt, floods, tornadoes, earthquakes and volcanic activity.

Various estimates have been given of the probable total human casualties in historic times arising from all these natural events; these estimates range from minima in excess of 10 million to maxima up to 30 million. It is a sobering thought when one bears in mind the much lower population densities of the past. The present average death toll from these disaster situations is reliably estimated to be approaching one million per decade.

Even these figures have been exceeded by deaths arising from disease and famine. Whilst a large number of diseases can have fatal results Mankind has suffered in particular from four ailments which from time to time produce disaster situations. The bubonic plague or Black Death of 1347 to 1351 is reliably estimated to have carried off 75 million people of whom some 800,000 were in Great Britain.

Influenza epidemics have occurred at frequent intervals from 1510 onwards with occasional pandemics of world-wide distribution. The great influenza pandemic of

1918 to 1919 resulted in over 21 million deaths of which some 225,000 were in the United Kingdom. The casualty rate for this pandemic was nearly three times as great as the total death toll in the First World War of 1914–18. The 1957 influenza pandemic was fortunately much less disastrous owing to the widespread availability of vaccines.

Cholera is another potential disaster disease. It is endemic to peninsular India and from the 16th century onwards numerous epidemics have been recorded radiating outwards from the Ganges delta along the main routes of human travel. The first major pandemic started in Lower Bengal in 1817 and during the next six years spread to Africa and China. Another pandemic began in 1826, reaching Russia in 1830 and Britain and North America in 1832. Other pandemics in 1852, 1863, 1881 and 1889 followed somewhat similar routes and probably caused millions of deaths although no reliable figures are available. Although now contained by modern medical knowledge, cholera remains a potential danger to the world.

Our fourth disaster disease, malaria, is still the single greatest cause of human mortality. Malaria is still rampant in many localities and rough figures of 300 million cases yearly resulting in 3 million deaths annually are frequently quoted. Until recently the annual death rate in India attributable to malaria was put at nearly 2 million. Whilst the control of malaria is rapidly being extended, it should be noted that as the principal victims are infants, elimination of the disease is soon followed by a rapid increase in population.

Famine can be equally damaging and may arise from either natural disaster situations or man's misuse of his environment. Climatic oscillation leading to drought, excessive flooding, late springs, frost damage and wind erosion, or over-breeding of destructive vermin such as locusts, mice and rabbits, and over-production of plant disease such as potato blight, are all attributable to Nature.

Wars and civil disturbances, rapidly increasing populations near subsistence level and failure to conserve the environment are all Man's contribution to famine situations. Records of famines in Europe, the Middle East, India and China exist from at least 500 BC and number several hundred. A great famine may be a national catastrophe lasting several years and carrying off millions of people. Such were the great Indian famines of 1769, 1790, 1866, 1869, 1876–78 and 1899; the great Chinese famines of 1877–78 and 1920; and the great Russian famine of 1921. Although no reliable casualty figures are available for these disasters, local incidents suggest overall population reductions of a third which would produce regional casualty figures comparable to the 75 million quoted for the 14th century bubonic plague. The Irish famine of 1846–47 is adequately recorded and this resulted in over a million deaths, which with emigration reduced the population of Ireland by 2,500,000 in ten years.

How has Man reacted to these disaster situations and what strategy for survival, if any, has he evolved? He has for many millenia been engaged in a perpetual struggle with Nature and many would argue that he is now in control of his environment. He is still, however, relatively powerless when Nature releases major forces such as those detailed above. As an individual there is little he can do except examine critically his environment (and this is where a study of geography helps) and if necessary take avoiding action. In an organised society, however, monitoring can be arranged and a prediction, forecasting and warning service built up, and in affected areas structures can be evolved to protect the inhabitants, from some, if not all of the forces unleashed. Some measures of adaptation, so that life in a disaster zone becomes a calculated risk, is therefore possible. Houses in river flood zones can be built on stilts, hurricane shelters can be constructed and modern building techniques can allow for earthquake hazards. There are already methods of avalanche control in the Alps and by embanking as in the North Sea area action can be taken to prevent disaster from minor coastal flooding.

225

There has even been talk in recent decades of hurricane control and earthquake manipulation but the prospect of these ideas becoming realistic seems at present remote. It is probably only in the field of disease that real control is possible. The other disaster situations must be recognised as natural and since we now know they are recurring we should endeavour to evolve standby organisations to deal with the disaster situations as they arise.

Our first need is for continuous monitoring, information storage, and then prediction. We probably now know all the natural hazards and where they are likely to occur but we do not know when. A first step in this direction was the 1971 request of the United Nations Office of Science and Technology to the Smithsonian Institute of Cambridge, Massachusetts, to undertake a worldwide survey of natural disaster, research and warning systems. A global Natural Disaster Warning System is the obvious objective. A preliminary survey of research and warning systems was published by the Smithsonian Centre for Short-Lived Phenomena in July 1971 and a Directory of National and International Environmental Monitoring Activities has also since become available. These surveys have revealed that a great deal of information is already in existence at the regional and national levels but has yet to be organised internationally to provide the basis for an international disaster warning system.

We are probably best equipped to deal with atmospheric disaster situations since there is already a good world meteorological coverage. River flooding in the U.S.A., hurricane situations in the Caribbean, tropical cyclones in the Bay of Bengal, tsunami waves in the Pacific, storm surges in the North Sea, etc. are all monitored and can be predicted some hours in advance. We are probably least well equipped to deal with geomorphic mass movement – earthquakes, landslides, avalanches, volcanic activity, etc. have not been monitored so rigorously as they have not until recently been recognised as natural and recurring.

Whilst it should be possible to reduce casualties in affected areas by adequate warnings, by taking precautionary steps and by building shelters against expected disasters this cannot prevent extensive damage and disruption of the social life when a disaster occurs. Experience has shown that a major disaster usually overwhelms the regional and national relief organisations of the country in which it happens. Few things unite world sympathy more than a major national disaster but the help which flows from this sympathy, however well-intentioned, arrives more often than not too late. Ad hoc arrangements must be made and muddling through with a loss of valuable time is a common result. We need regional depots and supplies located in strategic positions manned by trained personnel standing by with adequate transport ready to move into the disaster area at a moment's notice.

There are a number of bodies already in existence out of which an international disaster relief organisation might grow. Many countries have wisely retained their Civil Defence Corps and an International Civil Defence Organisation exists in Geneva. The League of Red Cross Societies which also has its headquarters in Geneva would be another candidate. The United Nations Organisation clearly springs to mind. The World Food and Agricultural Organisation, (FAO) and the World Health Organisation (WHO) are other obvious interested parties. Throughout the world numerous charitable organisations exist, some of which have grown to a considerable size. Thus, Britain's three largest charities, Oxfam, Save the Children Fund and Christian Aid, collectively raise over 10 million pounds a year and already have international links and a considerable expertise in dealing with disaster situations. Individually, however, these organisations may only touch upon particular aspects of a disaster problem and all have in-built defects – Civil Defence is war oriented, the United Nations is a political organisation, the Red Cross is non-political but cannot act unless invited. FAO and

WHO are not geared to a crisis action. The charitable organisations depend on uncertain income and a great deal of volunteer help. Collectively, however, these organisations undoubtedly have the know-how and the wisdom to evolve an efficient International Relief Organisation to work in with a Global Disaster Monitoring and Warning System.

We have so far been concerned very largely with the Man against Nature situation. It is sometimes argued that advancing technology, the industrial revolution and the creation of an urban environment have now placed Man above Nature and in control of his environment. Whilst it is true that the impact of some of the natural disasters has been reduced, Man has paradoxically produced a large number of disaster situations of his own making, although it might be more correct to regard many of these as accidents. Collectively, however, these accidents may add up to some thought-provoking totals.

The collapse of engineering works such as bridges, tunnels and dams; the collapse of buildings; subsidence and mining accidents; road, rail, air and ship disasters; fire risks, etc. are all hazards faced by individuals living in the man-made environment of a technological civilisation. The collapse of engineering works is more common than is realised but the loss of life is fortunately rarely great. Bridge failures may occur through wind, fire, ice, flood or collision and some notable disasters include the collapse of the Tay Bridge in 1879 (blown down), the collapse of the Niagara Falls Bridge in 1938 (wrecked by ice), the Tacoma Narrows Suspension Bridge failure in 1940 (wind resonance), the Chiromo Bridge disaster of 1948 (carried away by floods) and more recently the collapse of several box girder bridges. Dams for water reservoirs and flood prevention schemes have collapsed from time to time with more serious consequences as a result of the sudden flooding. The failure of the Malpasset Dam in the French Riviera in 1959 drowned 421 victims, whilst the landslide into the Vaiont Reservoir in Italy in 1963 caused an overtopping of the dam which swept away several villages and 2,000 people. The collapse of buildings is by no means uncommon and Ronan Point in London and some Spanish hotels immediately spring to mind.

Mining has long been notorious for disaster situations and despite modern techniques still remains hazardous. One hopes, however, that disasters such as the coal dust explosion of 1942 in Honkeiko Colliery, Manchuria, which resulted in a death toll of 1,572 will not now recur. The science of engineering is, however, all the time advancing, transport units grow in size, bridge spans are being increased, dams get higher and impounded reservoirs are made larger. The risk of disaster must therefore always be present since unforeseen hazards may arise as the limits of the engineers' knowledge are gradually extended.

Less dramatic, but more disastrous, is the annual loss from fire. In the United Kingdom an average of 600 persons are killed a year and 3,000 injured as a result of fires, whilst financial losses are now in excess of £100 million a year. Over 40% of the reported fires arise in domestic situations and there is a steady annual average of some three thousand fires in clubs, hotels and restaurants. Most of these are related to carelessness.

Collectively, however, the greatest loss of life that an advanced society faces today, in the disaster situations which we have been enumerating, arises from transport. The safest forms of transport, rail, air, and ship, often receive the maximum publicity when an accident occurs because incidents are much less frequent and large numbers may be involved. The loss of the *Titanic* in 1912, with 1,500 lives, or the loss of the *Wilhelm Gustloff* in 1945 with 4,000 lives naturally hit the headlines. As does the crash of an airliner with 150 on board. What is more insidious, however, is the steadily mounting toll of deaths arising from road accidents. If they have not already done so the debits will soon outweigh the credits on the balance sheet of the internal combustion engine.

Annual road deaths in the U.S.A. are now around the 50,000 mark and forecasts of 10,000 a year have been made for the United Kingdom. This figure was in fact nearly reached in 1941 when 9,169 deaths were recorded with but a fraction of the traffic which we now endure. The problem of road deaths is beginning to assume epidemic proportions in the advanced technological civilisations and it is quite likely that for the world as a whole around 5 million people have now died in this century as a direct result of the invention of the internal combustion engine.

In comparison with Nature's disaster situations most of the cases which we have dealt with in the preceding section are incidents or accidents, and the strategy for survival which has evolved to deal with such situations is essentially local or regional and highly specialised. Within the United Kingdom we look to the Police, the Fire Service, the St. John's Ambulance Service, the British Red Cross, the Special Constabulary, the Womens' Royal Volunteer Service, the Coast Guards and the Royal National Life Boat Service to deal with the various kinds of incidents and accidents. The main weakness in our strategy seems to be in the lack of any co-ordinating organisation which could integrate all of the available resources in the event of a major disaster. Lord Robens drew attention to this gap in 1969 when he proposed the formation of a National Rescue Service to replace the disbanded Civil Defence Corps. The value of a comprehensive service was seen in the rescue work undertaken in the East Coast Floods of 1953 and the Hither Green train disaster of 1967. We no longer have this protection and it will be tragic in more than one sense if we have to wait for another major disaster before the public at large realises the deficiency.

The problem of Man against Nature, control of the environment, and of life in the industrial and urban society, pales into insignificance, however, when we turn to consider Man's biggest problem – Man himself. Man has produced many major disaster situations as a result of an inability to live at peace with his neighbours. Wars and civil disturbances have exacted a heavy toll of life and caused a great deal of disruption but whereas in the past professional armies only were involved, the present century has witnessed total warfare involving both civil and military forces, whole nations being against each other. With rapidly increasing destructive powers, total involvement and increasing populations, casualty figures have grown exponentially. The Crimean War of 1854–56 had a death toll of 160,000; the Franco–Prussian war of 1870–71 a death toll of 180,000 and the Russian–Japanese war of 1904–05 a death toll of 140,000. In World War I from 1914–18, however, the death toll rises to eight million and in World War II from 1939–45 it is estimated that there were 54,800,000 civil and military deaths – and only two atomic bombs were dropped at the very end of this holocaust. The outlook would indeed be bleak if ever the U.S.S.R. and the U.S.A. let loose the armoury of atomic weapons which they have accumulated since 1945.

Not only have sovereign states engaged in bloody struggles but we have also witnessed in the present century a continuation on a massive scale of political and religious liquidations. The Great Purge of Yezhovshchina in the U.S.S.R. between 1936–38 has no official figures but fairly reliable estimates of the disappearance of between 8–10 million people can be made from the deficiency of males in the official census statistics. Hitler's 'final solution' for the German–Jewish problem led to the extermination of between 5–6 million Jews. In China the execution of counter-revolutionaries between 1950–55 in the Hsiao Mieh (deprivation of existence) campaign is reliably estimated to have totalled between 5–10 million. The Peking radio formally announced monthly totals of 'deprivations' during this period. It is a sad and ugly tale and Mankind still gropes for a solution to the problem of living together on planet Earth.

The realisation that an even larger and more ominous problem lies ahead may, however, provide the human species with the kind of shock therapy that seems so badly needed. Nature equipped Man to survive her own disasters by means of a high reproductive rate. High death rates have been matched and exceeded by high birth rates. Now that Man is mastering some disaster situations, however, his inbuilt capacity for survival could well be the cause of his ultimate downfall. The total world population increased very slowly through prehistoric and early historic times and it was not until about AD 1810 that a world population of 1,000 million was reached. It took another century before the 2,000 million mark was passed just after 1920, but only another 40 years before 3,000 million was reached around 1960. The latest world population figure we have is 3,632 million for the year 1970. If this rate of growth is continued then we would be adding a further 1,000 million people by each of the years 1975, 1984, 1992 and 1998, thus exceeding 7,000 million by the end of the century. Although these predictions are sometimes disputed the critics cannot deny that the mathematical curve is exponential and that we are now at the point where the curve rises steeply and dramatically. It is quite clear that in the absence of a world-scale disaster the world population of AD 2000 will be more than double that of 1960 and that we could be faced with 12,000 million by 2035; 25,000 million by 2065 and around 50,000 million by the end of the 21st century. Clearly growth such as this, which theoretically is of an infinite kind cannot continue indefinitely since we are dealing with a finite base, in this case planet Earth. Moreover all the evidence to date points to the fact that the Earth's resources, both renewable and non-renewable, cannot possibly sustain continued technological and agricultural expansion for very much longer.

Thus we arrive at what future historians may well regard as the great doom-debate of 1972 when Mankind as a whole first realised that it had a problem on its hands with implications which far exceed even the threat of atomic war. Those involved in this debate fall broadly into two groups that might be labelled pessimists and optimists. The optimists include names such as John Maddox, Wayland Kennett, Kenneth Mellanby, Norman Borlaug, Alvin Weinberg and Andrew Schonfield, and the general tenor of their argument is that we are merely in another Malthusian phase and that we need not worry too much since demographic transitions and future technology will provide an answer to the problem. On the other hand the pessimists such as Paul Ehrlich, John Davoll, Dennis Meadows, Aurelio Peccei, Barry Commoner, George Borgstrom, Hugh Montefiore, Julian Huxley, Max Nicholson, Frazer Darling and many others stress the fact that we are now on the point of an exponential curve of population growth where the rapid rise begins and that our finite earth cannot possibly sustain the growth for much longer. The analogy of the pond lily which doubles its size every day illustrates this situation: at first there is little change in the scene but by the 29th day half of the pond has been covered, and then in one day the remaining half is covered. So far as population growth on Earth is concerned we are perhaps in the 28th day.

There are two aspects to this problem, in one of which Mankind already has experience. The second is an entirely new situation in which we can only hazard a guess as to what might happen. Organised societies based fundamentally on agriculture of a self-sufficient kind can only cope with population increase by increasing the area of cultivation and/or increasing the output per unit area. Irrigation, fertilisers and the so-called green revolution have all helped push up production in the post-war period and output has in many areas kept ahead of population increase. However, the limits of improvement have now been reached and exceeded in some regions. Dust bowls may be created by indiscriminate farming whilst salt deserts may appear with over-irrigation and over-use of chemicals in agriculture. Nature soon exacts a toll if Man takes more out of the soil than is being put in. If population increase now races ahead of food production it can only lead to a repetition of the famines which were experienced in the then overpopulated parts of the world in the 18th and 19th centuries. But future famines must inevitably be of a much greater magnitude, for despite world knowledge and assistance it will be physically impossible to move in and maintain emergency subsistence supplies for the vastly increased populations. The outlook for India, China and South-East Asia in general, is indeed grim.

The second situation relates to the industrial society which poses new problems, since here we find other limiting parameters to growth in addition to food. These parameters might dominate before we are overwhelmed by sheer numbers. There is a fundamental difference between earlier hunting, pastoral and agricultural societies and modern industrial technologies in that in earlier societies Man still remained part of an ecological system, in harmony with Nature, which re-absorbed his waste products. Some agricultural societies almost reached a steady state ecology since the food grains, animal products, wool, leather and wood which formed the basis of their economies were continually being recycled. 'All are of the dust, and all turn to dust again.' (Ecclesiastes, 3, v. 20). Industrial man, however, bases his high standard of living upon the consumption of non-renewable energy resources such as coal, oil and gas; and upon the consumption of non-renewable mineral resources such as iron, copper, aluminium, silver, lead and zinc. In the process he creates vast rubbish dumps of inorganic material and pollutes the land, air and water in ways which Nature cannot absorb or recycle.

The combination of the natural desire to increase standards of living combined with continued population growth is likely to bring about a disaster situation in an industrial society much more quickly than is commonly realised since we have five limiting parameters:

(a) Energy resources will become increasingly difficult to obtain.
(b) Mineral resources will become increasingly difficult to obtain.
(c) Pollution may be so problematical that the population may be submerged in its own waste.
(d) Society may disintegrate with increased affluence and urbanisation.
(e) Food supplies may be difficult to obtain either because of falling industrial production which limits exchange, or because of rising world shortages.

Others have written at great length about world food production, the potential productivity of virgin lands, food from the oceans, of world energy resources and of the world consumption of minerals. My predecessor in this presidential chair, Dr. S. R. Eyre, has given us a valuable summary of the present situation and I need not enlarge upon these well documented topics. Mention need only be made now of the growing realisation that either pollution of the environment or social malaise might bring about a collapse before the exhaustion of energy, minerals or food. Man-made pollutants now abound in the environment, ranging from sulphur dioxide and carbon dioxide discharged into the atmosphere, to detergents containing phosphorus and phosphates discharged into rivers, and pesticides containing DDT sprayed on the land. Lead is discharged from car exhausts, oil pollutes the sea from tankers and oil wells. Raw sewage and industrial waste is added to our rivers and oceans whilst there is a constant trickle of radiation waste from nuclear power stations. Vast mounds of inorganic rubbish accumulate on land or are dumped at sea, indestructible materials such as plastics and glass are poured out in ever-increasing amounts from our factories. Cumulatively Nature is quite overwhelmed by all this productivity and Man himself might suffer the same fate in the course of time. The now famous M.I.T. (Massachusetts Institute of Technology) computer predictions presented in 'The Limits to Growth' have clearly revealed the danger of an industrial society being overwhelmed by its own

230

pollution and waste and then collapsing through rising death rates and declining food production.

Social malaise is another unknown parameter difficult to quantify. It is paradoxical that the more affluent a society becomes the more it is troubled by juvenile delinquency, rising crime rates, anti-social behaviour and social stress. Some of these troubles are undoubtedly related to the increased and increasing gap between rich and poor which affluence brings to inflation in the monetary system, to strikes and industrial unrest, to increased unemployment brought about by automation and efficiency, and to environmental problems related to city size and structure – statistics for instance show a clear correlation between city size and crime rates. There is a real danger that an industrial society might disintegrate from within as a result of crime, strikes, inflation, unemployment and anarchy long before the other parameters begin to bite. Although we are familiar from history with the collapse of pastoral and agricultural societies we have yet to witness the decline and fall of an industrial society. It may possibly be less dramatic but it might be more protracted and to that extent more painful than when famine overtakes an agricultural society and Nature rapidly brings numbers into balance with the available resources.

Some but by no means all of these problems were debated at the recent United Nations Conference on the Human Environment which was held in Stockholm in June 1972. Whilst this conference marks a notable step forward in our realisation of the problems ahead, the press reports suggest that a great deal of attention was given to methods of counteracting pollution rather than controlling or eliminating the root cause. Although the protagonists in the problem may dispute the time interval, with places like Rio de Janeiro erecting a 39 storey high-rise complex to house 21,000 corpses in separate burial vaults, the writing on the wall is clear enough.

If Mankind is to survive on Earth he must advance beyond his present strategies for dealing with natural disasters and evolve a major global strategy to meet his own man-made disaster situations. There are many who argue that a major world power is necessary to maintain a global peace and the question arises whether this state of affairs can be brought about by negotiation rather than by an atomic world war with a potential casualty rate of up to 500 million. Even devastation of this magnitude, however, would have but a limited effect on the population problem which is *the* major difficulty now facing Mankind. A biologist presented with the present graph of population increase would diagnose a 'swarming stage' situation. This is frequently observed in Nature when a population of a particular species experiences favourable environmental conditions in the absence of controls which have hitherto limited its numbers. This situation either results in an increase in predators which re-establish stability, or eventual collapse through food shortage and pollution of the environment from excessive waste. Either way uncontrolled expansion leads to mass mortality.

We have seen that the problem involves not only an increasing population but also a rising standard of living. Any long term strategy for survival must clearly aim at changing in the first instance the exponential curve of population growth into a straight line parallel with the time axis and at the same time standards of living must be held in check to reduce demands on environmental resources. The aim must be for stable societies with a minimum disruption of ecological processes, maximum conservation of materials and energy and static populations. The logic of this argument cannot be disputed but as we begin to translate it into necessary and consequential action it is then that we realise that it is fundamentally contrary to much of our current economic, industrial, political and religious thought. Politicians tend to see the answer to most of their problems in increased growth rates, whereas it would appear that we need immediately a zero growth rate and beyond that very likely a voluntary reduction.

231

Economists are mainly concerned with gross national product and the quantity of living standards whereas it would appear that we ought to be more concerned with the quality of life. Our industrial philosophy has been based upon obsolescence, short life and throw-away products whereas it now appears that we should aim at long lasting products, recycling of materials, recovery rather than disposal, and reclamation rather than elimination. The chemical revolution which has given us pesticides, detergents, plastics and artificial fibres emerges as a major environmental menace and it now appears that these products should be abandoned in favour of natural controls and natural materials such as wood, wool and cotton. Bearing in mind that one person in an industrial society such as the United States has an environmental impact 55 times as great as one person in say India, the argument is also advanced that standards of living in advanced technologies should be held down, energy consumption curbed, the use of cars restricted, water more carefully conserved, and more effort devoted to the elimination of pollution.

Stabilising a population into a steady state will be problematical with so many current religious and philosophical ideas completely contrary to control. The reduction of the death rate through improved health and living conditions equally demands a reduction of the birth rate. No longer should we pray that the married couple 'may be fruitful in procreation of children' nor should we grant family allowances beyond the second child. All countries now need population policies, birth control facilities, and laws which reflect the need to control family size and birth rates. A change of attitude along these lines will be difficult to bring about especially when it runs contrary to religious dogma. It will require extensive educational activity and the supply of full details to convince many of the need to change their cherished beliefs.

Neither the communist world, nor the capitalist world nor the 'developing' world are going to find it easy to adjust to this way of thinking. Moreover any sudden change might well wreck existing finely balanced economic political systems. The best that can be hoped for is that a new philosophy of restraint, reclamation, recycling, conservation, environmental protection and disuse of some man-made materials will gradually permeate world society before a disaster situation arises.

References

Carlo M. Cipolla, *The Economic History of World Population,* Pelican Books, London, 1964

H. M. Finniston, K. N. Ayers, W. Tye, J. H. Latter, H. K. Black, H. Shirley-Smith, Lord Robens, C. A. Adams, Disasters, their Prevention, Control and Social Effects, *The Advancement of Science,* Vol. 25, No. 126, June, 1969

Harold W. Elfrich (Ed) *Agenda for Survival,* Yale University Press, 1970

Max Nicholson, *The Environmental Revolution,* Hodder & Stoughton, London, 1970

Natural Disaster Research Centers and Warning Systems, Smithsonian Institute, 1971

Directory of National and International Environmental Monitoring Activities, Smithsonian Institute, 1971

S. R. Eyre, Population, Production and Pessimism, Presidential Addresses delivered at the Swansea Meeting 1971, *British Association for the Advancement of Science,* 1971

Paul R. Ehrlich and Richard L. Harriman, *How to be a Survivor – A Plan to Save Spaceship Earth,* Ballantine Books, London, 1971

A Blueprint for Survival, *The Ecologist,* Vol. 2, No. 1, January, 1972

The Case Against Hysteria, *Nature,* Vol. 235, Jan.14, 1972

Donella H. Meadows, Dennis L. Meadows, Jorgen Randers, William W. Behrens III, *The Limits to Growth,* Potomac Associates, Earth Island Ltd., London, 1972

Jeremy Bugler, *Polluting Britain:* A Report, Pelican Books, London, 1972

R. F. Dasmann, *Planet in Peril,* Penguin Books, London, 1972

J. Maddox, *The Doomsday Syndrome,* Macmillan, London, 1972

Guinness Book of Records, Guinness Superlatives Ltd., London, Annual

DEPARTMENT OF GEOGRAPHY
UNIVERSITY COLLEGE OF SWANSEA
UNIVERSITY OF WALES

STAFF AS AT 1st JANUARY 1979

Professor of Geography and Head of the Department
R. H. GREENWOOD, M.A. (Cantab)

Professor of Geography
N. STEPHENS, M.Sc. (Bristol), Ph.D. (Belfast)

Reader in the Geography of Russia
L. SYMONS, B.Sc. Econ. (London), Ph.D. (Belfast)

Reader
D. T. HERBERT, B.A. (Wales), Ph.D. (Birmingham)

Senior Lecturers
E. M. BRIDGES, M.Sc. (Sheffield), Ph.D. (Wales)
S. H. COUSENS, M.A., Ph.D. (Cantab)
H. R. J. DAVIES, M.A., B.Litt. (Oxon)
H. J. R. HENDERSON, B.Sc. (Sheffield), M.A. (Liverpool)
G. HUMPHRYS, B.Sc. (Bristol), M.A. (McGill), Ph.D. (Wales)
D. H. MALING, B.A., Ph.D. (Dunelm)

Lecturers
J. A. EDWARDS, B.A. (Wales) Ph.D. (Dunelm)
M. FIELDING, B.A. (Lancaster)
A. H. PERRY, B.A., Ph.D. (Southampton)
W. C. ROUSE, B.Sc. (Birmingham), Ph.D. (Wales)
C. J. THOMAS, B.Sc. (Wales), Ph.D. (Nottingham)
C. TOMLINSON, B.A. (Reading)
R. P. D. WALSH, B.A. (Cantab)

Tutors
D. G. LOCKHART, B.A. (Strathclyde), Ph.D. (Dundee)
J. M. LUFFRUM, B.A., Ph.D. (Birmingham)
NINA R. PIGGOTT, B.A. (Oxon)

P. J. ATKINS, B.A., Ph.D. (Cantab)
R. A. SHAKESBY, B.A. (Portsmouth), Ph.D. (Edinburgh)

Part-Time Tutors
GWYNETH M. DAVIES, B.A. (London)
ROSEMARY D. F. BROMLEY, M.A. (Cantab), Ph.D. (Wales)

Part-Time Map Curator and Cartographer
GLENYS BRIDGES, B.A. (Wales)
SHEILA M. HINTON

Cartographers
T. FEARNSIDE, B.Sc. (Glasgow)
G. B. LEWIS, B.Sc. (Wales)

Administrative Assistant
SUSAN E. ASHTON, B.Sc. (Bristol)

Technicians
D. E. PRICE, C. & G. Final Photo.
J. S. WILSON, M.S.S.T.
A. F. CUTLIFFE, Dip. Phot., C. & G. Photo. Tech.
MARIE PARKER
JULIE D. SAVAGE
SHEILA M. GEAR (part-time)
CONSTANCE THOMAS (part-time)

Secretaries
IRENE BELLENGER
R. MERYL MORGAN
E. WENDY VIITMAA

FORMER STAFF

Professor of Geography and Head of the Department
W. G. V. BALCHIN, M.A. (Cantab), Ph.D. (London) (now Emeritus Professor)

Professor of Geography
J. OLIVER, B.A., Ph.D. (Bristol)

Senior Lecturer
GILLIAN E. GROOM, B.Sc. (Birmingham)

Temporary Senior Lecturer
G. KAY, M.A. (Liverpool), Ph.D. (Hull)

Lecturers
W. K. D. DAVIES, B.Sc., Ph.D. (Wales)
B. H. FARMER, M.A. (Cantab)
D. M. HARDING, B.Sc., Ph.D. (Wales)
G. MANNERS, M.A. (Cantab)
D. T. WILLIAMS, M.A. (Wales)

Temporary Lecturers
K. S. O. BEAVON, B.Sc. (Capetown)
H. J. POLLARD, B.A. (Reading)
I. D. THOMAS, B.A. (Wales)
D. WATTS, B.A. (London), M.A. (California)
G. J. WILLIAMS, B.A., Ph.D. (Wales)
C. J. B. WOOD, B.A. (Wales), Ph.D. (McMaster)

Assistant Lecturer
F. V. EMERY, M.A., B.Litt. (Oxon)

Temporary Assistant Lecturers
PEGI HOPKINS (née JOHN), B.Sc., M.Sc. (Wales)
M. L. T. SINCLAIR, B.Sc. (London)

Tutors
DOROTHY ANDERSON (née TROTMAN), B.Sc., Ph.D. (Wales)
W. S. BELL, B.Sc. (London)
C. BOARD, B.A. (London)
R. J. BROMLEY, M.A. (Cantab)
P. A. BULL, B.Sc., M.Sc., Ph.D. (Wales)
M. A. BUSTEED, B.A. (Belfast)
D. CLARK, B.Sc.Econ. (Bradford), M.A. (Sussex)
M. J. CLARKE, B.A. (Sussex), M.Sc. (London)
D. E. COTTON, B.Sc. (Hull)
R. T. COUPE, B.A. (Oxon)
ELIZABETH G. FARRELL, B.A. (Wales)
R. L. GANT, B.A. (Wales)
C. HARRIS, B.Sc. (Dunelm), Ph.D. (Reading)
M. J. HARRIS, M.A. (Oxon)
VALERIE M. HAYNES, B.A. (Cantab)
R. H. KING, B.Sc. (Wales), M.Sc. (Aberdeen), Ph.D. (Saskatchewan)
D. KOPKE, M.Sc. (Rhodes)
H. L. MASON, M.A. (Cantab)
R. H. MORGAN, B.A. (Wales)
R. A. MOWBRAY, B.A., M.Sc.Econ. (London)

T. C. MUSSON, B.A. (Oxon), M.A. (Newcastle)
JUNE OLIVER, B.A. (Bristol)
A. S. POTTS, B.Sc. (Wales)
EDNA A. POTTS (née GRINTER), B.Sc. (Wales)
H. A. RANDALL, B.A. (Dunelm)
M. G. SHAW, B.A. (Birmingham)
P. M. SMITH, B.Sc. (Wales)
A. H. TAYLOR, B.A., Ph.D. (Southampton)
J. L. TERNAN, B.A. (Belfast)
I. D. WHYTE, M.A. (Edinburgh)
S. WILLIAMS, B.Sc. (London), Ph.D. (Wales)
B. J. WOODRUFFE, B.A. (London)
C. F. WOOLDRIDGE, B.Sc., Ph.D. (Wales)

Research Assistant
J. A. KINGTON, M.Sc. (London)

Administrative Assistant
E. JOAN MASON (née REES), B.Sc. (Liverpool)

Technicians
BARRY FORMAN
KINGSLEY F. HARNIMAN
CLAIRE E. HARVEY
KENNETH M. JONES
ADRIAN D. MORAN
ANGELA MORGAN
JANET MOSLEY
WENDY NELMES
JOAN PADMORE
HELEN PARKER
EDDIE THOMAS
PETER WHITE

Secretaries
MARY EDWARDS (née PETERS)
ELIZABETH EVANS (née WILLIAMS)
HELEN HODGES (née CARTER)
KATHLEEN HYDE (née BATCHELOR)
ANNE JENKINS (née EVANS)
ELINOR A. JONES
JENNY MORGAN (née JONES)
PHILLIPA K. NEWINGTON
MURIEL POLLOCK
JACQUI REES (née REES)
SUSAN SHACKLETON-BAILEY
CAROL S. SLACK
JENNY M. SMITH (née DAVIES)
NESTA THOMAS
ANNE WILLIAMS (née PHILLIPS)

LIST OF GRADUATES OF THE DEPARTMENT OF GEOGRAPHY

DEGREE OF BACCALAUREUS

1955

External Examiner: Professor R. H. Kinvig

FACULTY OF ARTS

Final Degree
Evans, Donald Stuart
Hendy, John Samuel

FACULTY OF SCIENCE

Upper Second Class Honours
Bucknell, Robert Evan Howell

Lower Second Class Honours
Knott, Brynley Howell
Rees, Denys Gethin

Third Class Honours
Evans, John Philip

Final Degree
Snow, Edith

1956

External Examiner: Professor R. H. Kinvig

FACULTY OF ARTS

First Class Honours
Williams, Michael
Yockney, John

Upper Second Class Honours
Davies, William Gareth
Plummer, Brian Alfred George
Trump, Marjory

Lower Second Class Honours
Bevan, John James Allen
Evans, Hywel Gwyn
Jenkins, David Edward
Tranter, Bernard Desmond

Third Class Honours
Beynon, Mary Elizabeth Eileen
Maher, Margaret Christina

Main Degree
Jones, Russell Griffith
Thomas, William Anthony

FACULTY OF SCIENCE

Upper Second Class Honours
Carragher, Terence Patrick

Lower Second Class Honours
Evans, Walter Lewis
Lloyd, Sheila Rosemary

Final Degree
Lloyd, Roland Stephen Ridge
Morgan, Mary Elizabeth Meriel
Stanfield, James Leon

1957

External Examiner: Professor R. H. Kinvig

FACULTY OF ARTS

First Class Honours
Williams, Geoffrey James

Lower Second Class Honours
Brown, Patricia
Davies, Emrys
Hamley, William
Jenkins, Shirley
Powell, Anne Shirley
Scott, Frances Gillian
Watkins, Gruffydd John

Third Class Honours
Roach, Trevor Pryce

Main Degree
Jones, Derek Gwyn
Owen, Tecwyn
Rees, Alan
Richards, Alun
Thomas, Geraint
Thomas, Glenys

FACULTY OF SCIENCE

Upper Second Class Honours
Griffiths, Michael Wyn
Ramsay, Elizabeth Ann
Williams, Haydn John

Lower Second Class Honours
Gerrard, Bernard William
Johnston, Raymond
Lloyd, John Owen
Mathews, Hywel Bowen
Thomas, Kenneth Michael

Third Class Honours
Meredith, Malcolm Morris

Final Degree
Dixon, James
Green, Richard
Harries, Alan Prosser
Marsh, Hedleigh Herbert
Vaughan, John Derek
Williams, Margaret Lois

1958

External Examiner: Professor N. Pye

FACULTY OF ARTS

Upper Second Class Honours
Acors, Margaret Elizabeth
Howells, Derrick Thomas
Morow-Griffin, Trevor Louis Charles

Lower Second Class Honours
Lloyd, Marian
Parker, Bertie John

Third Class Honours
Jenkins, Rowland
Morgans, Terence Lloyd
Mort, William John
Obianika, Christian Robinson Onyemaechi

Main Degree
Bailey, Gareth
Guy, Marjorie Louise
Morse, Brian

FACULTY OF SCIENCE

Upper Second Class Honours
Matthews, Roger Philip

Lower Second Class Honours
Jones, Gareth
Thompson, Duncan Russell

Final Degree
Brookes, Gerald
Charles, Ronald
Evans, Anne
Evans, Patricia Velmai
Gammon, John Frederick
Johnson, Edward George
Mynott, John James
Richards, Margaret

1959

External Examiner: Professor A. A. Miller

FACULTY OF ARTS

First Class Honours
Thomas, Sylvia Mary

Upper Second Class Honours
Baker, David Leslie
Barris, Robert George Norton
Herbert, David Thomas

Lower Second Class Honours
Hopkins, Christine Trembath
Jones, David John
Wooding, David John

Third Class Honours
Aston, Clive Derrick
Davies, Barbara

Main Degree
Davies, Brian Lloyd
Harries, Megan
Hopkins, Derek James
Jones, Helen Anita
Jones, John Morgan
Jones, Noreen Margaret
Lynch, Maureen Ann

FACULTY OF SCIENCE

Upper Second Class Honours
Hawes, Clive
Lewis, John Brian
Symonds, Clydesdale Wentworth
Williams, Janet

Third Class Honours
Evans, David Gerwyn

Final Degree
Bateman, David Nigel
Boyd, David
Davies, Marian
Evans, Marilyn
Filer, Roger
Jones, Ann Eryl
Thomas, Anne
Thomas, Royston
Williams, Cyril

1960

External Examiner: Professor A. A. Miller

FACULTY OF ARTS

Upper Second Class Honours
Clement, Gillian Rosemaret
Edwards, John Arwel
Price, Valerie Jocelyn
Thomas, Robert Geoffrey

Lower Second Class Honours
Edis, Anne
Evans, John Wallis
Shukla, Bhanukumar Labhshanker

Third Class Honours
Williams, Robert

Main Degree
Brake, Barbara Pauline
Chinnick, Jeannette Jessamine
Evans, Brian John Vaughan
Morgans, John Ivor
Pretorius, Leoni Paxton
Shand, Robert Maurice

FACULTY OF SCIENCE

First Class Honours
Trotman, Dorothy Mary

Upper Second Class Honours
Davies, Peter
Ellis, John Gwyndaf
Jones, Alan David
Williams, Vernon Hughes

Lower Second Class Honours
Bond, John Allan
Gibbs, Mary Bradley
Johns, Anita
Jones, John Llewelyn

Third Class Honours
Sims, Colin Norwood

Final Degree
Ayling, Anne Claire
Biggs, Windsor David
Brackston, Roy
Clarke, Jean
Ellis, Keith
Harding, Brian John
Hughes, Carwyn
Johnes, John Edmund
MacCreadie, Donald Stuart
Pearce, Craddoc Brian
Pitts, Ida Mary Kinglake
Skinner, Alan Alfred

1961

External Examiner: Professor A. A. Miller

FACULTY OF ARTS

Upper Second Class Honours
Jones, Gareth

Lower Second Class Honours
Acreman, John Roland Norris
Jones, Elizabeth Carrol
Waugh, John David

Third Class Honours
Butler, Brian James

Main Degree
Cook, Patricia Doreen
Edwards, David John
Foulkes, John William Irving
Johnson, John Anthony
O'Brien, Maura Patricia

FACULTY OF SCIENCE

Upper Second Class Honours
Bevan, John Roger
Grainger, Edith Maureen
Powell, Arthur Brynmor

Lower Second Class Honours
Davies, Kenneth
Davies, Pamela Maud
Edwards, Clive
Frame, Lyndon Stuart

Third Class Honours
    Roberts, Elizabeth Lyn

Final Degree
    Clark, Robert David
    Cornelius, Adrian Whitney
    Evans, Colin Thomas
    Grant, Alan
    Howell, Gwynne Richard
    Jones, Fay Clare
    Madders, Delia Maureen
    Matthews, Dyfed
    Mesch, Nina Mary
    Morgan, Annette
    Roberts, Barbara Rose
    Thomas, John Neville Rees
    Young, Wendy Jane

1962

External Examiner: Professor N. Pye

FACULTY OF ARTS

Upper Second Class Honours
    Boakes, Cecilia Adeline Russell
    Jones, Sheila Miriam
    Lubliner, Martin
    Penn, Joy

Lower Second Class Honours
    Rimes, Rosemary Lyn

Main Degree
    Duckworth, Barbara Phyllis
    Penfold, Valerie June
    Williams, David Thomas

FACULTY OF SCIENCE

Upper Second Class Honours
    Thomas, Brenda

Lower Second Class Honours
    Daniel, Geoffrey
    Gaynor, Arthur Jeffrey
    Harding, Valerie
    Kennedy, David Beverley
    Pugh, Eustace David Trevor
    Roberts, Barbara Rose

Third Class Honours
    Jones, Fay Clare
    Morris, Margaret Clare

Final Degree
    Berry, John Richard Malcolm

Besley Michael Kaye
Hansen, Gerald Peter George Ernest
Jones, John Elwyn
Jones, John Griffith
Marnell, Michael Joseph
Morgan, Gwynfor Edward
Morris, Arthur Clive Pugh
McCarthy, Michael Desmond
Short, Aubrey James
Smith, William Harold

1963

External Examiner: Professor N. Pye

FACULTY OF ARTS

Upper Second Class Honours
    Jones, Barbara Elizabeth

Lower Second Class Honours
    Thomas, Merfyn
    Watkins, Janet

Third Class Honours
    Taylor, Brian Griffith

Main Degree
    Daniels, Barbara Ann
    Hopkins, Brian Upton

FACULTY OF SCIENCE

Lower Second Class Honours
    Griffiths, Dianne
    Hughes, David Richard
    King, Roger Hatton
    Marnell, Michael Joseph
    Pattison, Judy Margaret
    Roberts, Janice Margaret
    Robling, William Leslie
    Wild, David Peter

Third Class Honours
    Brooks, Joan Margaret

Final Degree
    Bunt, Colin Harry
    Davies, Philip
    Griffiths, Pauline
    Handley, Ruth
    Jibb, Patricia Helen
    John, Philip David
    Pooley, Roderick John
    Rees, David Arfon
    Thomas, Richard William James
    Warren, John Dilwyn
    Williams, Helen Patricia

238

1964
External Examiner: Professor N. Pye

FACULTY OF ARTS

Upper Second Class Honours
Davies, Richard Rawlinson
Farrell, Elizabeth Grace
Jones, David Parry
MacKenzie, Thomas Douglas
Linyard, Graham Ansell
Paine, Roger Edward
Shaw, John Raymond
Woodward, David Alfred

Lower Second Class Honours
Button, Ann Elizabeth
Crossland, Rae
Evans, Gwilym John
Garnett, Margaret Rachel
Roberts, David Richard Brereton
Saunders, Glamis Hugh
Vowler, William Felton

Main Degree
Beynon, Margaret Andrea
Calford, Ira Mills-Calford
Daniels, Jonathan Frederick
Fursey, Peter Richard
Penny, Gillian
Rees, George Alun
Riley, Michael David
Rose, Muriel Elaine
Williams, Arfon Wyn
Williams, Clive

FACULTY OF SCIENCE

Upper Second Class Honours
Grinter, Edna Audrey
John, Janice Beatrice
Jones, Richard Glyn
Potts, Allan Stephenson
Thompson, Margaret Anne
West, Norman John

Lower Second Class Honours
Brown, Gillian Margaret
McLellan, Ian Clark Scott
Smitham, Peter
Strawbridge, Peter Robert
Taylor, Peter John

Third Class Honours
Parker, Stewart Leyshon

Final Degree
Bell, Jane

Black, Stephen Michael
Brown, Colin
Edmunds, David William Stanley
Frost, Denis Alfred
James, Margaret Amy
Jones, Brenda Claire
Kimmings, Geoffrey Alan Kenneth
Knight, Arthur Clifford Edwin
Parker, Edward Charles
Preece, Colin Douglas

1965
External Examiner: Professor S. H. Beaver

FACULTY OF ARTS

First Class Honours
Wright, Jennifer Howard

Upper Second Class Honours
Cooper, Ronald Raymond
Evans, Rosemary Smith
Evans, William Ronald Penny
Lloyd, Elizabeth Carole
Rowles, Nicholas Ian
Williams, Gillian Mary

Lower Second Class Honours
Abdulla, Yasmin Mohamedali
Leonard, Valerie Brenda Jacqueline
Prosser, Sonia Miriam
Thomas, John Arthur
Williams, Harwood Kerith

Main Degree
bin Isa, Mohamed Anis
Cameron, Pamela Anne
Davies, Fiona Janet
Eastwood, David Neil
Evans, Gillian Pauline
Frost, Harry
Hughes, Norman Howard
Humphreys, Valerie Joan
Jones, Glyn
Sadler, Elizabeth Mary

FACULTY OF SCIENCE

Upper Second Class Honours
Baker, Peter Randall
Harris, Elaine Gillian
Jones, William Edward
Lewis, Gillian Dorothy
Parkin, Albert
Philp, Anthony Charles
Sen, Lalita

Thomas, Colin James
Williams, John Hayden

Lower Second Class Honours
Bateman, Richard
Battersby, Hazel
Birtwell, Richard Ian
Clarke, David
Farrow, Stephen John
Hardie, William Ian
Hurford, Ioan Rhys
Jenkins, Jennifer Mary
Morgan, David Graham
Williams, Richard Thomas

Final Degree
Davies, David Stuart
Gurney, Glenis Anne
Hall, Christine Carol
Jenkins, Geoffrey Reginald
Jones, Thomas Charles
Penny, Valerie
Sullivan, Graham
Thomas, Jeffrey
Weeks, Anthony Michael
Wells, Barbara Fay

1966

External Examiner: Professor S. H. Beaver

FACULTY OF ARTS

Upper Second Class Honours
Arnfield, Anthony John
Bordessa, Ronald
Drage, Richard John
Hewings, John Meredith
Lehr, John Campbell
Mooney, Patrick Bernard
Shields, David John
Smith, Hugh Vaughan

Lower Second Class Honours
Brook, Clive Anthony
Davies, Griffith Hugh
Davies, Richard William
Fitzsimons, John Graham
Fowler, Terence Martyn
Gillard, Angela
Greenhalgh, Robert David
Honeyball, Valerie Frances
Lambert, Michael
Lewis, David Arthur
Lewis, Thomas Terrence
Short, Roger Beverley
Swann, Alan William

Main Degree
Barnes, Claire Denise
Craig, David Black
Hunt, Pauline Jane
Ling, Alan Clive
Mahoney, Sheila Mary
Rees, Gary
Scurlock, David Hugh
Turner, Philip Thomas

FACULTY OF SCIENCE

First Class Honours
Spence, Nigel Anthony

Upper Second Class Honours
Barnes, Karel Jennifer
Davies, John Breese
Olsen, Philip Vernon
Trenhaile, Alan Stuart
Williams, Jennifer Megan
Williams, Kenneth George

Lower Second Class Honours
Clement, David Willacy
Cullen, Mary Elizabeth
James, Peter Anthony
Willsmere, Ann

Final Degree
Arthur, Jean Olive
Carpenter, Michael Thomas
Clark, Jean Margaret
Davies, Howard Grenville
Evans, John Charles
Jordan, Pamela
McKenzie, David Stuart
Palmer, Heather Emilie Zoë
Simpson, Brian Charles
Williams, Alwyn Marie

1967

External Examiner: Professor R. W. Steel

FACULTY OF ARTS

Upper Second Class Honours
Binks, Gillian Margaret
Brewer, Neil
Buckby, Martin Thomas
Griffiths, Ann Rosemary
Hunt, Robert David
Jones, Enid
Nixon, Marilyn Helen
Richards, Lesley Cynthia
Turnquest, Harcourt Lowell
Wainwright, Philip

Lower Second Class Honours
Creek, Jocelyn Charlotte
Fitzpatrick, Josephine
George, Jean Rees
Kirchner, Richard Peter
Smith, Diana Gwendoline
Underwood, Christine
Waterfall, Patricia Ann
Wood, Robert John Havis

General Degree—Second Class
Cookson, Rosemary Angela Eluned
  (French)
Jessop, Anthony Stanfield
  (Economics)
Morgans, Margaret Anne
  (History)
O'Riordan, Christina Mary
  (History)
Waters, Richard Gwyn
  (Economics)
Williams, William Page
  (Economics)

General Degree—Pass
Burn, Colin Robert Westwood
  (History)
Carty, Margaret Anne
  (History)
Findlay, Diana Joy
  (History)
Hinder, Sally Joanne
  (History)
Jones, Brenda
  (History)
Jones, Enid
  (History)
Lavender, Daphne Christina
  (English)
Michael, David Glyn
  (History)
Morgan, Gaynor Wynne
  (History)
Richards, Robert William
  (History)
Stanway, Florence Elizabeth
  (Politics)
Travers, Robert John
  (History)
Wright, Nicholas
  (Politics)

FACULTY OF SCIENCE

Upper Second Class Honours
Banfield, Colin Edward
Grant, Keith Frank

Halliwell, Bridget
Holmes, Suzette Pamela
Marlborough, Joan Margaret
Maskell, Olwena
Milburn, Isobel Evelyn
Smith, Paul Martin

Lower Second Class Honours
Bond, Margaret Ann
Brown, Margaret
Burrage, Rosalind Kathleen
Jenkins, Thomas Berwyn
Pagdin, Jeanette
Wales, Valerie Jane
Wright, Susan Victoria

General Degree—Pass
Barry, David
  (Geology)
Davies, Dewi Prys
  (Geology)
Leopard, Jaqueline Ann
  (Geology)
Leyshon, Geoffrey Alan
  (Geology)
Penn, Adrienne
  (Geology)
Warrilow, Griffith John
  (Zoology)

1968
External Examiner: Professor R. W. Steel

FACULTY OF ARTS

Upper Second Class Honours
Ager, Brenda
Armstead, Jane Mary
Bailey, Peter Ian
Brett, Laurence Humphrey
Exton, Susan Mabel
Fitter, Stephenie Lynne
Gallant, Victor
Glass, Janet Ray
Haywood, Peter Edward
Kimpton, Laurence John
McCarthy, Terence John
Price, Andrew Christopher
Scott-Campbell, Grenville Adrian

Lower Second Class Honours
Barrett, David Neil
Dempsey, Geraldine May
Taylor, Richard Lloyd
Wykes, Julia Mary

General Degree—Second Class
   Bembridge, John Keith
      (History)
   Brown, Lynda Joyce
      (History)
   Field, Jane
      (English)
   Gunnell, Paula
      (History)
   Walker, Robert Brian James
      (Politics)
   Walters, Thomas Stuart
      (History)
   Warburton, Susan
      (Politics)
   Williamson, Richard William
      (History)

General Degree—Pass
   Chapman, Richard Lawrence
      (History)
   Darke, Richard Abberley
      (History)
   Fairclough, David Alan
      (History)
   Griffin, Kevin William
      (Economics)
   Machin, Alan
      (History)
   Middle, Philippe Charles
      (History)
   Miller, Susan Ann
      (History)
   Needham, Jennifer
      (English)
   Nicholson, Margaret Ruth
      (History)
   Payne, Susan Margaret
      (History)
   Rigby, Janet Ann
      (Geology)
   Tringham, Christine Gwen
      (Economics)

FACULTY OF SCIENCE

First Class Honours

   Moore, Timothy Richard

Upper Second Class Honours
   Coggins, Philip Christopher
   Cuthill, Robert John
   Day, Susan Maud
   Hobbs, Gordon Rowland
   MacCallum, Kenneth Dugald

   Roberts, Valerie
   Webster, Peter Naylor
   Wrigley, John David

Lower Second Class Honours
   Allen, Susan Mary
   Cornelius, Alison Margaret
   Haden, Patricia Elizabeth
   Hammond, Michael
   Hurdle, Bridget Mary
   Painter, Anthony Guy
   Rudd, John
   Smethurst, Sandra

Third Class Honours
   Brindley, Jane Veronica
   Clayton, Charles Allen

General Degree—Second Class
   Fromel, Gustav Heinrich
      (Geology)
   Healey, Christopher Martin
      (Geology)
   Mitchell, Howard Evan
      (Geology)
   Pugh, Michael
      (Geology)
   Scott, Elizabeth Alison
      (Geology)
   Smith, Brenda Elizabeth
      (Geology)
   Spratley, Lindsay Christopher
      (Economics)
   Thomas, Robert Wayne
      (Economics)
   Winter, David John
      (Geology)

General Degree—Pass
   Angus, David Russell
      (Geology)
   Clement, Carolyn Grace
      (Geology)
   Cornish, John Patrick
      (Geology)
   Davidson, Stephen Stanwix
      (Geology)
   Ellis, David John
      (Geology)
   Fewster, Kathryn Margaret
      (Geology)
   Flynn, Kerry Patricia
      (Geology)
   Hackett, Christine Elizabeth
      (Geology)
   John, David Gwyn Roderick
      (Geology)

Kerley, David Geoffrey
  (Geology)
Love, Angela Francis
  (Geology)
Morris, Sheila
  (Geology)
Moss, Christine Pamela
  (Geology)
Thomas, Anthony Richard
  (Geology)
Thomas, Bronwen
  (Geology)
Turner, John George
  (Economics)
Williams, Mair Lois
  (Geology)
Williams, Rita
  (Geology)
Wilson, Christine Frances
  (Geology)

FACULTY OF ECONOMIC AND SOCIAL STUDIES

Upper Second Class Honours
Jones, John Wynne
  (Social Administration)

Lower Second Class Honours
Allen, John
  (Anthropology)
Brian, Michael Anthony
  (Anthropology)
Leigh, Richard Francis
  (Sociology)
May, Robert Morley
  (Sociology)
Morgan, Sybil Margaret
  (Social Administration)
Nichols, Caroline Ann
  (Sociology)
Smithson, Carol Ann Messervy
  (Politics)

1969

External Examiners: Professor J. C. Pugh and Dr. W. B. Morgan

FACULTY OF ARTS

First Class Honours
Barrett, Gillian Frances
Parker, Dennis John

Upper Second Class Honours
Brown, Laurence Harry
Coulson, Martin Geoffrey

Darlington, James
Davies, Jennifer Lynne
Goodchild, Patricia Ann
Hoffman, Elizabeth Adeline
Latronico, Peter Aubrey
Price, Wendy Elizabeth
Thomas, Veronica

Lower Second Class Honours
Bowen, Eric
Harold, Patrick Christopher
Jones, Stephen Douglas
Kerry, David John
Leigh, Barry Franklin
Morgan, Rhiain
Morris, Christine
Nilen, John Michael
Parkin, Linda Elizabeth
Soopramanien, Vijaya Lakshmi
Ternent, Joan

Joint Degree—Upper Second Class Honours
Blacker, Janet Elizabeth
  (American Studies)
Dean, Christopher John
  (American Studies)

Joint Degree—Lower Second Class Honours
Cunningham, Rosalind Elizabeth
  (American Studies)
Garside, Valerie
  (American Studies)
Hughes, Jennifer
  (American Studies)
McGuinness, Patricia Anne
  (American Studies)
Salt, Susan Mary
  (American Studies)
Scott, Martin, Noel
  (American Studies)

General Degree—First Class
Ashton, Owen Robert
  (History)

General Degree—Second Class
Ash, Jennifer Anne
  (History)
Clare, Christine Elizabeth
  (English)
Nicholls, Gareth Walter Owen
  (History)
Oldham, Catherine Alison
  (History)
Price, Robert Dan
  (Economics)
Ryder, Pamela
  (Philosophy)

General Degree—Pass
Hones, Trevor Edward
  (History)
Jones, Creina Emily
  (Politics)
Lewis, Janet
  (English)
Morley, Robert
  (History)
Thomas, Paul Roger
  (English)
Wynes, Laurence John
  (History)

FACULTY OF SCIENCE

Upper Second Class Honours
Eales, Nicholas John
Halliday, Linda Jane
Jones, Alun Dudley
Reece, Craig
Stafford, Pamela Mary
Taylor, Alan Carruthers
Thomas Gwilym Hywel

Lower Second Class Honours
Chapman, Timothy John
Duggan, Allan Anthony
Inder, Raymond Arthur
Lewis, Anna Esyllt
Luckie, Lorna Margaret
Thynne, Robert Philip

General Degree—Second Class
Atkinson, David Alan
  (Geology)
Fergusson, Patricia Ann
  (Geology)
Williams, David Banner
  (Geology)
Woodman, Glyn Adrian
  (Geology)

General Degree—Pass
Brown, Jeffrey Aldred
  (Geology)
Foley, Margaret Mary
  (Geology)
Garland, Geraldine Susan
  (Geology)
Gwilym, Robert David
  (Geology)
Haywood, Ruth
  (Geology)
Hulse, Mary Elizabeth
  (Geology)

Ray, Christopher Charles
  (Geology)
Summerscales, Margaret Christabel
  (Geology)
Thomson, Sandra Lesley
  (Geology)
Webster, Joan
  (Geology)
Williams, Barbara Jane
  (Geology)

FACULTY OF ECONOMIC AND SOCIAL STUDIES

Upper Second Class Honours
Barrow, Graham Timothy
  (Sociology)
Maloney, Eileen Mary
  (Sociology)
Morgan, David William
  (Economic & Social History)
Powell, Elizabeth Jane
  (Psychology)
Strange, Derek William
  (Economic & Social History)
Taylor, Sheila Lynne
  (Economic & Social History)
Telford, Keith
  (Economics)
Woods, Margaret Elaine
  (Psychology)

Lower Second Class Honours
Blatchford, Elizabeth Ann
  (Psychology, Economic & Social History)
Bowers, Michael Randall
  (Anthropology)
Briggs, Michael Andrew
  (Sociology)
Cackett, Raymond Henry William
  (Economics)
Cox, Patricia
  (Sociology)
Davies, Martin Bowen
  (Economics)
Evans, Patricia Anne
  (Anthropology)
Hickson, Simon Barry
  (Anthropology)
Lawson, David John
  (Economics)
Nuttall, Donald Barry Alfred
  (Economics)
Sparrow, John Alexander
  (Economics)

Trevelyan, Linda
 (Social Administration)
Williams, David Howell Lloyd
 (Economic & Social History)

Third Class Honours
 Saunders, Christopher Philip
 (Sociology)

1970

**External Examiners: Professor J. C. Pugh
and Dr. W. B. Morgan**

FACULTY OF ARTS

First Class Honours
 Matthews, Michael Hugh

Upper Second Class Honours
 Ansell, Paul Murray
 Bancroft, Clifford Gordon
 Egerton, John Graham
 Lansley, Timothy John
 Meek, Cherrylyn
 Ryan, Stephen John
 Stokes, Ann
 Trebble, Dennis William
 Watkins, Robert Edward

Lower Second Class Honours
 Butler, John Leslie
 Clarke, Stephen King
 Fouweather, Jeremy
 Hughes, Meryl Elizabeth
 Kitchiner, Paul Dudley
 Lawrence, Stephen
 Richards, John Clifford
 Ripper, Helen Mary
 Stonehouse, Alan

Joint Degree—Lower Second Class Honours
 McAleer, James Raymond
 (American Studies)

General Degree—Second Class
 Thomas, Hadyn Samuel
 (History)

General Degree—Pass
 Bowman, Neil Barry
 (History)
 Buckley, Robert Andrew Rashleigh Rede
 (History)
 Caldon, Michael
 (Economics)
 Dodson, Jaqueline June
 (Economics)

Dryburgh, Margaret
 (Economics)
Evans, Ralph Stuart
 (English)
Hayward, Vivien Jessica
 (English)
Simpson, Monica Ann
 (English)

FACULTY OF SCIENCE

First Class Honours
 Sanders, Christopher James

Upper Second Class Honours
 Challinor, Philip Charles
 Mills, John Rickson
 Thomas, Barbara Ann
 Wilson, Wendy Lorraine
 Wooldridge, Christopher Frederick

Lower Second Class Honours
 Baker, Mary
 Browning, Hilary Margaret
 Browning, Sarah Catherine
 Davies, Huw Rhidian Clement
 Harrison, Martyn
 Horton, John Edward
 Howard, Aileen Mary
 Kettel, Geoffrey Alan
 Mellor, Graham Pugh
 Pearce, Christopher David
 Roberts, John Martyn

Joint Degree—Upper Second Class Honours
 Carver, Margaret Anne
 (Geology)
 Harper, Janet
 (Geology)
 Smith, Steven
 (Botany)
 Williams, Valerie Joy
 (Geology)

Joint Degree—Lower Second Class Honours
 Clarke, Maureen Mary
 (Geology)
 Clewer, Angela Mary
 (Geology)
 Hartston, James Frederick
 (Oceanography)
 Jackson, Susan Ann
 (Geology)
 Jones, Hilary Ann
 (Geology)
 Roberts, Ann
 (Oceanography)
 Twist, John Rankin Melville
 (Geology)

Joint Degree—Third Class Honours
Harris, Norman Graham
(Oceanography)

General Degree—Second Class
Newton, Daphne Gay
(Oceanography)
Tarbuck, Karin Elizabeth
(Oceanography)

General Degree—Pass
Charlesworth, Richard Gregory
(Psychology)
Davies, Alan Jeffrey
(Economics)
Furlong, Lorraine Alice Mary
(Geology)
James, James William Ceri
(Geology)
Lee, John Royden
(Oceanography)
Price, Malcolm John Teague
(Economics)
Rowley, Christopher Darryl Raymond
(Geology)
Thurlow, William James
(Oceanography)
Williams, Margaret Diane
(Oceanography)

Aegrotat
Perens, Reinhold Kirstjan
(Oceanography)

FACULTY OF ECONOMIC AND SOCIAL STUDIES

First Class Honours
Gebbett, Stephen Henry
(Social Administration)

Upper Second Class Honours
Aldred, David Harold
(Economic & Social History)
Bachmann, Nigel Werner Roger
(Economic & Social History)
Handford, Annette Rosemary
(Social Administration)
Hardman, Bruce Peter
(Economic & Social History)
Orchard, Kerry Jonathan
(Sociology)
Pond, Christopher
(Politics)
Shaw, Jennifer
(Politics)
Smythe, Reginald Lester
(Sociology)

Stephens, Freda Jane
(Sociology)
Walker, Raymond
(Social Administration)

Lower Second Class Honours
Billingham, Clive John
(Economic & Social History)
Burrell, David John
(Economics)
Castles, David George
(Sociology)
Collingwood, Ian Rodney
(Sociology)
Deery, Gregory Sean
(Sociology)
Duguid, Allan Garson
(Sociology)
England, Gillian
(Social Administration)
Fowler, Alan Bernard
(Sociology)
Irwin, David Michael
(Economics)
John, Vincent Nicholas Michael
(Sociology)
Joseph, Barbara Shan
(Sociology)
Mansfield, Christina Margaret Bentley
(Sociology)
Merrall, Richard Ewart
(Economics)
Mills, Ruth
(Politics)
Mortimer, Stephen William
(Economics)
McArdle, Colin James
(Politics)
Newton, Alice Veronica
(Social Administration)
Pearson, Robin Edward
(Politics)
Rathkey, Michael
(Politics)
Stevenson, Elaine Clare
(Economic & Social History)
Todd, Paul Richard
(Economic & Social History)
Wade, Ian Colin
(Sociology)
Wait, Donald
(Sociology)
Wilson, Raymond Trevor
(Economics)
Yarwood, Jennifer Renee
(Sociology)

Young, David John
(Sociology)

Third Class Honours
Sherwin, Joy Pauline
(Anthropology)

Pass Degree
Cawthron, Ian Neville
(Sociology)
Fenney, Christopher John
(Politics)
Hughes, Graham Harvey
(Economic & Social History)

1971

**External Examiners: Professor N. Pye and
Dr. P. R. Mounfield**

FACULTY OF ARTS

Upper Second Class Honours
Dykes, John Barry
Hall, Kevin John
Hampshire, Barry
Hewitt, Graham
Hume, Robert Arthur
Sharples, Graham
Wilson, Charles Morgan

Lower Second Class Honours
Best, John Henry
Blackman, Janet Avis
Evans, Stephen Peter
Halstead, Alan Hartley
Kedward, Alan John
Roberts, Geraint Jones
Williams, Mervyn Charles

Third Class Honours
Lang, Marian Heather

Joint Degree—Upper Second Class Honours
Wheatley, Philip Ormerod
(American Studies)
Williams, Cynthia Isobel
(History)

Joint Degree—Lower Second Class Honours
Bowyer, Paul Mitchell
(History)
Harrison, Lynne
(American Studies)
Phillips, Lyn
(History)
Silo, Stephen Laurence
(History)

Young, Nigel St. John
(American Studies)

Joint Degree—Third Class Honours
Downs, Rita Anna
(History)
Frith, Susan
(English)

General Degree—Second Class
Thomas, Malcolm David
(Politics)

General Degree—Pass
Lloyd, Mary Elisabeth
(Philosophy)
Walburn, John Hulme
(English)

FACULTY OF SCIENCE

First Class Honours
Deeley, Sheila Lynne

Upper Second Class Honours
Brown, David Derrick
Cook, Kevin
Davies, Stephen Vaughan
Draper, Susan Jennifer
Emms, Janet Elizabeth
Ireland, Nicholas Frederick
Naylor, Graham Leonard
Punnett, Laurence Michael
Rees, Marilyn Anne
Tervet, Peter Alexander

Lower Second Class Honours
Aitken, Roger William
Brock, David Michael
Coombes, Ann
Goddard, David John
Hatch, Elizabeth Anne
Hughes, John Mervyn
Keeble, Marston Charles
McGowan, David John
Paget, Henry Graham
Sunderland, Elaine Elizabeth

Third Class Honours
Davis, Anne Barbara Eileen
Pickthorne, Madeleine

Joint Degree—First Class Honours
Bent, Peter Francis
(Geology)

Joint Degree—Upper Second Class Honours
Jones, Ian Graham
(Geology)

Joint Degree—Lower Second Class Honours
  Davies, Marion Elizabeth
    (Geology)
  Fear, Michael Robert
    (Geology)
  Grierson, Donald Ian
    (Geology)
  Hughes, Kathlyn Moira
    (Geology)
  Roberts, Valerie
    (Oceanography)
  Thomas, Christopher John Arthur
    (Economics)
  Williams, Martin Robert
    (Geology)

Joint Degree—Third Class Honours
  Morgan, Janet Lydia
    (Geology)
  Morris, Peter John
    (Geology)
  Steel, Janet Elizabeth
    (Economics)
  Stocks, Andrew Elliott
    (Geology)
  Williams, Michael John
    (Geology)

General Degree—Pass
  Davies, Kerry Stephen
    (Economics)

FACULTY OF ECONOMIC AND SOCIAL STUDIES

Upper Second Class Honours
  Constable, Linda Joyce
    (Sociology)
  Foden, Helen Christine
    (Sociology)
  Hermet, Paula Howard
    (Psychology)
  Jepson, James Rodney
    (Economic & Social History)
  Line, David John
    (Economic & Social History)
  Little, Thomas Royston
    (Economic & Social History)
  Morrill, Glyn Perry
    (Economic & Social History)
  Osborne, Susan Mary
    (Anthropology)
  Prior, Robert Lloyd
    (Economics)
  Prowse, Michael John
    (Economic & Social History)

Redmayne, Terence Michael
  (Psychology)
Sayce, John Laverton
  (Politics)
Thomas, Keith
  (Politics)

Lower Second Class Honours
  Butler, Michael
    (Politics)
  Fennell, Kathryn
    (Sociology)
  Houghton, Rosemary Jane
    (Economic & Social History)
  Judd, Lydia Mary
    (Psychology)
  Leyland, Stewart Cliffe
    (Economic & Social History)
  Lyes, Susan Elizabeth
    (Sociology)
  Marrin, Alan
    (Politics)
  Matthews, David Lawrence
    (Sociology)
  Parker, Susan Annette
    (Sociology)
  Pittman, Catherine Mary
    (Politics)
  Puddifoot, Patricia Ann
    (Social Administration)
  Sands, John Arthur
    (Sociology)
  Smith, Susan Carole
    (Social Administration)
  Summers, Ann Caroline
    (Psychology)

Third Class Honours
  Holloway, David John
    (Economics)

Pass Degree
  Colegate, Peter Leslie
    (Sociology)

1972

External Examiners: Professor N. Pye and Dr. P. R. Mounfield

FACULTY OF ARTS

Upper Second Class Honours
  Brown, Christopher Leslie
  Chambers, Peter Robert
  Hopkins, Vivienne Ann
  Hurry, Graham Frank

Ilbery, Brian William
Packham, Richard William
Penn, Barry Edwin
Reed, John
Rolls, Philip Terence
Smith, Brian Robert
Timson, Valerie Jean Wreford
Way, Anthony Francis
Wiggett, Susan

Lower Second Class Honours
Atkins, Mary
Ault, James Christopher
Barton, John Allan
Bentley-Taylor, David Andrew
Braidwood, Christine Marjorie
Duffield, Philip John
Hardhill, Irene
Janes, Shirley Ann
Jordan, Neil Martin
Krejci, Teresa
Leighton, Norman
Rees, Michael Roderick
Rosney, Alan Stuart
Siddall, Lois Amanda
Smith, Alison Vernon
Stoker, Paul Timothy Parke

Third Class Honours
Amos, Christopher William
James, David Nicholas Llewelyn
Long, Doreen Judith
Neild, Pamela Diane

Joint Degree—First Class Honours
Grayson, Anatol Gregory
(American Studies)

Joint Degree—Upper Second Class Honours
Swaby, Clive Henry
(History)
Trower, Richard David
(History)

Joint Degree—Lower Second Class Honours
Fearnley, David Andrew
(History)

FACULTY OF SCIENCE

Upper Second Class Honours
Alderson, Susan Margaret
Bate, Thomas Hill
Bownes, John Stuart
Brocklehurst, Martin Stewart
Browne, Thomas Jarrold
Campbell, Vincent James
Faull, Ian Trevor

Greig, Neil Robert
Guthrie, Eleanor

Lower Second Class Honours
Amster, Rodney George
Beddoe, Pamela
Bell, Jeanette
Birch, Janet Lynn
Booth, Simon Mark
Brandrick, Susan Ann
Carder, Stephen John
Cox, Roger Alistair Douglas
Dellow, Allison
Humphries, Douglas Edwin
Jones, Martyn Eynon
King, Graham John
Lewis, Daniel Glyndwr
Morgan, Pamela Joan
Perkins, Beverley Anne
Radford, Alison Margaret
Thornton, Ian Parke
Tucker, Alastair Leslie Robert
Vick, Roger Ian
Wheeler, Mary Elizabeth
Wilcox, Brian John
Williams, Barbara Ann
Wisniewski, Stefan Richard

Third Class Honours
Dicketts, Geraldine Angela
Matthews, Anthony John
Powell, Christopher John

Aegrotat
Lusmore, Martin

Joint Degree—First Class Honours
Firstbrook, Peter Loveday
(Oceanography)

Joint Degree—Upper Second Class Honours
Tilley, Christine Gillian
(Geology)

Joint Degree—Lower Second Class Honours
Callingham, Peter
(Economics)
Culshaw, Simon Thomas
(Oceanography)
Jones, Edward Keith
(Geology)
Whitley, Norman
(Geology)

Joint Degree—Third Class Honours
Harrington, Philip James
(Geology)
Hart, Patricia Margaret Doris
(Geology)

FACULTY OF ECONOMIC AND SOCIAL STUDIES

First Class Honours
Williams, Allan Morgan
(Economics)
Williams, Colin
(Politics)

Upper Second Class Honours
Beardmore, David Arthur
(Russian Studies)
Bowen, Barry
(Politics)
Cheetham, Jane Ann
(Social Statistics)
Cox, Christopher John
(Economics)
Davies, Alun James
(Politics)
Fox, Jacqueline Mary
(Sociology)
Gaillard, Pauline Brenda
(Sociology)
Godwin, Brian George
(Economics)
Jones, Diana Susan
(Sociology)
Mellish, Dianna Maud
(Sociology)
Morgan, Derek John
(Economics)
Thomas, Alan Mathias
(Economics)
Watkin, Ann Elizabeth
(Politics)
Webster, David Charles Henry
(Sociology)

Lower Second Class Honours
Bateman, Christopher Dennis James
(Politics)
Cannon, Peter William
(Politics)
Evans, Elizabeth Marilyn
(Politics)
Hanton, Jonathan Joseph Alexander
(Sociology)
James, Stuart Hubert
(Sociology)
Jenkins, Pamela
(Economics)
Kirke, Robert Karl
(Economics)
Lewis, Judith Mary
(Russian Studies)

Morris, Richard Bryn
(Economics)
Mykura, Rosamund
(Economic & Social History)
Pyrke, John Robert
(Sociology)
Sharkey, John Francis
(Economics)
Slatter, Jennifer
(Sociology)
Sleeman, David Vincent Lloyd
(Anthropology)
Sugar, Caroline Joan Lorraine
(Social Administration)
Wiltshire, Avril Sheila
(Social Administration)

Third Class Honours
Bird, Graham Christian
(Sociology)
Eilbeck, Katherine Jean
(Sociology)
Prevett, Jennifer Ann
(Sociology)
Round, Priscilla Julia
(Sociology)

1973

External Examiners: Professor W. R. Mead and Dr. P. A. Wood

FACULTY OF ARTS

First Class Honours
Pritchard, Alan Poyner

Upper Second Class Honours
Bridges, David Newbold
Dinsdale, Susan Mary
Raine, John Watson
Stevens, Terence Richard
Wilkes, Keith Robert

Lower Second Class Honours
Basford, Michael
Bradley, Susan Elizabeth
Brettingham, Janet Christina
Clark, Anne Gillian
Clinton-Smith, Gwynyth Ruth
Farr, Martin Thomas John
Farwell, Edward Barry
Haines, Linda Jean
Kingston, Paul Charles
Langley, Peter
Leech, Patricia Anne
Lowden, Brian Joseph

Miles, Geoffrey Owen
Oliver, Mary Jane
Parry, Gordon Alexander
Reed, Frances
Stephens, Timothy Frank
Welbirg, Peter Julian Herbert

Third Class Honours
Allin, William Roy
Oakley, Katherine Mary
Spriggs, Christopher Michael

Joint Degree—Lower Second Class Honours
Andrews, Jeanette Winifred
  (History)
Anthony, Patricia Margaret
(American Studies)

FACULTY OF SCIENCE

First Class Honours
Harris, Philip Wynford Vernon

Upper Second Class Honours
Anstey, David Edward
Ash, Bernard Barrington
Buck, Gillian Patience
Faulkner, Ronald Henry
Ferguson, Marion Joan
Ferguson, Martin John
Kay, Jennifer Mary
Kennedy, Sheila Mary
Marston, Janet Margaret
Moffitt, Barry Johnstone
Parkins, Raymond John
Parry, Dinah Elizabeth
Samuel, Catherine Anne
Smith, Kelvin John
Svendsen, Christen

Lower Second Class Honours
Anderson, Diane Patricia
Cardis, Stephen William
Fenge, Terence Alfred Edward
Foster, Peter
Friend, Philip
Hall, Martin John
Holmes, Malcolm Alexander
Jerman, Susan
Keating, Philip Kenneth
Lidstone, Michael David
McCormick, David Thomas
Morris, Charles Edward
Murray, Kathleen Joan
Parkinson, Philip Michael
Pittis, Lynn Christine
Ralph, Alexandra Mary
Rees, Meurig Lewis

Rose, David
Smith, David Mark
Smith, David Robert
Tester, Anita Marion
Thomas, Peter
Townley, Frances Patricia
Wilkins, Adrian Christopher Charles
Window, Catherine Mary

Third Class Honours
Coates, Margaret Elaine
Gay, Malcolm
Stead, Paul Gregory

Joint Degree—Upper Second Class Honours
Bull, Peter Anthony
  (Geology)
MacPhail, Richard Ian
  (Geology)
Tomlinson, Shirley Elizabeth
  (Oceanography)

Joint Degree—Lower Second Class Honours
Reynolds, Robert Charles
  (Geology)

FACULTY OF ECONOMIC AND SOCIAL STUDIES

Upper Second Class Honours
Abbott, Howard Craig
  (Social Statistics)
Bishop, Margaret Ann
  (Russian Studies)
Clements, Malcolm Adrian
  (Economics)
Evans, Ian Leroy
  (Russian Studies)
Farnsworth, Vanessa Jeannette Emile
  (Sociology)
Garland, Beverly
  (Russian Studies)
Grover, Ruth Marian
  (Psychology)
Howard, Barbara Jane
  (Sociology)
Howes, Susan Winifred
  (Economic & Social History)
Martin, Geraldine Ada
  (Economic & Social History)
May, Judy Elizabeth
  (Anthropology)
Newman, Beti Bowen (Mrs)
  (Economic & Social History)
North, Elspeth Julia (née Bowyer)
  (Sociology)

Ogden, Frances Claire
(Psychology)
Thomas, Meryl Elizabeth
(Sociology)
Walsh, Patricia Jean
(Economics)
Warner, Susan
(Russian Studies)

Lower Second Class Honours
Barrow, Clive
(Economic & Social History)
Bourlet, Sheila Anne
(Anthropology)
Cavanagh, James
(Economic & Social History)
Clement, Peter John
(Russian Studies)
Crompton, Brenda Marion
(Social Statistics)
Evans, Christopher Paul Canton
(Economics)
Evans, Paul William Hywel
(Economic & Social History)
Gibbs, Jonathan James
(Russian Studies)
Hicks, Martin Frederick
(Russian Studies)
Hicks, Peter Lawrence
(Economic & Social History)
Hodgson, Jane Cecilia
(Psychology)
Howell, Lyn David
(Psychology)
Lodwick, Ceridwen
(Psychology)
Morris, Janet Helen
(Sociology)
McQuillan, Wendy
(Sociology)
Partridge, Ann
(Russian Studies)
Powell, John Evan
(Economic & Social History)
Reardon, Timothy
(Economics)
Reeves, Michael Frank
(Economic & Social History)
Roach, Wendy
(Psychology)
Steel, Carol
(Russian Studies)
Taylor, Pamela Elaine
(Anthropology)
Watling, Lynn Alison
(Social Administration)

Weekes, Jane Alison
(Psychology)
Williams, Caroline Anne
(Sociology)

Third Class Honours
James, Philip Douglas Reeby
(Economics)
Watkeys, Mary
(Social Administration)

Pass Degree
Waugh, William Blair
(Social Administration)

1974
External Examiners: Professor W. R. Mead and Dr. P. A. Wood

FACULTY OF ARTS

Upper Second Class Honours
Bardon, Keith Sellers
Cattle, Larry Alan
Cowell, Mary Elizabeth
Evans, Kenneth Royston
Grose, Susan Carol
Hopkin, Jean Margaret
Mellor, Kathryn Jane
Molyneaux, Ann Elizabeth
Peace, Sheila Marjorie
Price, Jane Elizabeth Dagwell
Rendell, Eileen Elizabeth

Lower Second Class Honours
Bootherstone, Trevor
Brown, Alison Lindsay
Crowther, Winifred Louise
Dickins, Michael Anthony
Fancett, Derek John
Farnham, Timothy Charles
George, Robert
Giddings, David John
Gregg, Ian
Harris, Eleanor Frances
Mercer, Edward Charles
Monk, Jane
Morgan, Christine
Pritchard, Richard Adrian
Reed, Kenneth Anthony
Richardson, Jayne Mary
Robson, Stephen Richard
Taylor, Grahame John
Tripp, Jane Elizabeth
Walters, Sally Ann

Third Class Honours
Dalgliesh, Alexander Douglas Robertson
Fawdry, Christopher Stephen
Morrison, Robert Richard
Redman, Wendy Elizabeth
Ruck, Gary Neville

FACULTY OF SCIENCE

Upper Second Class Honours
Barnes, Chistopher Thomas
Bell, Margaret Joan
Griffiths, David James
Hughes, Mary Erica
Keith, Barbara Ann
Robinson, David Martin
Rogers, Kevin William
Tily, Sheila Barbara
Wells, Rosemary Catherine

Lower Second Class Honours
Beasley, Martin Thomas
Campbell, Rosanne Elizabeth
Cooke, Janet Elizabeth
Flaherty, Josephine Ann
Lewis, Kenneth John
Lyons, Shirley Ann
Moffatt, Keith Anthony
Morgan, Susan Elizabeth
Nelms, Carole Ann
Reed, John Bulkeley
Warren, Elizabeth
Watling, Pamela Joy
Williams, Clive Graham

Third Class Honours
Hearne, Jane

Pass Degree
Matthews, David Brian

Joint Degree—Upper Second Class Honours
Astin, Julie Kay
(Oceanography)
Banner, Jacqueline Ann
(Oceanography)

Joint Degree—Lower Second Class Honours
Anthony, Peter John
(Oceanography)

Joint Degree—Third Class Honours
Curtis, Julia
(Oceanography)

FACULTY OF ECONOMIC AND SOCIAL STUDIES

First Class Honours
Littler, Alison Susan
(Economic & Social History)
Littler, Stephen Maurice
(Economics)
Phillips, David
(Economics)
Phillips, David Rosser
(Russian Studies)

Upper Second Class Honours
Bedford, Robert Laurence
(Anthropology)
Bostel, Linda Margaret
(Social Administration)
Cooper, Alec
(Social Administration)
Cushway, Elisabeth Margaret
(Economic & Social History)
Hardman, Anne
(Russian Studies)
Jones, Sian Eleri
(Russian Studies)
Mizen, Julia Constance
(Social Administration)
O'Boyle, Rita Elizabeth
(Anthropology)

Lower Second Class Honours
Anelay, Juliette Mary Elizabeth
(Social Statistics)
Baker, Jonathan Paul
(Economics)
Brannon, Alan John
(Social Administration)
Broderick, Hanoria Helena
(Social Administration)
Clark, John Alexander
(Economics)
Davies, Mark Wright
(Russian Studies)
Davis, Elisabeth Anne
(Economic & Social History)
Eaglesham, James Hastings
(Economics)
Evans, Marshall Owen
(Economics)
Faull, Arlene Moyra
(Russian Studies)
Fudge, Lynda Christine
(Russian Studies)
Hawkins, Janet Anne
(Russian Studies)

Jones, Lynne
(Russian Studies)
Law, Judith Ann
(Politics)
Lee, Marion
(Sociology)
Levison, Stephen
(Russian Studies)
Matthews, Jeffrey Thomas
(Russian Studies)
Naylor, Lynne
(Sociology)
O'Brien, Philip Edward
(Economics)
Purcell, Alison Mary Osment
(Sociology)
Randle, Deborah Mary
(Psychology)
Slee, Veronica Mary
(Economic & Social History)
Smith, Patricia
(Economic & Social History)
Smout, Linda Jane
(Anthropology)
Spencer, Geoffrey
(Sociology)
Stoker, Marilyn Denise
(Anthropology)
Washbrook, Keith Leonard
(Social Administration)
Westbury, Anthony Mark
(Russian Studies)
Wright, Jennifer Coral
(Psychology)

Third Class Honours
Tooker, Paul Gregory
(Politics)
Yates, Julie Margaret
(Social Administration)

Pass Degree
James, Michael Foster
(Sociology)

1975

**External Examiners: Professor J. H. Bird and
Dr. I. B. Thompson**

FACULTY OF ARTS

Upper Second Class Honours
Bird, Stephen Dennis
Bowie, Mary
Fletcher, Stephen
Goddard, Nigel

Harrington, Jane Victoria
Hopkin, John William
Jeffrey, Anita Lynne
Laverick, Colin John
Little, Christopher Richard
Nicol, Simon Paul
Rogers, Audrey
Victor, Christina Rita

Lower Second Class Honours
Borton, Diana
Carpenter, Ian Robert
Dewberry, Rosalynd Patricia
Gilliland, Kevin Nigel
Hodgson, Carolyn Mary
Hulin, Albert Norman
Latty, Ann Elizabeth
Smyth, William Stephen
Thomas, Alun Richard
Trotman, Paul John
Vinicombe, Keith Edgar
Webb, Elizabeth Mary
Wilson, James Andrew

Joint Degree—Upper Second Class Honours
Battye, Robert Anthony
(History)
Brown, Richard
(History)

Joint Degree—Lower Second Class Honours
Davies, Gerald Clive
(Politics)
Finch, David Graham
(English)

Joint Degree—Third Class Honours
Cookson, Michael Andrew
(Politics)

FACULTY OF SCIENCE

First Class Honours
Costigan, Gillian Irene

Upper Second Class Honours
Clarke, Derek
Coles, Hilary
Evans, David William
Hogarth, Janice Elizabeth
Hollowood, Stephen John
Joy, Raymond James
Knights, Penelope Clare
Lewis, Janet Louise
Lloyd, Patricia Ann
Smith, David Allison
Streatfeild, Christopher David
Wayman, Janet Ann

Lower Second Class Honours
Bewick, Colin Trevor
Bishop, Marilyn
Hughes, Richard Geraint
Kennedy, Barbara Eileen
Lane, Christopher Andrew
Martin, Sarah Elizabeth
McLean, Neil Playel
Mole, Miriam Ann
Phillips, Rhian Mair
Phillips, Robert Bernard
Poole, Melanie Christine
Rawsthorne, Malcolm John
Thorne, Sandra
Twemlow, Mark
Unwin, Allason Rosemary

Third Class Honours
Bevan, Kathryn Ann

Joint Degree—Upper Second Class Honours
Matthews, Charles Lewis
(Oceanography)

Joint Degree—Lower Second Class Honours
Doughty, Richard Charles
(Oceanography)
Saganowski, Angela Rose
(Oceanography)
Smith, Michael John
(Oceanography)

FACULTY OF ECONOMIC AND SOCIAL STUDIES

Upper Second Class Honours
Arthur, Stephen Vincent
(Economics)
Evans, John Andrew
(Russian Studies)
Keene, Judith Helen
(Sociology)
Light, Byron
(Politics)
Marston, Judith Margaret
(Sociology)
Muir, Andrew Robert
(Economics)
Powell, Simon Rhys
(Anthropology)
Roberts, Elaine Clare
(Russian Studies)
Scott, Frances Kay
(Anthropology)
Strange, Keith
(Economic & Social History)

Thomas, Wendy Annette
(Russian Studies)
Turtle, Anne Catherine
(Social Statistics)
Wardley, Peter
(Economic & Social History)

Lower Second Class Honours
Ajao, Adenihun Olanrewaju
(Economics)
Bale, Nicholas Mark
(Social Statistics)
Beacham, David Morgan
(Social Statistics)
Castiaux, Donald Philip
(Anthropology)
Chrostowski, David
(Russian Studies)
Cleaver, David
(Economic & Social History)
Coates, Colin Roy
(Social Statistics)
Commons, Anthony Gerrard
(Sociology)
Cove, John Patrick
(Politics)
Donoghue, Carole Lucy
(Russian Studies)
Dumelow, Keith
(Economic & Social History)
Farnell, Roger
(Anthropology)
Ford, Richard Anthony Jack
(Sociology)
Guthrie, Rosalyn
(Social Administration)
Higgins, Ronald Peter
(Politics)
Jackson, Keith Robert
(Sociology)
Johnson, Anne Hilary
(Russian Studies)
Kilgallon, Anthony John
(Russian Studies)
Knowles, Inga Margaret
(Social Administration)
Lasky, Anne Beverley
(Social Administration)
Morgan, Margaret Elizabeth
(Sociology)
Murphy, James John
(Politics)
Palmer, Jill
(Russian Studies)
Pomeroy, David John
(Social Administration)

Pritchard, Doris May
(Russian Studies)
Smellie, Sarah Louise
(Psychology)
Snowdon, Michael John
(Economic & Social History)
Thomas, Anne Marie
(Russian Studies)
Vaughan, Judith Ann
(Economic & Social History)
West, Elizabeth Anne
(Anthropology)
Wildy, Sarah
(Anthropology)
Williamson, James Christopher
(Economics)
Wood, Nicholas Charles Haddon
(Russian Studies)

Third Class Honours
Tkaczenko, Igor
(Russian Studies)

Aegrotat
Jones, Wynne
(Economics)

1976

External Examiners: Professor J. H. Bird and Dr. I. B. Thompson

FACULTY OF ARTS

First Class Honours
Neil, Heather Joy

Upper Second Class Honours
Dennis, Keith Frederick
Hitchenor, Anne
Jaeger, Deborah Olwyn
King, Michael David
Lawler, Damian Maurice
Lewis, Cheryl Anne
Lewis, David Hywel
Page, Judith Mary
Watts, Christine Alicia
Williams, Joy Christine
Williams, Rhian

Lower Second Class Honours
Beckett, Kevin John
Dewhirst, Susan Lesley
Duggan, Jennifer Jane
Dye, Phyllis Michele
Gell, Brian Crompton
Gower, Joanne Mary
Harwood, George
Hill, Elisabeth Mary

Jones, Byron
Jones, Sheryl Ann
Male, Peter
Marsden, John Clifford
McKevitt, Philip John
Mullet, Jane Hilary
Quarrell, Gerald Martin
Tansley, Gwendoline Vivien
Targett, Vivienne
Weaver, Nigel James

Third Class Honours
Watkins, Linda Anne

Joint Degree—Lower Second Class Honours
Targett, Adrian Neil
(History)

FACULTY OF SCIENCE

Upper Second Class Honours
Ames, Denise
Bartlett, Linda Audrey
Cooper, Paul Anthony
Cullen, Geraldine Bridget
Day, Terence Edward
Douglas, Anthony Denard
Hawkins, Clive
Hickey, Christine Sheila
Keble, Clive William
Le Hardy, Jane Allison
Liddell, John Michael Robert
Palmer, Gillian Rosemary
Thompson, Susan Joan
Widdows, Julia Carol
Williams, Allan Geoffrey

Lower Second Class Honours
Bruce, Leonard Kevin
Davies, William Ivor
Dewhirst, Rachel Margaret
Dole, Sheridan
Edwards, Gareth Roy
Gill, Gerald Patrick
Hewlett, Michael Edward Kilby
Hill, Tony
Irving, Diana Hilary
Knowles, Richard Burbidge
Mitchell, John
Randy, Nigel Ernest
Tarris, Philip Geoffrey
Taylor, Christine
Thomas, Peter Jack
Yates, Catherine Wendy

Third Class Honours
Lawrance, John Deacon
Liggett, Iain Richard

Lucas, Mark Charles
Trevis, Anthony William Harold

Joint Degree—Upper Second Class Honours
Booker, Ian Robert
(Oceanography)

Joint Degree—Lower Second Class Honours
Howard, Nina Elizabeth
(Biology)
Sanday, Paul Victor
(Geology)
Hildred, Keith
(Oceanography)
Stogdon, Lucy Christian
(Geology)
Glydon-Jones, Elizabeth Claire
(Oceanography)

Joint Degree—Third Class Honours
Rees, John Blain Minto
(Oceanography)

FACULTY OF ECONOMIC AND SOCIAL STUDIES

Upper Second Class Honours
Coatham, Veronica Mary
(Social Administration)
Fox, Susan Elizabeth
(Social Administration)
Goodwin, Aneurin Bennett
(Russian Studies)
Greenwood, Anthony Philip
(Social Administration)
Lawrence, Kim
(Economics)
Lovering, Rosemary Ann
(Social Statistics)
Mawe, Michael Charles
(Russian Studies)
Sawey, Mary Patricia
(Politics)
Webb, Janet Mary
(Politics)
Williams, Ann Elizabeth
(Economic & Social History)
Williams, Anne Penelope
(Social Administration)

Lower Second Class Honours
Blezard, Raymond Andrew
(Economic & Social History)
Butler, John David
(Economics)
Clarke, David Ellwood
(Social Administration)

Cowell, Jane Elizabeth Mahala
(Social Administration)
Davies, Derek Vivian
(Social Administration)
Davies, Peter Roger
(Social Administration)
Evans, David Henry
(Economics)
Fidkin, Maureen
(Economic & Social History)
Henley, Susan June
(Psychology)
John, Anthony Wayne
(Economics)
Kelly, Susan Mary
(Social Administration)
Kinsella, Margaret Clare
(Social Administration)
Mason, Timothy
(Economics)
Murray, Hilary Anne
(Economic & Social History)
O'Shea, John Timothy
(Politics)
Parker, Kathleen Anne
(Anthropology)
Powicke, David John
(Politics)
Rigby, Martin William
(Politics)
Thomas, Dewi Alun
(Social Administration)
Thomas, Lynne
(Russian Studies)
Wildash, Susan Mary
(Social Administration)
Wilkes, Heather Josephine
(Sociology)
Williams, Gareth Leslie
(Psychology)

Third Class Honours
Stephens, Patricia
(Sociology)

Pass Degree
Wootton, Philip Bruce
(Politics)

1977
External Examiners: Professor S. Gregory and Mr. A. Hunt

FACULTY OF ARTS

Upper Second Class Honours
Breeze, Eleanor Sara

Hall, Elaine Margaret
Jones, James Victor Hogarth
Langridge, Alison Jean
Leach, Nigel
Ley, Diane Clare
Murdoch, Brian Maxwell
Parry, Mary Penelope
Quinn, Valerie Jane
Rodway, Sian Ellen Margaret
Thomas, Helen Louise
Tyler, Douglas John

Lower Second Class Honours
Brown, Susan Anne
Burry, Angela Maria
Cotton, John Frederick
Cox, John Robert
Davies, Brian
Garrett, Peter Michael
Jones, Brian Glynne
Jones, Gruffydd John Phillips
Keville, Christopher Francis
Lamarque, Rene Colin
Lingard, Sarah Elizabeth
Pegum, Diana Julie
Samuel, Lyndon
Smith, Christine Margaret
Warr, Julie
Watson, Dianne Jane
Whittington, Marion Edith

Third Class Honours
Gravelle, Glenda Mary
Hodgetts, Keith David

FACULTY OF SCIENCE

Upper Second Class Honours
Anderson, Robert
Ashworth, Paul Francis
Bland, Graham Clive
Brown, Philip Andrew
Davis, Timothy John
Dorman, Philippa Mary
Evans, Geoffrey Barton
Harper, Robert Lindsay
Jones, Gwynfa Vanessa
Jones, Robert Douglas
McGoldrick, Edward Peter
Morland, Christine Mary
Pearson, Jacqueline Moira
Thomas, David
Wright, Elizabeth Margaret Jeanetta

Lower Second Class Honours
Bevan, David Paul
Bickley, Amanda Jane

Davies, Mary Yvonne
Dawes, Susan Marina
Dickinson, Jonathan Andrew
Edwards, Ceri
Goodwin, Sarah
Gray, Paul Stanley
Hunt, Michael Joseph
Mason, Malcolm Asquith
Scott, Laurence Charles
Webster, Martin
Whitehead, David Gerard
Willcocks, Steven Roy
Wormington, Sharon Jane

Third Class Honours
Griffiths, Paul Richard
Spear, Clare Maria

Joint Degree—First Class Honours
Goodwin, Karen
(Botany)

Joint Degree—Upper Second Class Honours
Knight, Michael Peter
(Geology)

Joint Degree—Third Class Honours
McGlynn, John
(Geology)

FACULTY OF ECONOMIC AND SOCIAL STUDIES

Upper Second Class Honours
Babbage, Susan Elizabeth
(Russian Studies)
Dragun, Anna Lucja
(Russian Studies)
Fry, Nicholas Richard
(Economics)
Hay, Susan Alexandra
(Social Administration)
Langdon, Amanda Clare
(Social History)
Morgan, Huw James
(Social History)
Neal, Julie Carolyn
(Social History)
Tonks, Stephen George
(Social History)

Lower Second Class Honours
Bailey, Graham Denis
(Social Administration)
Barron, Heather
(Psychology)
Duke, Penelope Jane
(Social Administration)

Easton, Guy Jonathan
  (*Politics*)
Edwards, Pauline Ann
  (*Russian Studies*)
Evans, Christopher Frank
  (*Economics*)
Gatis, Robert Ewen
  (*Social Statistics*)
Hinds, John Gwynn
  (*Economic History*)
Hopkins, Kenneth Michael
  (*Economics*)
James, Alistair John
  (*Politics*)
Jones, Helen Anne
  (*Russian Studies*)
Jones, Susan Felicity
  (*Anthropology*)
Margerison, Nigel John
  (*Sociology*)
Merry, Susan Cowan
  (*Anthropology*)
Morris, Kathryn
  (*Social Administration*)
Morris, Sharon Ann
  (*Social History*)
Nash, Susan Gail
  (*Social History*)
Pierce, Susan Mary
  (*Sociology*)
Ryder, David
  (*Psychology*)
Stowe, Nigel Justyn
  (*Social Administration*)
Thomas, Ann Turnbull
  (*Social Administration*)
Triscott, David Reginald Stewart
  (*Economics*)

Third Class Honours
Crockett, Kim Joanne
  (*Economic History*)
Glapinski, Gordon Zenon
  (*Economics*)
Nunn, Angela Elizabeth May
  (*Economics*)

1978
External Examiners: Professor S. Gregory and Mr. A. Hunt

FACULTY OF ARTS

First Class Honours
Taylor, Thomas Geoffrey

Upper Second Class Honours
Booker, Jane Mary
Day, Christine Gillian
Fletcher, Debra Mary
Hawkins, Alan Charles
Jones, Kathryn Margaret
Maddy, John Donald Macrae
Matthias, Anthony Christopher
Mosley, Julie
Penny, Nicholas James
Quinn, Derek John
Sadler, Iona Margaret
Taylor, Lynn Patricia
Trollope, Denise Elizabeth
Vaughan, Elizabeth Tegwen
Williams, Glynis

Lower Second Class Honours
Brereton, Donal Marius
Colville, June Betty
Coster, Susan Jane
Dew, Christopher John
Draycott, Kay
Foster, Stephen Geoffrey
Haines, Marion Christine
Hawkings, Dylan John
Horwat, Elzbieta Teresa
Mundy, Ian Douglas
Perks, Lindsey Anne
Perry, Anthony David
Tidd, Andrea Jane
Todd, Charles James Graham
Walton, Nicola Anne

Third Class Honours
Dowdall, Jayne Penelope
James, Rhiannon
Sanchez, Elvira
Stephens, Glenn Melvyn
Turner, Christopher David
Woods, Michael Ellis

FACULTY OF SCIENCE

Upper Second Class Honours
Aust, Martin John
Bridges, Karen
Harwood, Rosalyn
High, Frances Clare
Humphrey, Norman Ian
Lockey, Roger John
Moore, Andrew
Rowland, Richard Arthur
Smettem, Keith Richard John
Tickle, David William
Williams, Philip James

Lower Second Class Honours
Atkinson, Pamela Miriam
Barr, Linda
Bate, Martin Edward
Charles, Gareth Wyn
Clark, Alan James
Evans, Janet
Hockridge, Gerrad Allen James
Lamboll, Richard Ian
Long, Paul Robert
Martin, Michael David
Moran, Paul Anthony
Stirk, Peter John
Swain, Stephen Andrew
Trickett, Anthony Charles
Walters, Linda
Watkins, Julia Cathryn
Welsh, Peter Anthony
Widdows, Deborah Jane
Williams, John Keith

Third Class Honours
Chidgey, Janie
Griffiths, Elizabeth Ann
Thomas, Hywel John

Joint Degree—Upper Second Class Honours
Keeble, David Martin
(Oceanography)

Joint Degree—Lower Second Class Honours
Dunlop, Alastair Douglas
(Oceanography)
Rickett, Elinor Jane
(Biology)
Rose, Christopher Martin
(Oceanography)
Turner, Jillian Margaret
(Biology)

Joint Degree—Pass
Haxell, Michael Robert
(Oceanography)

FACULTY OF ECONOMIC AND SOCIAL STUDIES

Upper Second Class Honours
Alderman, Lyndsey Ann
(Social Statistics)
Bliss, Christopher Jan Andrew
(Social Statistics)
Davies, Nicholas John
(American Studies)
Dee, Gillian Mary
(Russian Studies)
Gaffney, Suzanne Margaret
(Psychology)

Jones, Elsbeth Watkin
(Social History)
Machin, Elizabeth Anne
(Social History)
Steele, Jane Helen
(Social History)
Tabram, Alan
(Social Policy)
Tidmarsh, Celia Ruth
(Social Anthropology)
Timson, John Dennis
(Russian Studies)
Weston, Carol Jayne
(Social History)

Lower Second Class Honours
Ashton, Lesley Carol
(Social Anthropology)
Cadel, Timothy Arthur
(Russian Studies)
Charlesworth, Dorothy Ann
(Social History)
Corrall, Brian Kenneth
(Social Policy)
Currie, Alison Gillian
(Sociology)
Dargue, Christine Margaret
(Social Policy)
Davidson, Duncan Neil
(Social History)
Dawson, Stephen Eric
(Psychology)
Evans, Jacqueline
(Social Anthropology)
Foxley, Alison Margaret
(Social Policy)
Fryer, Alison Jane
(Social History)
Granger, Catherine Jennifer
(Russian Studies)
Green, Andrew Berkeley
(Economic History)
Jones, Christopher Neil
(Social History)
Kellett, Michael John
(Russian Studies)
Lander, Julian Christopher
(Russian Studies)
Mason, Andrew Nicholas
(Russian Studies)
McCann, Jane Ada
(Social Policy)
Miller, Derek Murdoch
(Economics)
Nash, Andrew John
(Russian Studies)

Owen, Anne
  (Economics)
Root, Carolyn Jill
  (Psychology)
Sharman, Matthew C. Lewis
  (Economics)
Summerfield, Carol Ann
  (Social Statistics)
Tate, Robert Maurice
  (Social History)
Vaughan, Stephen Gareth
  (Social History)
Waring, Stephen Andrew
  (Politics)
Willcocks, Sharon Gwenyth
  (Social Anthropology)
Williams, William Ellis
  (Politics)
Wood, Laurence Thomas
  (Economics)
Worby, John Spencer
  (Russian Studies)

Third Class Honours
James, Stephen Rowland
  (Economics)
May, Phillip Stephen
  (Politics)
Rossiter, Richard James
  (Social Policy)
Thomas, Hugh David Gabe
  (Russian Studies)
Young, John Clifford
  (Economics)

Pass Degree
Williams, Hugh Gareth Woods
  (Russian Studies)

1979

External Examiners: Professor S. Gregory and Mr. A. Hunt

FACULTY OF ARTS

Upper Second Class Honours
Beck, Paul Anthony
Durant, Gillian
Fidler, Christopher Michael
Griffin, Leigh Russell
Hudson, Robert Noel
Israel, Roger David
Morgan, Susan Margaret
Mullineaux, Joanna Mary
Thwaites, Janette Lois
Tooke, Karen Jane
Williams, Rhian

Lower Second Class Honours
Booker, Rachael Anne
Clark, Antonia Mary Anderson
Clowes, David Michael
Cottam, Nicholas John
Dugdale, Steven Deric
Hirst, Richard Philip
Jefferies, Roy Anthony
Jones, David
Jordan, Irona Jane
Knowles, Judith Elizabeth
Mapstone, Joseph Jerome Alexander
Moore, Peter Anthony
Mullins, Helen Iona
Parry, Karen Pamela
Read, Philip Ashley
Scourfield, Susan
Smith, Helen Elizabeth
Ward, Stephen Gregory
Whittle, Brian Lawrence
Whycer, Elizabeth Jane
Worley, John Morris

Third Class Honours
Cole, Robert Arthur
Oldroyd, Lesley Jennifer

Pass Degree
Phillips, David Geraint

Joint Degree—Upper Second Class Honours
Grimes, Sandra
  (Russian Studies)
Offord, John
  (American Studies)
Trilsbach, Anthony
  (History)

FACULTY OF SCIENCE

First Class Honours
Campbell, Stewart

Upper Second Class Honours
Brossard, Christopher Ivan
Carroll, David James
Dawson, Nicholas James
Jones, Hilary Anne
Kindred, Ashley Desmond
Owens, Jennifer Anne Elisabeth
Playle, Merrin Laura
Shuttleworth, Anne
Sutherland, Fiona Jean
Wilcox, Elizabeth Mary
Williams, Paula
Woodhouse, Lorraine Faith

Lower Second Class Honours
Ackerley, Rosalind Marie
Baur, Peter John
Bond, Ian Douglas
Bradshaw, Suzanne
Broughton, Anne Olivia
Colyer, Jacqueline Anne
Deeley, Jayne Anne
Donnelly, Adrian
Evans, Eric Cadwgan
Haggard, Jane Elizabeth
James, Jonathan
Jennings, Brian George
Ross, Nicholas William Andrew
Stearns, Barbara
Voss, Michael John

Third Class Honours
Lundy, Susan Mary

Joint Degree—Upper Second Class Honours
Howes, Jonathan David
(Oceanography)

Joint Degree—Lower Second Class Honours
Kelly, Brian John
(Oceanography)

Joint Degree—Third Class Honours
Brooks, Susan Elizabeth
(Geology)
Fraser-Harris, William Lovat
(Oceanography)
Johnson, Leigh
(Biology)

FACULTY OF ECONOMIC AND SOCIAL STUDIES

Upper Second Class Honours
Atkins, Susan Jennifer
(Psychology)
Baker, Julia
(Economics)
Davies, David Llewellyn
(Economics)
Donkersley, Paul Martin
(Economics)
Fear, Paul Gareth
(Economics)
Lloyd, Anthony Derek
(Economics)

Lower Second Class Honours
Appleby, Sandra Denise
(Psychology)
Bailey, Philip
(Economics)

Baldwin, Christopher
(Social Administration)
Baxter, Kathryn Anne
(Social Administration)
Bell, Andrew John
(Social History)
Booth, Helen Rebecca
(Psychology)
Bridgeman, Harry Patrick
(Economics)
Bridgman, Steven Mark
(Economic History)
Brown, Peter James
(Economics)
Chick, Julie Elizabeth
(Social History)
Chillington, Christine Faith
(Psychology)
Clinton-Smith, Lyndsey Paula
(Social Administration)
Colman, Louise Wendy
(American Studies)
Cullen, Declan Anthony
(American Studies)
Cushion, Maria Elizabeth
(Sociology)
Dowe, Susan Patricia
(Social Administration)
Evans, Ruth Marjorie
(Social History)
Green, Deborah Lynne
(Social Administration)
Hassell, Catherine Margaret
(Economics)
Heryet, Amanda Elizabeth
(Social Administration)
Jones, Alison
(Social Administration)
Llewellyn, Huw
(Economics)
O'Sullivan, Paul John
(American Studies)
Penton, Leslie Albert
(Social History)
Pugh, Hywel Andrew
(Psychology)
Rogers, Ann Margaret
(American Studies)
Share, Alan Joseph
(American Studies, Social History)
Tarbet, Stephen Howard
(Politics, Russian Studies)
Trimby, Gillian
(Psychology)
Walters, Gregory Charles
(Social History)

Weaver, Tessa
(Social Statistics)
Welch, Josephine Sheila
(American Studies)
Whitehorn, Helen Jane
(Social History)

Third Class Honours
Crowther, Richard Vernon
(Economics)
Doogue, Patrick Joseph
(Politics)

Garrod, Janet Penelope Susan
(Economics)
Rees, Christopher David
(Social Statistics)
Shapton, Eira Noreen
(American Studies)
Taylor, Richard John
(Economics)
Thomas, Jaqueline
(Sociology)

LIST OF GRADUATES – MASTERS

DEGREE OF MAGISTER IN ARTIBUS

The Degree of M.A has been awarded to the following, for the theses whose titles are given.

1956
JOHN CURTIS GROVE, B.A. (Wales)
Land Use Changes in West Gower 1840–1950.

1960
BRIAN ALFRED GEORGE PLUMMER, B.A. (Wales)
An Investigation into Human Influence on Marsh Development in the Burry Estuary, South Wales.

1964–65
MUSTAFA MOHAMMED KHOGALI, B.A. (Khartoum)
The Significance of the Railway to the Economic Development of the Republic of the Sudan, with a Special Reference to its Western Provinces.

1969–70
ELIZABETH GRACE FARRELL, B.A. (Wales)
Essex Rural Settlement – Some Aspects of its Evolution with Particular Reference to the Sixteenth Century.

1973–74
ALLAN ROBERT RAYBOULD, B.A. (Wales)
A Geographical Analysis of the Effects of Socio-economic Class on Consumer Movements.

SHANTI KUSUMSIRI DE SILVA, B.A. (Sri Lanka)
Socio-Spatial Patterns of the City of Colombo: a factorial ecology.

JOHN YOCKNEY, B.A. (Wales)
Modern Developments in the Ports of Eastern England.

1974–75
WILLIAM HAMLEY, B.A. (Wales)
The Urban Structure of Colchester.

DEGREE OF MAGISTER IN SCIENTIA

The Degree of M.Sc. has been awarded to the following, for the theses whose titles are given.

1938
EMRYS JONES HOWELL, B.Sc. (Wales)
Movements of Mining Population in the Anthracite Mining Area of South Wales, 1861 to the Present Day.

1966–67
RUSSEL DUNCAN THOMPSON, B.Sc. (Wales)
Some Aspects of the Glaciology and Glacio-Meteorology of Signy Island in British Antarctic Territory.

1968–69
BRIAN JOHN WOODRUFFE, B.Sc. (London)
Land Use in Worcestershire: a Study in Land Use and Land Use Change between 1939 and 1963.

KENNETH DAVIES, B.Sc. (Wales)
The Development and Growth of Population and Settlement in Flintshire.

1972–73
RICHARD TINDALL ARNOLD, C.Eng., F.I.C.E., F.I.W.E.
A Water Resources Survey of South West Wales.

1973–74
THOMAS DENZIL BENJAMIN JOHN, C.Eng., F.I.Mur. E., F.I.W.E.
The Implementation of the Water Resources Powers of the Water Resources Act 1963 in general and with regard to South West Wales in Particular.

1974–75
KINGSLEY FRANCIS HARNIMAN, B.Sc. (London)
> The Application of Computer Simulation in Geomorphology (with Special Reference to the Random Walk Simulation of River Networks).

1975–76
PETER ANTHONY BULL, B.Sc. (Wales)
> An Electron Microscope Study of Clastic Cave Sediments from Agen Allwedd, Powys.

RAYMOND ARTHUR INDER, B.Sc (Wales)
> Residential Areas in Cardiff: Alternative Approaches to Definition and Analysis.

1976–77
ROBERT CHARLES REYNOLDS, B.Sc. (Wales)
> The Stratigraphy and Selected Micro-Fossil Analysis of Recent Coastal Sediments Taken from Borings in Oxwich Marsh Gower, Glamorgan.

1978–79
GERALD ELDRIDGE, B.Sc. (Southampton)
> The Geomorphological Development of Ogof Ffynnon Ddu, Powys.

JANE ALLISON EVANS (née LE HARDY), B.Sc. (Wales)
> Recreation and the Estuarine Environment: a Case Study of the Milford Haven Waterway.

DEGREE OF MAGISTER IN SCIENTIA ECONOMICA

The Degree of M.Sc. Econ. has been awarded to the following, for the theses whose titles are given.

1970–71
TERESA FLORENCE SHEWRING, B.Sc. Econ. (London)
> A Study of Industrial Estates in the Regional Development of South Wales.

1972–73
EDWARD VAN DER VLIET, B.A. (Natal)
> The Nature of Farming on South West Gower: a Study of some Factors Influencing Farmers' Choice of Enterprises.

1975–76
DEREK WILLIAM STRANGE, B.Sc. Econ. (Wales)
> Some Aspects of Housing in South Wales, 1919–1969.

LIST OF GRADUATES – DOCTORATES

DEGREE OF PHILOSOPHIAE DOCTOR

The Degree of Ph.D. has been awarded to the following, for the theses whose titles are given.

1959–60
MICHAEL WILLIAMS, B.A. (Wales)
The Draining of the Somerset Levels.

1963–64
DOROTHY MARY TROTMAN, B.Sc. (Wales)
Data for Late and Post Glacial History in South Wales: a Pollen Analytical study of Three Peat Bogs, Waen Ddu, Cwmllynfell and Bryn House, Swansea.

PETER DAVIES, B.Sc. (Wales)
A Study of Some Aspects of Landsliding and Slope Development in an area of South Wales.

VERNON HUGHES WILLIAMS, B.Sc. (Wales)
A Study of the Solutional Processes and Phenomena in Limestone with Special Reference to the North Avonian Outcrop of the South Wales Syncline.

1965–66
STEWART RABY, B.A. (Oxon), M.Sc. (Alberta)
Stream Quality and Water Resource Management in England and Wales.

1967–68
GRAHAM HUMPHRYS, B.Sc. (Bristol), M.A. (McGill)
Economic Change in Industrial South Wales: Post War Patterns and Developments.

1967–68
GEOFFREY JAMES WILLIAMS, B.A. (Wales)
Contributions to the Pleistocene Geomorphology of the Middle and Lower Usk Valley.

1968–69
ALLAN STEPHENSON POTTS, B.Sc. (Wales)
The Glacial and Periglacial Geomorphology of Central Wales.

EDNA AUDREY POTTS (née GRINTER), B.Sc. (Wales)
The Geomorphology of the Sand Dunes of South Wales with Special Reference to Gower.

1969–70
HUGH LAURENCE MASON, M.A. (Cantab)
The Development of the Urban Pattern of Ireland 1841–1881.

WILLIAM COLIN ROUSE, B.Sc. (Birmingham)
An Investigation of the Stability and Frequency Distribution of Slopes in Selected Areas of West Glamorgan.

ALAN STUART TRENHAILE, B.Sc. (Wales)
A Geomorphological Investigation of Shore Platforms and High Water Rock Ledges in the Vale of Glamorgan.

1970–71
COLIN EDWARD BANFIELD, B.Sc. (Wales)
The Influence of Situation, Site and Meteorological Factors Upon Atmospheric Pollution in South-East Wales.

SUNITI DANISSARI GUNASEKERA, B.A. (Ceylon)
A Study of the Social and Economic Geography of the Coastal Fishing Industry of Ceylon.

1971–72
DAVID CLARK, B.Sc. Econ. (Bradford), M.A. (Sussex)
Urban Linkage and Regional Structure in Wales – a Systems Approach.

DAVID PARRY EDE, B.Sc. (London)
An Investigation into Some Factors Influencing the Hardness of Streams and Springs on Limestone with Particular Reference to South Wales.

HENRY JAMES STEWARD, B.Sc. Econ. (London)
Cartographic Generalisation – Some Aspects of the Automation Problem.

1973–74
EDWIN MICHAEL BRIDGES, M.Sc. (Sheffield)
An Investigation into the Origin and Development of Selected Soils of the Gower Peninsula.

NAFTALI KADMON, B.A. (Jerusalem), M.Sc. (Glasgow)
Automated Cartography for the Atlas of Israel.

1974–75
KAREL JENNIFER HUGHES (née BARNES), B.Sc. (Wales)
The Nature and Origin of Pleistocene Deposits in the Avan Basin of Southwest Glamorganshire.

MICHAEL HUGH MATTHEWS, B.A. (Wales)
The Changing Location of the Early Modern Chemical Industry in Great Britain 1736–1890.

EDUARD VAN DER VLIET, B.A. (O.F.S.), B.A. (Natal), M.Sc. Econ. (Wales)
Decision Making in Agriculture – a Comparative Study of Selected Aspects Affecting Rural Landscapes.

1975–76
BRIAN WILLIAM ILBERRY, B.A. (Wales)
Decision Making in Farming: A Study of Some of the Factors Affecting the Agricultural Land-Use Patterns of North-East Oxfordshire.

ALUN DUDLEY JONES, B.Sc. (Wales)
Rainfall, Runoff and Erosion in the Upper Tywi Catchment.

1976–77
DENNIS JOHN PARKER, B.A. (Wales)
Socio-Economic Aspects of Flood Plain Occupance.

PETER ANTHONY BULL, B.Sc. (Wales), M.Sc. (Wales)
Contributions to the Study of Clastic Cave Sediments with Particular Reference to Agen Allwedd, Powys.

JOHN WATSON RAINE, B.A. (Wales)
Social Interaction and Urban Neighbourhood: a Social and Geographical Study in Cardiff.

WILLIAM JOHN CHAMBERS, B.Ed. (London)
Aspects of the Limestone Geomorphology, Hydrology and Water Chemistry of the Gower Peninsula.

YAHYA ISA FARHAN, M.A. (Cairo)
A Geomorphological Engineering Approach to Terrain Classification.

JOHN ALEXANDER BRIGGS, B.A. (London)
Aspects of the Development Process in Africa: a Study of the Southern Gummuiya Area of Central Sudan.

ADRIAN ALUN SEABORNE, B.A. (Wales), M.A. (Saskatchewan)
Socio-Economic Adjustment Associated with Changing Patterns of Industrial Location in South Wales.

CHRISTOPHER FREDERICK WOOLDRIDGE, B.Sc. (Wales)
A Study of the Movement of Beach Sand and the Interpretation of Shallow Water Marine Morphology in Whitesand Bay, Pembrokeshire.

1977–78
BARBARA ANN THOMAS, B.A. (Wales)
Medieval and Sixteenth Century Field Systems in Surrey.

ROSEMARY DULCIE FOLLETT BROMLEY (née ASHWORTH) M.A. (Cantab)
Urban Growth and Decline in the Central Sierra of Ecuador 1698–1940.

SHEILA MARJORIE PEACE, B.A. (Wales)
 The Elderly in an Urban Environment: a Study of Spatial Mobility and Neighbourhood Interaction in Swansea.

KEITH SELLERS BARDON, B.Sc. (Wales)
 The Recreational Use of Selected Inland Water Sites in South Wales.

1978–79
DAVID JOHN EVANS, B.A. (Birmingham)
 Urban Structures and Social Problems in South Wales.

HARB ABDEL KADER AL-HUNATI, B.A. (Jordan)
 Regional Developmental Planning in the Third World with Special Reference to East Bank of Jordan.

DAVID ROSSER PHILLIPS, B.Sc. Econ. (Wales)
 The Utilisation of, and the Attitudes of the Public to, General Practitioner services: a Geographical Study in West Glamorgan.

DAVID MARTIN ROBINSON, B.Sc. (Wales)
 The Geography of Augustinian Settlement in Medieval England and Wales.

COLIN HASLEHURST WILLIAMS, B.Sc. Econ. (Wales)
 Language Decline and National Resurgence in Wales.